D0962670

CONTAINS GMOs

SEEDS *of* REPRISAL

Monsanto vs. Michael White

J. SOMERVILLE PARK

Provident House, LLC

Library of Congress Control Number: 2013915712
ISBN: 978-0-615-85625-4

Photograph on back cover of Michael White by Emily White

Photograph on back cover of J. Somerville Park by Annie

www.seedsofreprisal.com

Published by
Provident House, LLC

Third Edition 2014

With admiration and respect, for
all the Davids . . . past and present.

"Nothing that you do in science is guaranteed to result in benefits for mankind. Any discovery, I believe, is morally neutral and it can be turned either to constructive ends or destructive ends."

– Arthur Galston

ACKNOWLEDGEMENTS

With genuine appreciation, I wish to thank those who helped me with this book, as well as a few of the many people who helped me along the way on life's journey. Several people asked to remain anonymous, and so they shall. Please note: I never met two of these people, yet they played crucial roles in my writing and I am forever in their debt.

Dan & Martha Akens, Rob Barrett, Steve Beeson, Mike Belancsik, Rick Bragg, Jim Broaddus, J. R. Brooks, Barbara L. Burton, Teresa Eubanks, Peachie Dornan, Larry Gordon, Betsy Gray, Dr. Marian Huttenstein, Joseph Kasmer, Jim Kirby, Glenda Lammers, Nelle Harper Lee, Jim Mann, Jay Marquardt, Wayne Medlock, Dennis Miller, Julie Miller, Anne Morgan, M.D., Linda Page, Ann Park, Bill Park, Leroy Pendelton, Thomas Pope, Megan Pratt, Steve Rollison, Dr. James Salem, Demetrius Smith, Col. Michael Snell, Rebel Steiner, Jan Walsh, Dr. Kevin Walsh, David Ward, Walt Wells, Martha Whitt, Sloan Wilson, and Don Word.

I want to express my gratitude to Michael White's family. From his late father, Wayne, to his wife, Pam, and children, Emily, Quentin, Valerie, and Shad & Heather, they have all been more than kind, as well as helpful in making this book possible.

When I met Michael he was not long removed from his harrowing ordeal and was, naturally, wary of strangers. Even so, for some reason he opened up to me. And his saga was so riveting and intriguing that I immediately wanted to help bring it to the public.

During the course of this project Michael not only invited me into his home where I was treated like family, but he also openly shared his ordeal, warts and all. And I can say without any reservations that he is a man of true faith, integrity, honesty, decency and courage. For those reasons he detests whenever anyone uses the 'h' word in conjunction with his name. Nevertheless, I believe that after reading his story more than a few people will conclude that Michael White is a bona fide hero.

AUTHOR'S NOTES

This is a dramatization of a true story. A friend who helped me with this project has referred to it as a non-fiction novel.

The names and identifying traits of some people have been changed to protect the innocent, as well as those who are not. Some people were—understandably—reluctant to be interviewed and for that reason their names and identifying traits were changed so they could remain anonymous.

The locations where some events took place have been changed, again, to protect the identities of those involved. The same goes for some other aspects of the book.

In some cases I used poetic license to make the story flow, such as when information was no longer available. Ex: Chapter 3 indicates the tag on a late model GMC pickup was registered to an old Cadillac. The tag on the truck was indeed a fake and placed on it to deliberately hide the driver's identity, and done so in violation of the law. Even so, I did not find anyone who could recall the make and model of the vehicle to which the tag was actually registered. Succinctly, it may or may not have been registered to an old Cadillac, but it most certainly was not registered to the late model pickup that was using it.

The timeline was recreated to be reasonably accurate. Nevertheless, there is a possibility that some events are not in the exact order in which they occurred.

Some of the information about Agent Orange, GMOs, Monsanto and other matters did not come to the attention of Michael White until after his case was settled. It was included because it is relevant and established a historical backdrop.

During my research I consulted a number of resources and they are noted in the 'end notes.' Many of them hold a wealth of information that simply could not be included in this book, so I urge you to read them for yourself. Please note: A valid effort was made to acknowledge all sources. However, if one was used but not cited, the omission was unintentional.

Some of the personal conversations and interactions between Michael and his former wife were edited to protect their privacy, as well as that of their children. The same goes for the personal conversations and interactions with his parents.

In some instances a conversation between Michael and his friends, confidants, allies and/or attorneys was presented as having occurred during one meeting when, in real time, it was based on more than one encounter.

This is not Michael's story in its entirety; far from it. For various reasons, a number of conversations, meetings, incidents and even critical information he acquired during this ordeal were 'left on the cutting room floor.' Case in point: Several highly charged encounters between Michael and Monsanto's private investigators were not included.

All of the encounters depicted in this book between Michael and Monsanto's private investigators were based on at least one eyewitness account, and they were recreated to be reasonably accurate using that information. The same holds for events that took place in courtrooms, sightings of unmarked aircrafts, as well as vehicles operating with illegal license plates. Additionally, information about Agent Orange, PCBs, rBGH, TCDD, the Vietnam War, the plight of farmers in India, Monsanto's history and other news worthy items, both past and present, were based on sources from the 'end notes' and were written to be reasonably accurate based on that information.

Finally, regardless of whether you love this book or loathe it, I encourage you to thoroughly educate yourself about the complicated and highly contentious matter of GMOs because sheep do not make good citizens.

PRELUDE

The low ebb for Dan Quayle's often beleaguered term as U.S. Vice-President came on June 15, 1992. The ambitious but seemingly hapless politician—generally regarded as a good person but a lightweight in matters of intellect and state—traveled to an elementary school in New Jersey on that fateful day for a photo-op. It was the kind politicians do all the time, one meant to boost his flagging image. Instead, he sealed his fate for all-time as a chronic punch line and the butt of a thousand-and-one jokes.

Taking part in a spelling bee, a 12 year-old student wrote the word "potato" on the chalkboard. Quayle, seated only a few feet away, "corrected" the youngster, gently chiding him that an "e" was needed at the end of the word to make it correct. Doing as he was told, the student dutifully added an "e," thus making it "potatoe." And when he did, Quayle instantly mugged for the cameras with a big politician's smile as he pronounced, "There ya go!" It confirmed he was sure the word was now spelled correctly. Sadly for Quayle, there is no "e" in potato, not in the first part, not the middle, or the end.

From comedians to political pundits to everyday citizens and even staid college professors, it seems everyone had a big, long and hearty laugh at the expense of the Vice-President. As the clip was played over and over on television, the blunder became a defining moment for Quayle.

A few weeks prior to "the gaffe heard round the world," Quayle gave a speech that garnered little attention at the time. But that was not unusual. A number of people felt the powers that be in President George H. W. Bush's administration gave Quayle short shrift; they were more likely to send the Vice President to a ribbon cutting ceremony for a remote state park than to deliver a speech of any consequence.

At the time, Quayle's speech appeared to be little more than a bit of cheerleading to promote the President's push for "regulatory relief initiative." In this instance the Food and Drug Administration's new policy regarding genetically modified foods was highlighted. Quayle said the U.S. biotech industry stood to reap enormous profits, but only if it wasn't saddled with complicated rules and restrictions. In theory, it sounded good. Here was a new and emerging industry and if the government didn't harness it with regulations like those for parachute makers and pharmaceutical companies then American based companies stood to control it; certainly better than having a country with few checks and balances take the lead. However, there's a reason why some industries must be regulated, especially those that directly affect the safety and well-being of the public.

The FDA's hands-off policy hinged on the premise that GM plants are "substantially equivalent" to natural plants. It's generally believed that Quayle had little to do with shaping the policy. Michael R. Taylor, an attorney working for the FDA at the time and who would later become a vice-president for Monsanto, crafted the policy.

The policy Quayle spoke of that day is still in place. Much to the consternation of concerned citizens, scientists and medical practitioners, companies that produce genetically modified organisms that wind up in our food supply operate with only minimal oversight.

More than two decades later, the painful irony is still hard for many to swallow: a politician who could not spell "potato" set in motion a directive that dictates U.S. policy for GMOs, meanwhile, our food supply hangs in the balance.

CHAPTER 1

Fall of 2002

Michael White edged a bit closer to the bluff's rim and looked down with anticipation. More than six hundred feet below, he heard the faint sound of the deep, dark, slow-moving waters of the Tennessee River, though he couldn't see it because it was still dark out.

From his earliest recollections, right up until this day, the best times of his life had been spent growing-up on Sand Mountain. Springs, summers, autumns and winters, they all had their own particular beauty, majesty, and a special place in his heart here in the picturesque foothills of the Appalachians.

Life on the mountain was hard, to be sure. Most people struggled just to make ends meet, and Michael's family had been no exception. But his parents, Wayne and Virginia, were good, honest, decent, and honorable people; the proverbial salt of the earth. And although Michael was brought up in a home where money was always tight, there was no shortage of love in the family, and that extended to nature and the outdoors. Long before the term 'environmentalist' was in the common vernacular, the Whites were teaching their son how to take care of the land and nature so that they would be around for his children, and grandchildren, to enjoy.

The White's immense respect for nature was reinforced by the lightning-charged faith preached every Sunday at the Scottsboro Church of God where they were loyal and devoted members. The congregation was taught that the earth was only on loan to mankind from God, and it was their sacred obligation to be good stewards.

Their Christian faith was a vital part of the White's life, a world with no moral ambiguities. They were admonished to walk the straight and narrow, and when confronted with evil and wrongdoers, it was their duty to face them head-on.

Given the lessons in faith Michael had been taught during his formative years, it was no wonder that he was drawn to the beauty and serenity of Sand Mountain. It was a remarkable place, particularly this area because it provided an awe inspiring panoramic view that reached out all the way to the horizon.

Unfortunately, even as dawn broke, all Michael saw was a massive curtain of thick and mottled fog, the sort that obscured everything from sight. He was sorely disappointed, yet resigned to the fact that he would not see anything from the bluff on this day, save for the fog.

Seemingly out of nowhere, as if God had waved a magic wand, fine points of light began to pierce the dense curtain of fog; those delicate fingers of silver-white then reached down to earth until they touched the river below. Their reflections danced on the water's dark surface like a symphony of sparkles exploding from prisms, transforming the murky abyss into one of the greatest light shows on earth.

This extraordinary spectacle siphoned the oxygen right out of Michael's body, filling his heart with something indescribably intense, inspiring, and powerful. He knew instinctively that what he was witnessing was beyond merely amazing; it was a tiny glimpse of heaven . . . or at least as close as man ever gets to it on earth.

CHAPTER 2

Between raising a family, caring for his elderly parents, running the family farm, managing his seed business, doing volunteer work in the community and helping out at his church, Michael often found himself waking up only a few hours after he'd kicked his boots off the night before. Plain and simple, Michael loved watching a sunrise and contemplating God's handiwork, but it was a luxury he rarely had time for. And this day was no exception. The minute his boots hit the ground he was on the move.

Fortunately, Michael had a simple philosophy that came in handy when dealing with a life of grueling 110-hour work weeks without overtime pay, benefits, or a pension: "Ya don't like it, don't farm."

Easing off the main road, Michael steered his old Dodge pickup onto a dirt road that provided access to the 80-acre field he'd sown several weeks ago. There was little uniformity to the spider-web of dirt roads on the mountain. Most were little more than wide muddy trails snaking through the woods. This one, however, was a veritable interstate by comparison. But that was because Michael had maintained it over the years.

Once again, his diligence and hard work had paid off. Even on rain-soaked days, the dirt road was more than passable. And in no time he was in his field, down on one knee, carefully examining the sprouts of winter wheat that were peeking up through the ground.

A farmer lives for the moments when he can touch the seeds he's planted as they come to life. Although it's a relationship that eludes most, it's nothing short of sacred for those who till the soil for their livelihood. But this time, Michael was distracted. The longer he crouched, the more he felt the teeth-gnashing aches and pains that blitzed through his knees and back.

By contemporary standards Michael was a hearty boomer in his prime who could still strike out and explore the four corners of the world if he chose. But his tall, rugged good looks belied the toll that decades of farm labor had taken on his body. Luckily, he was content with his own tiny corner of the earth in Northeast Alabama. He had no intention of ever leaving Sand Mountain, not now, not ever. Someone else would have to conquer the world.

With a favorable nod of his head, Michael noted that his winter wheat was coming along nicely, although it could use more sun. But he also realized with a start that he was lacking another essential element, that of time. Staring through the fractured crystal of his old Timex, Michael saw it had slipped away and he'd have to really hustle or his seed business wouldn't open on time.

Farmers can't count on much. From unpredictable weather to fluctuating crop prices to fickle bankers, there's not much of their environment they can control. So Michael prided himself on being one of the few things his farmer friends and customers could rely on. Being available to meet their needs wasn't some hack ad man's slogan—it was a fundamental principle about the way he did business.

Adjusting the brim of his ever present tattered baseball cap to block out the sun, Michael glanced over at a shortcut he'd taken a time or two in the past. The old rutted and overgrown logging road was now treacherous, and seemingly all but impassable. Yet that's where he spied a pickup. It was parked on the old rollercoaster-esque road, though quite a distance away from his location.

The truck was partially obscured by the woods, but Michael could see the driver. He was standing beside the vehicle and looking through a pair of binoculars. Hunting season wasn't far off, so he was probably spotting deer trails as well as seeking a good location for his deer stand for opening day, common practices among hardcore hunters.

Locking eyes with Michael, the man hesitated for just the briefest of moments, and then hopped into his truck for a quick getaway. That meant he didn't have permission to be where he was; it was blatantly obvious he was trespassing. Why else would he be so intent on abruptly fleeing the scene?

Although Michael pegged this stranger for a poacher, it wasn't the first one he'd seen of late poking around his farm and home. Actually, in the past few months there had been several of them lurking around. The obvious thing that made the earlier sightings odd was that most poachers don't start scouting for places to hunt until much closer to the time of the official hunting season. They had no qualms about hunting without permission on someone like Michael's land. But most of them would rather avoid the wrath of the game warden.

Far more than a mere nuisance, poachers created an undue financial burden for farmers on Sand Mountain, and most of them were already strapped to the breaking point. Over the years they'd trampled countless newly planted fields and bulldozed more than a few fences with their vehicles. Michael grabbed his own binoculars to get a good look at the stranger.

The poacher's truck was already shooting rooster tails of mud and laying tracks by the time Michael could focus. Nevertheless, he got a decent look before it sped away. It was a late-model GMC, white with Z/71 stickers on the rear fenders. He also got the tag number. In fact, he double-checked because it was a local plate. Michael was usually proud to say, "Folks around Sand Mountain ain't the sort to hunt without permission." But even he couldn't deny that in his otherwise cozy little corner of the world there were some reprobates who would.

Michael didn't have time to spare; he had a business to run. He would turn the poacher's tag number into the sheriff's office later on if he had a free minute or two and let them handle it.

Focusing on the task at hand, Michael reasoned to himself that if he drove like a moonshiner running from the revenuers—not an unheard-of sight on Sand Mountain—he might just make it to work on time.

CHAPTER 3

The first thing a customer notices when they walk into White's Seed Cleaning on a crisp fall day is the scent of freshly brewed coffee mingled with the smell of seeds. It's a distinctive, pleasing aroma. The next thing they notice, especially on Saturday mornings, is the flurry of activity. And this one was even busier than most.

Since the moment Michael arrived, just a few minutes before opening time, he'd been working nonstop. From unloading trucks on the dock, pulling invoices, checking inventory, to the all-important glad-handing with customers, he'd been a busy man. But that's the way he liked it.

Back in 1982, when Michael was just getting started, he was a struggling one-man operation battling a host of competitors, companies that had been serving the same farmers for decades, some for generations. The well-entrenched competition gave his rookie shop little chance for survival. Yet twenty-odd years later, Michael had several employees during the busy season and a reputation for quality service. What's more, in an industry that was contracting, Michael's store was actually growing.

But the truly amazing accomplishment was that he'd turned out to be one of the last men standing, so to speak. One by one, his competitors had gone under, and all for the same basic reasons. Each year there were fewer farmers, so companies that wanted to remain in the seed game not only had to out-think and out-work their rivals, but they also had to keep up with the evolving world of agribusiness. And Michael, the new kid on the block, had kept up better than the old guard.

To be fair, the seed business had changed quite a bit in recent years, and change often favors an upstart over the old guard, especially those who are set in their ways. Gone were the simple days when farmers merely retrieved the seeds they'd plowed up from their fall harvest, tossed them into Auntie Em's storm cellar for the winter, and then replanted them at springtime. They now answered to agribusiness savvy lenders, and they required concrete answers to tough questions, such as, "What's the germination rate of your spring planting seeds?" For many types of seeds, anything less than 85 or even 90 percent was now unacceptable. Substandard seeds can derail a crop loan, and without one, a farmer's out of business.

The germination tests must be done by a certified and bonded lab, a significant expense for any small business, but especially so for farmers because they operate on razor-thin margins. A factor in controlling lab costs can be volume. And when Michael got a discount for doing a volume of business with a lab, he gladly passed the savings along to his customers.

However, germination tests were only part of the equation. Seeds must remain in top condition throughout the cold, wet winter months. To insure this, first they must be thoroughly cleaned, and then stored in specially designed bins that provide the ideal environment right up until the day they're planted.

The process of cleaning seeds is labor intensive and requires specialized equipment, and the cost of quality bins is also no small matter. Toss in utilities, maintenance, repairs, warehouse space, employees and insurance, and it's a daunting proposition for a family farm. So, for a number of farmers, the responsibility has to be outsourced. And this is where Michael trounced his rivals. While they slowly withered on the vine—making do with antiquated equipment and often cutting corners on service—he flourished by investing in new equipment and always going the extra mile for his customers.

Michael was also adept at keeping his staff happy. On busy days he often treated them to lunch. It was a small gesture, yet one they genuinely appreciated. It also meant everyone would sit down together for a few minutes. On a hectic day, it was crucial that Michael knew what his employees were doing, and vice versa. As a student of the seed business, he had learned a valuable lesson while watching his competitors fail: duplicating work in a labor-intensive venture is a recipe for ruin.

But Michael's myriad of duties didn't end with the lunch detail. He was the de facto errand boy and head bottle washer, as well. Whatever needed to be done, especially away from the store, Michael did it, such as make a run to Dilbeck's general store during the course of a day if needed. For generations, Dilbeck's was the epicenter of life for many of Sand Mountain's residents. People went there to buy the flour they needed to bake their bread, cloth to make their clothes, nails to build their barns, jars to put up preserves, and sugar to cook moonshine. Long before there was Facebook, they swapped news and gossip under the store's slow turning ceiling fans, at one time the only way to stay connected with friends and community. Although Mr. Dilbeck was now long deceased, his store was still a focal point for the locals. One person even pronounced, "It was the Wal-Mart of Dutton back in its day." In fact, keeping with rural Southern tradition, if you asked an old-timer for directions he would still be far more likely to use Dilbeck's as a navigation point than the shiny new convenience mart down the road.

During the course of his errands Michael encountered a deputy. It wasn't uncommon for members of the sheriff's staff to stop and chat with Michael because they knew him through his devotion to the Jackson County Rescue Squad. The County's Chief Investigator described Michael as "the most selfless volunteer" they had. Over the years he'd donated countless hours of his time, plus tens of thousands of dollars worth of work with his bulldozer during a number of crises. On several occasions he even picked up the tab for the enormous cost of diesel fuel required to operate the big dozer. And he gladly did this at times when the cash strapped county simply didn't have the funds to pay anyone to perform this vital service, often done in the middle of horrendous storms—even with tornado warnings in the forecast—and under the most grueling conditions.

Michael and the deputy were, at best, only nodding acquaintances. However, he knew the man by reputation. Flashing his badge, blasting his siren, or flaunting his authority just wasn't his style. If anything, he went to the opposite extreme because, in a small town, there's a fine line between respect and ridicule for law officers. Unless dealing with a criminal matter, a deputy who takes himself too seriously will wind up as a chronic punch line, the butt of a thousand jokes. And a rural county like Jackson that's perpetually in a cash crunch simply can't afford a real-life Barney Fife.

After a bit of perfunctory small talk, the deputy asked Michael about the fellow he'd seen with the binoculars earlier in the day. And it was obvious he was keenly interested.

For a moment Michael had no idea what the deputy was talking about. So he repeated his words, turning them into a question. "Fellow with the binoculars?" The day had been so chaotic Michael had forgotten that he'd called the sheriff's dispatcher soon after getting to work. He had given her the truck's description and tag number and then said something akin to, "Run this when you got time. No rush, just a poacher on the mountain that's long gone."

Obviously, someone had found time to run the plate. More importantly, the information they'd uncovered made the deputy take the matter seriously. Yet Michael simply couldn't understand why he was so intrigued by an ice cold lead on a poacher sighting. Sure, poachers were prosecuted when they were caught red-handed, but in a county with limited resources a rigorous field investigation isn't feasible for every report that comes in. That piqued Michael's curiosity and made him wonder exactly what the man with the binoculars had done to warrant the deputy's undivided attention. "What's up? This fellow done something I need to know about?"

Instead of answering, the deputy countered with a few questions of his own. "You sure he was driving a late model GMC? Maybe it was so far off that you might not have gotten the tag number right? Maybe it wasn't even a truck?"

Michael didn't mince words. "It was a GMC, alright; a white pickup. Saw it through my binoculars. Got a pretty good look 'fore he took off like a bandit. And I know I got the tag right."

The deputy then informed Michael that the suspicious stranger was, in all likelihood, up to no good. And odds were he had far more than poaching on his mind.

Intrigued and a bit taken aback, Michael couldn't help interrupting, "We're talking about the fellow in the pickup I saw today, right?"

The deputy fiddled with his holster a moment, a nervous habit he had when he needed to buy himself some time, then grimaced. "All I really know for sure at this point is that the tag on the truck you saw is a fake. It's registered to an old Cadillac Coupe de Ville that got totaled-out years ago, definitely not a late model GMC truck."

Several thoughts pinballed through Michael's head. Why would someone be nosing around his property? There was nothing of value to steal, not unless they wanted to do the sweaty, back-breaking labor of picking crops by hand. And who in their right mind would use a tag from a junked vehicle on a new truck?

It occurred to Michael that salvage yards in Alabama tend to keep tags on cars and trucks that have been wrecked, junked and abandoned.

Doesn't matter how they end up on the scrap heap, seems their tags remain in place until they're crushed, probably to maintain an easily accessible record of the car's history. But that also made it fairly easy for anyone willing to break into a salvage yard to steal a tag. The question was, "Why would they? And why put a stolen tag on a new truck?"

The deputy surmised that the only logical reason anyone would put a fake tag on a new truck was to avoid detection. That made Michael's mind spin. The pieces of the puzzle might possibly be coming together for the deputy, but Michael couldn't make any sense of this. Why on earth would a poacher go to such extremes to avoid detection? It just didn't fit the profile he had of them.

The poachers on Sand Mountain were, for the most part, males who lived in surrounding towns and cities. Few, if any of them, had felony records, though they had a well earned reputation for damaging fences and trampling freshly planted fields, which meant they were far more than merely a nuisance for farmers and land owners.

Michael had no regard for poachers, yet he didn't think of them as hardened career criminals. Driving with stolen plates was taking it to another level altogether. It wasn't the act of some misguided men hunting without permission on Sand Mountain, but rather the sort of sleazy subterfuge that was indicative of something far more sinister. Child molesters, burglars and career criminals drove around with stolen tags to hide their identity, but not poachers, not on Sand Mountain.

Michael rubbed his forehead in confusion. "I'm lost; none of this adds up." Looking the deputy in the eye, he asked point blank, "Shoot straight with me. What do you think's going on here?"

Instead of answering, the deputy fumbled with his holster, cleared his throat, then hit Michael with a chain of fully loaded questions spoken with an official tone. "Is anybody you know of mad at you? Anybody out to get you? Do you harm?"

Michael wasn't sure how to respond. Should he be dumbfounded or insulted? After all, not only was he a man of peace, he was also devoutly religious, the kind of person who considers it his duty to put down his plow in the middle of a field and come to the aid of his friends and neighbors— even strangers—in their time of need. And everyone on Sand Mountain knew it.

As he stared off into the woods, trying to make sense of the deputy's disturbing questions, Michael tried to focus in on the mental image he had of the man with the binoculars. No longer preoccupied with making it to work, Michael came to a startling realization. The stranger had not been spotting deer. He'd been watching Michael, and had gone to extreme lengths to do so without being caught. And odds were the other strange vehicles he'd seen over the last month or so snooping around on his property, ones that took off before he could get their tag numbers, were also stalking him.

The thought of one stalker was enough to lose sleep over, but multiple stalkers? Then toss in the fact that at least one of them—if not all—was using a bogus tag to hide his identity elevated this situation from merely unsettling to beyond unnerving. Michael slowly leaned against his truck to steady himself. He tried to look nonchalant so the deputy wouldn't know just how much the revelation had rattled him. Yet try as he might, the official tone of the deputy's words kept echoing in his brain like a baleful omen. 'Is anybody out to get you? Do you harm?'

On the same mountain where Michael had gotten a glimpse of heaven on earth, he now had a sinking feeling that the devil himself was on his heels. Not only was someone stalking him, perhaps the stranger even intended to do him harm, or worse, do his family harm.

To compound matters, whoever this stalker was, and whatever his motives, he had already gotten dangerously close, and Michael hadn't even realized he was being followed until now.

CHAPTER 4

City life can be frenetic and impersonal, fueled by a controlled chaos that's unfathomable in a place like Sand Mountain. The harmony found in the remote nooks and hollers made it easy for natives to believe they were immune from the ills of the modern world. Even those living "downtown" in the smattering of villages dotted here and there found the pace and quality of their lives a gentle throwback to simpler times.

The people on this picturesque mountain were apt to believe the outside world would not—could not—encroach on their way of life. But suddenly all indications were that a very shady interloper was stalking Michael; perhaps his safety and well-being were at stake. It caused him no small amount of concern, especially since he was a family man. As the primary breadwinner for his family, which included his wife, Debbie, and young daughters, Valerie and Emily, he had to consider the big picture. If he was under siege, so was his family. So naturally, thoughts of the mysterious stranger stalking around and hiding behind stolen plates haunted Michael and kept him up into the wee hours of the morning. He found himself looking over his shoulder everywhere he went.

The deputy had assured Michael that he'd track down the stalker before any harm came to him. But Michael knew law enforcement could only do so much. He'd have to have help from people on the mountain who had their own methods of getting to the root of a problem like this one.

There was a time when a prodigious amount of moonshine was distilled on Sand Mountain and the potent liquor—often 150 or even 190 proof—was as readily available as soda pop and licorice whips. Not everyone was a moonshiner, not even close, but most people had a friend, relative or at least an acquaintance who at one time or another had dabbled in whisky making. Eking out a living on the mountain had never been easy, so some of the older folks viewed moonshining simply as an obligatory workaday task required for daily survival.

Although the heyday of bootlegging was long past, a number of the mountain's rural most residents, especially old-timers, looked askance at law enforcement officers. Most of the hostilities were reserved for the federal "revenuers," but local law enforcement officers were not immune. Their probing questions often generated only cold, blank-eyed stares of impenetrable silence from locals. So when Michael put out feelers among friends, relatives, and acquaintances about the stranger stalking him, he went to great pains to stress that they should cooperate with the law. Yet he knew he couldn't persuade some of them to go back on a way of thinking that had been handed down from generation to generation.

A few days later, just before dusk, Michael made his way over to the Reliford Cafe, a favorite among locals. The lure of the place had never been décor or even cuisine. The portions were generous enough to suit even hearty mountain appetites, but pretty much every eatery in the area could boast the same. The draw was that indefinable "local feeling"— the comforting sensation that the customer is part of the family. So, naturally, the place was a magnet for those who wanted the latest news and gossip and a sense of belonging.

A gaggle of old geezers, all retired and limping along on Social Security, held court at the cafe practically everyday. Huddled around a timeworn table, they could often be found from early morning until late in the day, sharing photos of their grandkids and swapping stories, news and the latest gossip with everyone who came in the restaurant. And during the daily lulls—usually right after breakfast and lunch when they were the only customers—the members of the over-the-hill-gang occupied themselves with tales from their youth. After years of retelling, their life stories were massaged to the point where a mediocre high school quarterback had become a legendary passer and a five-pound bass had morphed into Moby Dick. Their tall tales weren't lies, at least not in the strictest sense. They were merely the vainglorious ramblings of old men who secretly wished their lives had been a bit more interesting, more fruitful, more memorable.

One man who occasionally sat in on this septuagenarian coffee klatch had no desire to relive his past. Although Sammy Joe Denton had, at one time, owned a large and successful farm, he was not the sort to stare for long in the rearview mirror of life. He was far more focused on the future. And what made it all the more odd was that one day without notice in 2002, after almost thirty years of running a highly productive farm, he simply called it quits. Just like that, no explanation, no nothing. He sold off his equipment and called it a day.

Some said it was his health; he'd suffered through several serious medical issues in recent years. But there was something else, something Sammy Joe wasn't telling. A man like him didn't just hang up his boots on a whim. It went against the very nature of his being. But he was also a very private man. You didn't ask Sammy Joe a lot of personal questions. People respected him and didn't pry into his affairs.

Although he'd given up farming, he kept busy. He had a couple of small businesses that kept him on the go and put a few dollars in his pocket. And from time to time—usually late in the afternoon and only once every week or so—he'd drop by Reliford's for a cup of coffee and the latest news on the mountain.

Although Sammy Joe enjoyed the tall-tales and anecdotes that were part of his friends' daily ritual, he had little taste for rumors and malicious gossip. That's why he was thought of as a clearinghouse for hard news and information.

As sundown approached on a cold and bleak day, Michael entered the little cafe, wandered over to the counter and ordered a cup of coffee. He greeted the patrons seated at the old Formica-topped counter by name, but avoided the standard small talk expected. Neither socializing nor a hungry belly had brought him to Reliford's; he was there to see Sammy Joe. And Sammy Joe knew it, as did pretty much everyone else.

After getting his coffee, Michael made his way to the back table where Sammy Joe was seated with the septuagenarian coffee klatch. As if on cue, the old men fumbled with lame excuses about 'time to go home' and then one by one they exited, finally leaving Michael alone with Sammy Joe.

"How you making it?" Michael asked as he made himself comfortable in a chair still warm from its previous occupant.

"Fair to middlin', " Sammy Joe replied, employing the standard term he used. It was a diplomatic way of saying, 'I've felt a lot better, but I'm not gonna bore you to tears with a recap of all my health issues.'

Michael toyed with the clunky old salt shaker on the table. It wasn't easy for him to speak about certain things, especially anything that suggested weakness, so keeping his hands busy helped. "You hear anything yet about this fellow that's been spying on me?"

Old men with time on their hands often needlessly draw things out. It comes with the territory. No need to get to the heart of the matter until you've circled it a time or two . . . or even three. But Sammy Joe abstained from the practice. He was still a busy man in his own right, plus he saw the worry in Michael's eyes. A devoted family man himself, Sammy Joe understood Michael's concern. Being stalked by a stranger wasn't a situation he would wish on anyone, especially not a decent and honorable man such as Michael.

Sammy Joe fixed a sympathetic gaze on his old pal. "I hate to say it,

Michael, I really do, but I ain't got a damn thing for you. Ain't nobody got nothing on this fellow. He must be part ghost. That or he's the slipperiest SOB that ever slithered out from under a rock on this here mountain."

Michael took a deep breath. When Sammy Joe couldn't find out anything about someone on Sand Mountain it was far more than unsettling, it was cause for genuine concern.

The look on Michael's face said it all and caused Sammy Joe to promise he'd redouble his efforts. "Hell, Michael, whoever this is, well, I bet ya I'll have the goods on him before you can say grace over your Sunday dinner." Michael nodded. He truly appreciated his friend's assertion that this would all soon be resolved. However, he recognized that Sammy Joe's 'promise' was more a good friend trying to alleviate a father's worst fears than an actual commitment for a quick conclusion as to the stalker's identity and intentions.

* * *

Several days after meeting with Sammy Joe, Michael was driving home one evening after a long, tedious and hard day. He had a lot on his mind, and sometimes he did his best thinking behind the wheel. So with a faint drizzle clouding the windshield, he took the long way home.

The road he took over Sand Mountain was a series of steep 'S' curves broken up only by a few short stretches of marginally straight roads. Nevertheless, if you drove with a modicum of common sense it was anything but a treacherous drive. However, a coat of mist could change everything. Whereas a heavy rain would wash away the residue of oil left behind by vehicles that used the road, a mist, instead, sat on top of the oil laden asphalt and turned it into a slippery glass-like surface that could tax the skills of even the best drivers. So Michael backed off his normal speed, keeping the needle around 30 mph, 35 tops. And he kept one eye on the woods, lest a deer dart into his path and turn this night into disaster.

As he slowly wound around the mountain roads, Michael couldn't shake the notion that whoever was stalking him was up to no good. In fact, they had to be up to something bad, very bad. There was absolutely no reason to use a fake tag other than to hide one's identity. And that meant they anticipated breaking a far more severe law than driving with stolen plates—the latter no small crime itself. That's what had been keeping him up night after night. What did they intend to do? And why did they have it in for him?

Of all the emotions Michael had wrangled with since finding out he was being stalked, the dread of the unknown was the one driving him most crazy.

Trying to focus on both the slick winding road and pitch black dark woods, Michael suddenly realized someone was behind him, though he wasn't sure where the headlights came from. It could've been a faster moving vehicle that simply caught up with him. Or, it could've been someone who entered the roadway from one of the many paved and dirt roads that intersected it.

Coming up on one of the most dangerous curves on the mountain, Michael braked and then hugged the centerline to maintain control of his truck while steering clear of the mountain's edge. The last thing he wanted was to get too close to the edge of the road where little more than an old, perfunctory guardrail stood between him and a perilously steep drop off—several hundred feet down to the bottom.

Taking extra care on the sharp curve, Michael glanced momentarily in his rearview mirror at the vehicle behind him. What if it was the stalker he had seen with the binoculars? A chill ran through Michael's body as a frightening notion entered his mind. The stalker could easily ram into his truck at the apex of this curve, causing him to lose control and career over the side of the mountain. When he finally hit bottom his corpse would be a bloody and mangled mess and his truck would be a crumpled wreck; it would be all but impossible for law officers to figure out that it was no accident and, just the opposite, he'd been rammed off the mountain on purpose.

Over the years more than one person had taken the fatal plunge off Sand Mountain. The crashes were almost always ruled 'driver error,' even when the gaggle of geezers at Reliford's speculated that foul play might have been involved. However, in the absence of ironclad evidence, the law had no choice but to blame the deceased driver for his own death.

As Michael rounded the apex of the perilous curve the tailgater got even closer; he was riding his bumper in a most aggressive manner. Then he hit his brights, all but blinding Michael. It took every ounce of concentration in his body to blindly maintain the course he was on, lest he slip up and take a fatal plunge over the mountain's edge. He was tempted to look in his rearview mirror again, hoping to get a better glimpse at this interloper, but experience had taught him that it would all be for naught. It would actually add to his blindness, and take his concentration off the treacherous curve in front of him.

With sweat beading up on his forehead, Michael quickly yet gently tapped his brakes . . . not to slow down too fast and exacerbate an already dangerous situation, but to warn the antagonistic tailgater that they were on a collision course if he didn't back off.

The warning did no good whatsoever. The driver somehow actually got even closer to Michael's bumper. The distance between them was now only inches and a precarious situation appeared to be turning deadly. Michael had done everything but pray, which was out of character. Normally he prayed before a situation got out of hand, but this one had manifested itself in the beat of a hummingbird's wings.

Just as Michael began to pray and, simultaneously, clear the curve, the car behind him pulled out and shot by at breakneck speed. In no time the car's tail lamps disappeared into the dark, drizzly night as it rounded the next curve at a dangerously high rate of speed. With a deep sigh of relief, Michael realized it was not the stalker at all, just some fool driving with reckless abandon, perhaps under the influence of alcohol or meth, the latter having long ago surpassed moonshine as the drug of choice on the mountain.

With the image of the stalker fresh in his mind, it occurred to Michael that a scant week or two ago he wouldn't have given a stranger driving behind him a second thought, even one behaving recklessly. Now, however, he realized that until he found out who was after him and why, and they were locked away, he'd have these kind of eerie and unsettling moments over and over again, and the nightmares to go with them, that is, on the nights when he could sleep.

CHAPTER 5

On a cold, damp, and miserable night when most people were either home beside a warm fire or under the covers, Michael had a clandestine meeting with James "Buddy Jim" Rendell in an old, drafty ramshackle barn. From a comfort standpoint, it would've been difficult to find a worse place. However, when Buddy Jim contacted his old friend he stressed that their meeting had to be absolutely private; it had to be someplace where no one would see them or overhear their conversation. So Michael made sure of that, even if it meant doing without creature comforts most take for granted, such as plumbing and electric lights.

Buddy Jim had spent a number of years in Montgomery, Alabama's State Capitol. During his tenure there he had figured out how to gain access through the front and back doors of some highly placed people. Although the machinations of career politicians left a sick taste in his mouth, he understood that sometimes you have to play poker with the devil in order to get anything done in a world where sleazy and corrupt politicians hold far too many cards.

On one level Michael admired Buddy Jim because he had spent so many years in the cesspool known as Montgomery without ever getting tainted by all the graft and corruption that seemed to flow through the town like the rapids of a rushing river. Yet on another level he wondered why an honest man would willingly work with and beside the scores of bandits, schemers and charlatans that inhabited the state's capitol.

When in Montgomery, Buddy Jim had to play convoluted games when talking with people. Conversations ranged from those that required coded language, to ones where the subject was danced around, but never quite broached. With Michael, however, he could get right to the point, and did. "Michael, you ever heard of a company called Monsanto?"

"Sure, they make Roundup."

Buddy Jim leveled a heavy gaze on Michael. "They make a lot mor'n just weed killer, a helluva' lot more."

Because of his farm and seed business alone, Michael knew a great deal more about Monsanto than the average person. But he instinctively realized this was not the time to showcase his knowledge. This was a time to listen.

With tongue firmly in cheek, Buddy Jim pronounced. "Monsanto's saying they're an agricultural company now, they're gonna feed the world, make sure nobody goes hungry." Buddy Jim grimaced, "Heck, I always thought of 'em as a company that made butt ugly orange and lime green shag carpet." He sighed and gestured dramatically with his hands. "How does a company that made fruit colored shag carpet now claim it's the leader in providing the world with food?" His question hung alongside the damp chill in the air, and both were cause for immense discomfort.

After a moment or two of silence had passed, Buddy Jim asked, "I guess you heard about what Monsanto did over in Anniston?" With a look of disgust, Michael nodded. Quite a few people in Alabama had heard or read about it. Actually, there were a number of people from all around the world who knew about it.

* * *

Monsanto indiscriminately buried millions of pounds of PCBs (Polychlorinated Biphenyls) in the ground and flushed tens of thousands of pounds of them into streams and creeks that flowed in and around the east Alabama town of Anniston. Although it dodged justice for decades, Monsanto finally had to answer for its crimes on February 22, 2002, when a jury found the conglomerate liable of "negligence, wantonness, suppression of truth, nuisance, trespass and outrage." It also found Solutia, the conglomerate's former chemical division, liable as well. Under Alabama law, the claim of "outrage" is almost never used because it generally requires conduct that is *so outrageous in character and extreme in degree as to go beyond all possible bounds of decency so as to be regarded as atrocious and utterly intolerable in civilized society.*[1]

Tragically, the "outrage" came far too late to save all the people who had been diagnosed with cancer, suffered and died prematurely, the scores of babies born with birth defects, and the numerous residents of Anniston suffering with chronic health problems attributed to PCB exposure. Although it served as little comfort to the victims and their families, their attorneys did prove that Monsanto went to great lengths to cover its tracks, suppressed information, and intentionally kept residents in the dark for decades about the vile toxins.

When you've been robbed of your health, is there any amount of money that can adequately compensate you for your loss? Doubtful. Nevertheless, the conglomerate and its ex-chemical division—Solutia— eventually agreed to pay approximately $700 million to settle up with the victims and clean up the toxic nightmare they'd left behind. Sadly, even when faced with irrefutable and damning evidence, Monsanto defiantly refused to acknowledge it did anything wrong to the city of Anniston or any of its residents.

Although Monsanto would not acknowledge the facts, people from across the country and around the world applauded the outcome of the lawsuit, especially since it came from a state not generally known for its environmental conscience.

---

[1] The italicized words in quotes are the legal definition of "outrage" in the State of Alabama.

During the legal proceedings it came to light that back in 1966 Monsanto hired a biologist, Denzel Ferguson, to test the streams and creeks where the plants' waste was being dumped. In Snow Creek, a small waterway that flowed right past Monsanto's plant, Ferguson put twenty-five healthy bluegills into the water to determine if it was indeed safe or not.

In a report sent directly to Monsanto, Ferguson went on record stating, "All 25 fish lost equilibrium and turned on their sides in 10 seconds and all were dead within 3½ minutes." One of his assistants at the time, Dr. George Murphy, went on to a highly distinguished career at Middle Tennessee State University where he not only Chaired the Biology Department, but oversaw Tennessee's first ever degreed program in forensic science. Murphy recalled the test at Snow Creek that caused the bluegills to spurt blood and shed their skin and scales by stating, "It was like dunking the fish in battery acid."

The results were beyond frightening. Nevertheless, to be absolutely sure Monsanto understood the gravity and cause of this crisis, Ferguson included this warning in his report, "Since this is a surface stream that passes through residential areas, it may represent a potential source of danger to children." He concluded that the root of the problem was the "extremely toxic" wastewater flowing straight from Monsanto's plant into Snow Creek. And he urged the conglomerate to not only clean up the creek, but also stop dumping its toxins there.

Snow Creek wasn't some out-of-the-way stream that led to nowhere. It was well known that it fed into the town's water supply, and it was also a place where children routinely played and people were baptized. A local mortician, Sylvester Harris, said he felt for a long time that he was burying too many kids, "I knew something was wrong around here."

Despite Ferguson's report, along with an abundance of additional damning evidence, Monsanto never warned the citizens of Anniston about the potential dangers the toxins in their water supply posed to them and their children. In fact, the conglomerate went to great lengths to cover up the truth and hide it from unsuspecting residents. About a year or so after Ferguson warned the company about Snow Creek, Monsanto circulated a confidential memo that contained an ominous line: *"We should begin to protect ourselves."* And, eventually, it seems that's exactly what the conglomerate did.

In 1997 Monsanto 'spun off' Solutia, which then became the proud owner of the toxic nightmare Monsanto left behind in Anniston. A number of people believed this move was little more than an abominable legal ploy that allowed Monsanto to wash its hands of some of its ghastly sins. Unfortunately for the people in Anniston, they would never be able to wash their hands again without wondering whether or not the water from their taps contained deadly poison.

Dr. David Carpenter, Professor of Environmental Health at the State University of New York in Albany, said about Anniston, "In my judgment, there's no question this is the most contaminated site in the U.S." But the fallout wasn't confined solely to the city limits of Anniston. In all likelihood, taxpayers in all fifty states will eventually get stuck with the colossal tab for the massive cleanup job, one that could go on for decades, much like the seemingly endless environmental decontamination efforts for Love Canal in New York and Times Beach in Missouri.

Many residents of Anniston felt that Monsanto had gotten away with nothing less than the murder of their town, with its poorest residents and minority community bearing the brunt of the toll. And when they found out that Monsanto had been covering up the truth for decades, a cynical saying circulated that "Solutia" was *Monsanto-speak* for "solution" to the despicable nightmare it left behind in Anniston.

* * *

With Anniston less than sixty-five miles as the crow flies from his own front door, Michael had heard some of the horror stories about the town. Like so many others, he felt that what Monsanto had done there was beyond unconscionable. It was an atrocity, to be sure, one that many felt defined the character of Monsanto . . . or the lack thereof.

Michael was beginning to sense where Buddy Jim's conversation was headed; his old friend hadn't specified a secret meeting and then brought up Monsanto on a whim. As a seed merchant, Michael was well aware that the giant conglomerate was 'the' major player in the emerging and often controversial business of genetically modified organisms as they pertained to seeds.[2]

Like a number of farmers, Michael had heard that Monsanto had filed suit against some farmers for planting GM seeds without permission, claiming the farmers had infringed on their patents—something that had never happened before in the history of farming, which dates back to the beginning of mankind. Worse, the farmers were threatened with financial ruin if they chose to battle the conglomerate. These were not rumors or idle gossip; this was information being discreetly passed from farmer to farmer, brothers quietly alerting each other of a ticking time bomb right outside the barn door.

Buddy Jim locked eyes with Michael, "Those creepy strangers that have been spying on you, it's gotta be Monsanto." There was no doubt whatsoever in Buddy Jim's pronouncement. He was giving his old friend

---

[2] There are several terms for laboratory derived crops (LDCs). Genetically modified organisms (GMOs), genetically modified (GM) and genetically engineered (GE) are the terms used by the industry that created them. However, all three distinctly imply that LDCs are always better than natural ones, when that is not the case. Therefore, some people prefer the term generically altered (GA), instead of GMOs, GM or GE, because it implies nothing about the quality of the crop, yet simply imparts information about its origin.

inside information, the kind that he had verified and double checked to make sure it was accurate.

This was troubling information indeed to know that a multi-billion dollar company was behind the spying and stalking. It was enough to make the hair standup on the back of Michael's neck as his blood drained all the way down to his toes.

CHAPTER 6

More often than not, when Michael was working on his farm he skipped lunch. He usually worked right through lunch time and didn't take a break until late in the evening; typically, it was the only way he could get everything done. But Oren Cantrell was working with Michael on this day so it was crucial to break for lunch.

Ever mindful that his helper had some health issues, not the least of which was that he'd lost his left arm, Michael felt it was important for Oren to eat on schedule.

Because of his health issues, it was difficult for Oren to get work, much less a steady job. A number of farmers thought he couldn't pull his end of the load, were afraid he might get injured, or both. Several people had even warned Michael against hiring Oren. One man cautioned, "That boy falls into a ditch and breaks his leg then you're gonna get sued." Never mind that someone with two arms could just as easily fall or stumble into a ditch and break their leg.

Even with the proliferation of sleazy lawyers, lawsuits against farmers were extremely rare on Sand Mountain; still, no one was immune from them. Nevertheless, Michael knew Oren loved farm work and believed everyone deserved a chance to do what made them happy and fulfilled. He'd taken more than a chance on Oren. Some would describe it as a leap of faith, but it was one he had never regretted.

He did have to make a few accommodations for Oren's special needs, but Oren more than made up for it with his loyalty and eagerness. That was more than Michael could say for some of the very people who had warned him to avoid Oren like the plague.

The Dairy Bar made Oren's favorite meal—a good, thick, juicy old-fashioned cheeseburger and fries. So whenever Oren was working for Michael, that's where he got their lunch. Even though Michael employed Oren as much as he could, the work was still sporadic, so he often picked up the lunch tab because he knew that it was difficult for Oren to make ends meet. Eating out was probably a luxury for Oren, even at the Dairy Bar where the prices appeared to have been frozen in the 1980s.

Given all the things Oren had going against him, there was never any doubt about the depth of his spirit. Michael thought the old farmer's adage 'he has a tough row to hoe' fit Oren's situation rather well, which was why he admired the man so much. Oren was neither a whiner or complainer, nor was he bitter about his lot in life. He just wanted to be accepted and have a chance to make his own way.

Loaded down with burgers and fries, Michael parked beside the field where Oren was working. As soon as Oren saw him, he shut down the tractor he was driving, hopped off, and sprinted the sixty or so yards to Michael as fast as he could. He was screaming and waving his arm; something was obviously wrong.

By the time he got to Michael, Oren could barely breathe, much less talk. It took a bit before he could catch his breath and share with Michael a series of incidents he conveyed as if disclosing top-secret information, "There's a black truck, a Toyota. I think it's a right new full-size one. And it keeps running by here, back and forth, back and forth. I counted fourteen times already since 'round eight this morning."

Michael felt that Oren sometimes could get a bit unhinged by little things that might not faze others, and there was certainly no law against anyone driving by fourteen times, or even two-hundred-and-fourteen, on a public road. Still, considering recent events it was more than merely odd that a truck would simply drive by all morning, over and over again, in an area where there wasn't a single store, gas station or restaurant for miles. Michael's wife and children had also seen suspicious people and vehicles lurking around. It was long past the point where they felt safe anymore, even in their own backyard. Realizing he couldn't take this lightly, not with all the spies snooping around and hiding behind fake tags, Michael wanted to have the facts straight. "Say it was a full-size Toyota?"

Oren nodded vigorously, "Solid black. And it looked right new."

Although most of the farmers in the area owned full-size Ford, Chevy, or Dodge trucks, a few had Toyotas, though Michael couldn't recall a single one of them being black. At that moment, while he racked his brain trying to think of someone with a full-size Toyota truck—any color—who might have a reason to pass by his farm time and time again, as if operating on cue a truck came cruising by. And just like Oren had said, it was a solid black, late-model Toyota Tundra. Both Michael and Oren just stared with gaping mouths. The timing couldn't have been better. Oren finally broke the silence by yelling, "That's it! That's it!" and jumping and pointing with a combination of vindication and distress.

"You stay put." Michael commanded as he hopped in his Dodge truck. In no time Michael was kicking up an enormous cloud of dust as he raced along beside his field, then squealed the tires as he veered onto the paved county road. It was enough to alert the Toyota's driver that Michael was after him, and a puff of smoke shot out the Tundra's tailpipe—the tell-tale sign its driver had accelerated like a thief to flee the scene.

Standing on the gas and gripping the steering wheel hard, Michael lasered in on the Toyota as the asphalt between the trucks disappeared beneath him. And in short order he was flooring his brakes just to keep from ramming the Toyota from behind.

It wasn't until Michael was on the Toyota's bumper that the occupants of the Tundra, a male driver and female passenger, realized he had caught up with them. The driver did a double take, and then kept glancing in his rearview mirror. Finally, in an effort to make a run for it, he floored the Toyota, but Michael quickly and easily caught up. He wouldn't let these spies come into his world and get away with scaring Oren half to death. Oren hadn't done anything to deserve that kind of treatment, and whatever it was these two were up to, he didn't need to get sucked into their sordid scheme.

Toyotas are thought of as rock solid by many, but they're not powerhouses, and it was no match for Michael's Dodge, not in a street race. It didn't take long for the Tundra's driver to realize this. So he slowed down to a pedestrian cruising speed of about 50 mph. But that presented a problem all its own: if the man knew his way around these back roads, ones with few signs or markers, this could go on for hours, basically until the Toyota or the Dodge ran out of fuel.

Although Michael's tank was almost full, he quickly evaluated the situation and reasoned that it wasn't wise to burn that much fuel along with hours and hours of his valuable time pursuing this truck. He had a farm and a business to run. He certainly didn't have time for an asinine game of follow-the-leader.

Just as Michael was about to peel off and the let stranger win this round, he caught a break. The Toyota came to a fork in the road and took the left side, which was not only a detour off the main road, it was a dead end.

Michael had to wonder, did the driver know what he was doing? Did he know he had turned onto a dead end? A half dozen different scenarios shot through Michael's head, and they were all extremely unsettling. Was it a trap? Did the interloper have a gang of thugs down there ready to ambush Michael if he followed?

Once on the dead end road, the Toyota slowed down considerably. Michael slowed down, as well, staying close enough so that the driver of the Toyota knew he wasn't going away. Without realizing it, Michael had made the decision to play this out to the end.

Finally, the Toyota went from a slow rolling crawl to a complete stop. Yet it was so gradual Michael never even saw its brake lights turn on.

Still mindful there could be a trap in store, Michael carefully maneuvered his Dodge behind the Toyota to block its escape, while still offering him the option of a quick getaway, if needed.

Neither the man nor the woman in the Toyota made an attempt to get out and confront Michael. Instead, they sat perfectly still, as if it was the most normal thing in the world to stop their truck on a dead end country road in the middle of nowhere and then just stare straight ahead, totally ignoring the vehicle behind them.

For a minute or two Michael simply sat in his truck. He figured a bit of the old "waiting game" wouldn't hurt at this point. If the people in the Toyota thought they were playing mind games with Michael, he'd deal them a hand of the same. In the meantime, he jotted down the Toyota's tag number, and double checked it to be absolutely sure he got it right.

Exhaling loudly, Michael decided it was time to end the stalemate. So he stepped out of his truck and, using caution but going to great lengths to appear casual, walked toward the Toyota. Although he'd already had a bird's eye view of the tag, Michael took an even closer look as he approached the truck. It was not only current, even the sticker on it was up to date.

Reaching the Toyota's passenger side, which was far more accessible than the driver's side because of overgrown weeds and brush, Michael tapped on the glass. Instead of rolling down the window, the woman opened the door. Michael's instant reaction was to jump back, almost certain that either the man or woman or possibly both had a gun. But if he jumped, that might spook them and make them shoot. So he bit his lip and remained calm, at least on the outside, and didn't even flinch.

With the door of the Toyota now wide open, Michael had a clear view of the truck's interior, including the occupants. The man, probably fifty-something, perhaps even in his sixties, was short, thin, with snow white hair and a mustache to match. The oversized mustache reminded Michael of someone who was trying to look like a cowboy from the 1800s, yet couldn't pull off that masculine look. This wannabe cowpoke was staring straight ahead, as if Michael didn't exist. The woman, however, was looking directly at Michael. She was probably ten years younger than the driver, but it was hard to tell for sure because she was wearing far more makeup than Michael was accustomed to seeing on women out here in farm country. She looked a bit like a young girl who was experimenting with makeup for the first time, and thought more meant better. Of course, it did occur to him that it could actually be a surreptitious disguise. Without it, there was probably no way he could pick her out of a police line up.

Realizing that neither the man nor woman would be the first to break the awkward silence, Michael stepped up. "Y'all scared my hired man," he said. "Had him pretty shook up."

"That so?" the lady asked innocently. "How'd we do that?" She made it sound as if she had no earthly idea how they could have upset anyone. Michael quickly surmised that lying probably came very easy to her, and that she was likely quite good at it.

"You run by my farm about fourteen times this morning. Didn't you?" Michael didn't make it sound like a criminal accusation, more like he'd caught an aimless teenager without a hall pass.

When the man finally spoke, his voice was laced with pompous sarcasm. "Ain't no law against using a public road," he said, locking eyes with Michael for the first time. "Is there now?"

"Naw, there sure ain't. But my hired hand, well, sometimes he gets spooked by things. And this time I can't say I blame him." Michael let out a deep breath. He decided to play another card altogether. "You see, we've had some creepy strangers spying on us, snooping around, taking lots of pictures of us - - - me and my family, that is, and I got young kids - - - and taking 'em without anybody's permission." Even as Michael said the words he saw part of an expensive telephoto lens poking out from under the front seat of the truck, right where the woman's feet were trying to hide it. But what really caught his eye was a piece of paper lying on the seat between the man and woman. On it, Michael clearly saw his own name and the notation "400 acres," a figure that closely corresponded with the number of acres of soybeans he was cultivating. But instead of confronting them, Michael decided to play along with their little game. He wanted to see where it would go, and what kind of lies the man and woman would tell him.

The man loosened up a tad, probably because he'd pegged Michael for a country bumpkin, and figured he was clueless. Most likely, the man felt he was already two steps ahead of this rube. "We're just out here looking for old cemeteries," he casually explained. "Doing genealogy research on my family."

It was a rather inventive lie, but Michael knew exactly how to counter it. "I've lived around here all my life. Matter of fact, my family's been around here for generations. Maybe I can help," he offered. "What's your name?"

Michael could see the lie forming before the man even opened his mouth. The man hesitated, then repeated Michael's question to buy some time. "What's my name? You wanna know my name?" Michael nodded.

He wasn't going to repeat his own question for this sleazy character and give him any extra time to cook up a bogus answer.

Without batting an eye, the driver of the Toyota announced in a haughty voice, "Blackman. My name's Blackman. Lowden Blackman." Michael was certain he'd conjured the name out of thin air, which was all the more odd because the man actually appeared to be proud of his fabricated lineage.

Perhaps fearing that Michael might ask a probing question that would trip "Lowden" up, the passenger jumped into the conversation to take the pressure off her partner, "Know any cemeteries around here with any Blackmans in 'em?"

All Michael could do was shake his head. "No, I can't say I do," he answered. Then, almost as an after thought, he added "I know of some cemeteries around here with Blacks in 'em, but no Blackmans."

The man instantly shook his head and gestured with a sweep of his hand, "I'm not talking about black people." Then he cocked his head and with a voice just above a whisper, the kind someone might use when requesting confidential information that would be 'off the record,' added, "By the way, we ain't seen any blacks since we've been here. Don't you find that kind of strange?"

Michael knew immediately that the pseudo cowpoke hiding behind a fake name was trying to set him up and goad him into making a racist remark. But Lowden wasn't just barking up the wrong tree, he wasn't even in the right forest. It was diametrically against Michael's religion to be prejudiced. Michael leaned his head inside the truck so that he could go eyeball to eyeball with the sleazy spy. But the interloper claiming to be Lowden Blackman was having none of it; he wouldn't even look in Michael's direction.

It was important for Michael to not only be cool, calm, and collected, but to also telegraph his demeanor to the man who refused to look his way. So in a pleasant yet firm voice he explained, "There's black people buried in cemeteries around here. But what I meant was, there's some people named Black in some cemeteries, but no Blackmans. Nobody with that last name that I know of."

Lowden seemed to realize his little trap had been used on the wrong person, so he clammed up, averted his eyes and let the woman take over. "Where's the cemetery with Blacks in it?" she asked. "The people named Black?"

At that point, Michael decided to go out of his way to be exceedingly cordial. He gave the two the impression that he believed every word of their half-baked story and genuinely wanted to assist them in finding the graves of their long-lost relatives.

There were several cemeteries with Blacks in them. But Michael gave them directions to one in particular, one on a dead end road just like this one. Then, without further ado, he wished them good luck finding their relatives and then walked back to his truck.

As Michael got inside and started the engine, he was already working on his next two moves, one of which would require expert timing.

* * *

Vern Phelps was an old pal of Michael's, and all too happy to oblige his friend's request for a favor. He didn't even have a lot of questions when Michael asked him to drive to an old cemetery that had been neglected for a number of years and perform a confidential reconnaissance mission. He trusted Michael and knew him well enough to know there had to be a genuinely good basis for all this intrigue and secrecy.

Riding his trusty Kawasaki ATV, Vern scooted across one of his pastures and then quickly maneuvered his way through a forest so dense it looked like dusk even at high noon. Coming to the edge of the forest, he was less than seventy-five yards from the old cemetery. Then, doing just as Michael had instructed, he dismounted his handy yet noisy ATV and walked the rest of the way to avoid detection.

No more than thirty or forty feet from the fence surrounding the old cemetery, Vern took cover behind some heavy foliage. A life long hunter and former soldier, he was quite adept at blending into his surroundings. Looking through his binoculars, he got a bead on the area. And it was just what he expected. No one had been buried in the graveyard since the 1950s or 60s, so the old road leading to it was forlorn and in danger of being taken over by kudzu and other weeds.

After less than fifteen minutes of standing at the ready—just as Michael had calculated, Vern watched a black Toyota truck drive up to the cemetery. Michael had figured, rightly so, that Lowden would have to at least pretend to follow up on the information he gave him, or risk being exposed as a blatant fraud. Of course, Michael already knew he was a spy. But Lowden didn't know that.

With Vern safely hidden from prying eyes, he watched intently as a man and woman got out of the Toyota, ones who matched the description Michael had given him to a 't'. Lowden immediately made a call on his cell phone while the woman busied herself loading film into an SLR camera, one with a very long and large lens. Vern had never seen one that big in real life, but he saw them all the time on TV on the sidelines of football games. It was the kind of high-dollar telephoto lens that pros use to get perfect shots from long distances in situations where you don't get any second chances.

Lowden appeared to be quite agitated during his phone call, though Vern couldn't hear anything being said because of the distance between them. Once Lowden ended his call, the couple got back into the truck and drove off. Vern noted that, just as Michael had predicted, neither the man nor woman ever looked at a single tombstone. In fact, they never even entered the cemetery, nor did the female ever aim her camera at it.

* * *

The vast parking lot of the Wal-Mart was beginning to empty on this cold and dreary night. The store would be closing soon. Michael slowly drove to the back of the lot until he spotted what he was looking for, an unmarked patrol car. He parked beside it so that his driver's side window was facing the driver's side window of the patrol car.

The deputy let his window down, and Michael did the same. They both exchanged perfunctory greetings, then the deputy confirmed Michael's suspicions by telling him what he was expecting to hear. "The plate on that black Toyota truck you called in is bogus, just like the one on that white GMC truck. The tag on the Toyota came off a wrecked Oldsmobile; got totaled-out years ago."

"The tag had a new sticker on it; looked up to date." Michael said. "I saw it myself."

"They probably made it on a computer. Wouldn't be hard," the deputy responded. "Besides, anybody who'd use a bogus tag wouldn't think twice about counterfeiting a sticker for one. Crooks'll do anything to try and keep from getting caught."

Michael nodded in agreement, then looked the deputy in the eyes. "A pretty good source tells me that a great big company called Monsanto is behind this," he said. "I figure these people are their spies."

The deputy was obviously taken aback, if not more than a little skeptical. "What in the world is a big company after you for?" Left unsaid was the fact that, like most people, he thought it was absurd to even insinuate that a multinational conglomerate employed spies to watch farmers in rural

Alabama, especially not spies using stolen tags.

"I'm not one-hundred percent sure yet."

Speaking more like a friend than a law officer, the deputy told Michael, "Next time you see any of these spies, or whoever it is, you call me." The deputy was convinced that Michael was being followed, and by someone using fake tags, but not for a moment did he buy into the 'utterly preposterous' notion that a multi-billion dollar company was behind the stalking. Even so, he had enough respect for Michael not to voice his opinion.

"I'm hoping to do better than that," Michael responded as he got out of his truck and headed toward the Wal-Mart, all the while realizing that the deputy had serious doubts about who was stalking him. Truth is, Michael could easily understand the deputy's skepticism. If it wasn't happening to him and his family, he'd probably be a doubter himself, because what was going on was so outlandishly bizarre and sounded so farfetched that it would have taxed the credibility of Honest Abe.

As the deputy drove off, Michael slowly made his way across the enormous parking lot all alone; never had he felt so small and vulnerable. Even at that moment one of Monsanto's henchmen could be watching him. A corporation that size could blanket the mountain with spies. He wanted to scan the area and check for prying eyes, but realized it would be playing into their hands. Michael had been incredibly lucky that his confrontation with Lowden turned out reasonably cordial, even if the spy had dumped a barn load of lies on him. Next time he might not be so fortunate. That meant he had to document this harassment so no one could write it off as a figment of his imagination.

Michael didn't know much about cameras, but he had come to the conclusion that he needed one. He would have loved to have caught the pseudo Mr. & Ms. Blackman on videotape. After all, he reasoned, if

Monsanto's spies were taking pictures of him, he certainly had a right
to do the same to them.

* * *

A few days later, Michael and Buddy Jim met again at their secluded
location. Buddy Jim pulled a manila envelope from inside his jacket. He
stared at it a moment, then looked up at Michael. "You know any folks
down in Florida?" he asked.

"No, can't say I do." Michael said with a shrug. "Why?"

Buddy Jim took a medium-sized photo out of the envelope and held
it up for Michael's inspection. "Ever seen this fellow before?"

Michael nodded. "Sure have. That's the man that was driving the
black Toyota I told you about."

"He's from Florida and his name's Lowden, Lowden Brown."

"He told me that his first name's Lowden. But said his last name was
Blackman." Michael cleared his throat "Said he was doing genealogy
research; looking through old cemeteries for his relatives." He grimaced
as he said, "But I didn't believe him."

Buddy Jim put the photo back in the envelope. "I'm told he's
Monsanto's lead investigator. And from what I hear they must want
you bad, because they're pouring money into this thing. That means
Lowden's gonna have help, lots of it."

Upon hearing this chilling news, Michael tried mightily to keep his
emotions in check, but it was an extremely difficult task for a father with
two young children, what with sleazy spies lurking about, hiding their
identities behind stolen tags. There was simply no way around it:
Michael feared down in the pit of his gut that if these slimy stalkers were
to do something to his family it might be impossible to track them down,
much less hold them accountable.

The mere notion that any company, big or small, would knowingly subject a human being to this kind of mental anguish and torture was a flagrant American tragedy. Yet there was more. Buddy Jim locked eyes with Michael and told him what he'd heard from a man representing Monsanto, and it was certainly not the kind of thing any friend wants to tell another friend. "That fellow mentioned your name in particular. I think they're gonna make an example out of you."

CHAPTER 7

As days, weeks, and months slipped away, the spying and stalking only got worse. Monsanto's goons got more brazen with time, and although they were still hiding their true identities behind illegal tags, it seemed as if there were now more of them than ever before. To compound matters, calling in a spy's tag to the sheriff's department was a complete waste of time. All they could do was confirm that a tag didn't match the vehicle it was on. Worse, Michael suspected he was being tailed on a daily basis.

After a farmer and one of Monsanto's henchmen got "entangled" it was obvious that the situation was a tinderbox, the kind with the potential for violence. So an influential local politician, Edwin Dobbs, called a secret meeting to address the concerns of farmers about the interlopers. Only a select few farmers were invited, people who were the backbone and leaders of the farming community, which included Michael. But farmers weren't the only ones invited. Buddy Jim was there, as was a high ranking state official. Although Dobbs was clearly running this show, it was the state official who provided some decidedly sobering news. He pronounced that he had gotten word straight from the horse's mouth that Monsanto was planning to sue seventy-five farmers in Alabama for patent infringement. However, he didn't say if that was an estimate or an exact number. Regardless, it was a chilling pronouncement to every farmer at the meeting, especially so for Michael given that he was already directly in the crosshairs' of Monsanto's spies.

* * *

The brass and intrusive behavior of the spies, nor the threat of a lawsuit, could change the fact that Michael still had to earn a living, he still had to keep his farm and seed business running and take care of his family and watch over his elderly parents.

Although it hurt Michael deeply to see his mother wasting away from terminal cancer, he cherished every moment he had with her. But visiting her wasn't always easy. Determined not to let Monsanto's spies interfere with his visits, he had to vary his routine, never stopping by to see her at the same time on any two consecutives days.

On days when Michael was headed to his mother's and spotted a tail, invariably, he took them on a wild and wooly ride down a hodgepodge of old logging roads that were more obstacle course than roadway. Once he had shaken them, which could be quite difficult, only then did he go visit his mother. He would not let these spies—little more than thugs who knew full well his mother was terminally ill and in great pain—have the satisfaction of invading his privacy during the precious visiting time he had left with her.

Leaning back in a chair beside Virginia's sickbed, Michael let out a deep sigh and then just tried to breathe easily. It was nice to think he could. The stress brought on by the stalkers had made it increasingly difficult for him to relax. Just being near his mother provided him with a calming effect. She was his haven from the merciless storm that engulfed him.

Moving ever so carefully, Michael reached over and gently took his mother's hand, then leaned close to her, "Momma, I gotta get back to work. But don't you worry, I'll be by tomorrow to visit." He gently kissed her forehead and then whispered, "I love you."

* * *

One particular day at White's Seed had been tedious and frustrating. To compound matters, Percy McCulver, a crotchety old fellow, had been in the store most of the morning complaining about everything from politics to potholes.

Although Percy could be a real pain sometimes, Michael had a soft spot for him because he was from his parent's generation. He appreciated that Percy brought life experiences to the table he didn't have, particularly that he had endured extreme poverty during his childhood, the kind most people can't imagine, much less have survived. That alone meant Percy had a far different perspective than most.

Still, as much as Michael appreciated and respected Percy, he could try the patience of Job. With Percy gnawing on his ear relentlessly, Michael had suffered through one of his most unproductive days in quite awhile. That meant as soon as supper was over, he'd be headed straight back to the store to take care of all the work he hadn't gotten done during the day. Of course, that would be on top of a pile of paperwork he needed to sort through for his farming operation.

As he pulled into his driveway, Michael was already sorting out in his mind how he'd accomplish both the leftover tasks at his seed business as well as the paperwork for his farm, all before his normal bedtime of midnight. No matter how he juggled things, it appeared sleep was going to be the loser tonight.

Michael had been so preoccupied that he hadn't even noticed a late model sedan in his driveway. Leaning against it was a skinny young man, probably no more than twenty-four or twenty-five, wearing a dark blazer and a tie.

Naturally, Michael was now leery of anyone he didn't know, especially a stranger this far from town wearing a coat and tie. Although the young man looked harmless enough, that didn't mean anything. After getting out of his truck, Michael greeted the man with more than a bit of trepidation. "What can I do for you?" he asked.

"You're Michael White, right?"

"Yeah," Michael said, though not quite sure if he should have divulged that information to the stranger.

With a quick and agile gait, the young man headed toward Michael and when he got within five or six steps thrust his hand inside his jacket. The motion was swift and fluid; it was obviously a practiced move. Michael instantly figured he had a gun. Was he a hit man? Was this how Michael would die?—right on his own front lawn? Would his young children be the ones to find his bullet riddled body?

Before Michael had time to react the young man forcefully stuffed a large envelope in the crook of his arm and pronounced. "Michael White, you've officially been served."

Michael wanted to throw the envelope down on the ground and walk away in disgust. But he realized it was too late. Instead, he handled it gingerly, keeping the envelope at arms-length from his body as he grimaced. "This can't be good." then sighed. "Guess this is from Monsanto, right?"

The young man ignored Michael's question as if it was irrelevant and then, pulling a second envelope from inside his jacket, asked one of his own instead. "You got a relative named Wayne White?"

The question blindsided Michael as if the young man had slammed a baseball bat into his gut, and it felt like he was swinging for the fences. Michael had to steady himself before he could answer. "Wayne's my daddy." Even though a sickening feeling told him he already knew the answer, he had to ask the obvious question. "That envelope's for my daddy, ain't it?"

"If his name's Wayne White, then 'yep,'" the process server replied. "Mind telling me where he lives? I had a devil of a time finding your house."

Michael spoke from his heart. Given the circumstances, it was the only way he could respond. "My daddy'll be eighty years old in a few days. His health ain't good. And my momma, God bless her, she's dying of cancer. She's bedridden and Daddy's the only one she'll let look after her." Michael exhaled a deep breath. "Momma and Daddy ain't never had a day of trouble with the law in their lives." Moving his hand very slowly and deliberately, Michael reached out to the process server. "Lemme deliver this one for you. A thing like this could kill Daddy. And Momma couldn't last a week without him. You wouldn't want their blood on your hands. You ain't that sort. I can see it in your eyes."

It's doubtful that a seasoned process server would have been swayed in the least by Michael's heartfelt appeal, but this young one mulled his words over carefully. Finally, the process server asked a pointed question. "You swear you'll give it to him?"

Michael nodded. "You've got my word."

A brief moment passed, yet it was time enough for the young man to read Michael. The lines of time and hard work on Michael's face told his story. In a world overrun by crooks, liars, cheaters, and thieves, Michael was a dying breed, a man whose word was still his bond. He was an honorable human being, and the process server instinctively knew it.

Cocking his head ever-so-slightly, the young process server gently put the envelope meant for Wayne White in Michael's hand. "If I say this was delivered and it's not, well . . . " He hesitated for a long moment before adding. "I can wind up in jail."

"If whoever you work for would even think about throwing you in jail for helping an old man who's caring for his terminally ill wife, well, if I was you I'd be looking for a new line of work." The process server nodded in agreement as he released his hold on the envelope. With his business concluded, he got in his car and drove away. Michael waited until the sedan was out of sight before he felt he could breathe. But even so, he was still reeling from the news that his father was also being sued. Michael never knew when spying eyes and their cameras were watching, and he definitely wanted to open his envelope in private. Although he already had a good idea as to its contents, he didn't want Monsanto's spies to see how it affected him. He made it a point to walk casually into his garage and then close the door, but once inside he ripped open the envelope as if it were on fire. He quickly unfolded the official legal document and read it aloud to himself.

Filed on October 15, 2003
United States District Court
Northern District of Alabama
Northeastern Division
Monsanto Company, Plaintiff,
vs.
Michael White, Wayne White,
White's Seed Cleaning, and
White Farms Feed & Seed, Inc.,
Defendants

The suit against Michael was not unexpected. The state official had specifically warned him awhile back about Monsanto's plan to sue seventy-five farmers in Alabama, and he'd been told he was one of the main targets. Even so, no one said anything about Wayne being on the dreaded list. Plus, the last thing Michael wanted to do was cause his family any more grief. They were upset enough without this latest bombshell, what with all the spying and stalking. So he put the document back in the envelope, exited the garage and walked back to his truck. He often kept important documents in the glove box, sometimes for days or even weeks. He might need one document or another to conduct business, and driving back and forth between his business, farm, home, and safe deposit box at a bank in town simply wasn't remotely convenient or feasible in a rural area like this.

Moments after Michael opened his glove box his blood went cold. For a long time all he could do was stare with anger, revulsion, frustration and disbelief.

The papers inside had been completely rearranged. Had one of Monsanto's spies rifled through them? If so, they had probably used gloves so it would be hard if not impossible to prove. Regardless, this meant every document would have to be moved to a safer place. Fighting the natural urge to scan the area for prying eyes, Michael wondered if he was being watched even now. It was the most unsettling feeling imaginable, to think that at any moment, no matter where he was, a stalker for hire with no conscience could be peeping on him and his family during the utmost private and intimate moments of their lives.

Before leaving his truck he discreetly stuck a twig in the bottom of each door in a way that wouldn't draw attention, yet would let him know if someone opened either of them. It was sad that he had to booby trap his own truck, but he'd had enough noses stuck into his business for one day.

* * *

It was after midnight when Michael left his seed business. Although he had finally gotten everything done, he was beat. Unfortunately, the paperwork for the farm that had piled up didn't care how tired he was. There was no getting around the fact that it had to be done, so as soon as he got home he took a seat at the old desk his father had once used and set to work. The desk wasn't an heirloom, not by any stretch, or even anything special. Wayne had probably bought it at a local furniture store, or maybe he had swapped something for it. Wayne never had much cash, especially back when he was farming. It was the reason he parked his plow for good way back in 1971, back when Michael was still in high school. His father hated to give up farming, but he'd been offered a good job working for the Tennessee Valley Authority, and he just couldn't deny his family the security and benefits a position like that provided.

As he shuffled through the paperwork, Michael tried to focus on the task at hand. But his mind kept wandering over to the strongbox in which he'd locked up the papers for the lawsuit. He'd never actually finished reading the entire document. It had turned his stomach so much that he figured he'd just hold off until morning. After all, from the little he had read there was nothing good in it. And he was willing to bet the more he read the worse it would get. Still, he couldn't concentrate. The unknown was haunting him.

With a deep sigh, Michael slid his chair back and wheeled around so that he was within arm's length of his strong box. It was an antiquated metal box with a tiny Master Lock safeguarding its contents. The lock was probably thirty or forty years old, maybe even older, but it was in great shape. Perhaps that was partially due to the fact that no one had ever tampered with it; it had only been exposed to honest people. Inserting the key, Michael popped open the old lock. Even though the box was filled with important papers, the envelope he'd just received from the process server was right on top and sticking out like an open sore. For a long time all he could do was stare at it, and it appeared to almost stare back at him.

Finally, after what seemed like a very long time, Michael gently picked up the envelope, removed the documents from it, and then leaned back in his chair. It was time to find out exactly what Monsanto had cooked up.

Michael read the lawsuit through once from beginning to end, and then read it again. In total he read the document four times before he finally felt he had a basic grasp of the convoluted legalese.

In essence, Monsanto was claiming that he had saved their GM seeds without their permission, and that by doing so he had infringed on their patent, simply known as "605." The suit went on to claim that Michael had knowingly cleaned Monsanto's patented seeds for another farmer so that the seeds could be "replanted" the following year, an action that was in direct violation of the "technology agreement" Monsanto claimed every farmer had to sign before they could use their GM seeds.

Even if a farmer hadn't signed the agreement, the conglomerate claimed that by merely opening a bag of its GM seeds the farmer automatically entered into an agreement with the conglomerate. Apparently, the fine print on the bag of seeds made a farmer totally accountable to Monsanto, and—seemingly—anybody who did business with that farmer, as well. It meant that third parties were bound by and accountable to an agreement they had not signed . . . or even seen.

Michael could only imagine how much Monsanto would demand in 'damages' from him—as if a farmer in rural Alabama could 'damage' a multibillion dollar conglomerate. He read the word "treble" in the suit, and took it to mean that Monsanto was asking for triple the damages it 'felt' it was due. No doubt, it would probably demand more than he had, even if he sold off everything he owned, including the old desk and strong box.

The thought of losing everything was overwhelming, so Michael tried to clear his head of the matter. But he couldn't. Something else was eating at him, something that happened a number of years ago. Back around '96 and '97, maybe even '98, Monsanto was passing out free seeds to some farmers. Their reps were claiming the seeds could increase yields and would allow farmers to spray their fields with the company's Roundup weed killer without harming the crop. Essentially, they were touted as the answers to a farmer's problems. These seeds purportedly produced higher yields at less cost and weeds, with the aid of Roundup, would no longer pose a problem. And to prove these exalted claims farmers could try the seeds for free with no obligation or commitment. No strings attached. But even back then someone had been suspicious enough to raise a red flag.

It had been none other than Percy McCulver.

Michael let his mind wander back several years, back when Percy had squawked and grumbled, "Mark my words, these big old companies don't just hand out stuff for nuthin'. Sooner or later, this'll cost you."

Of course, no one had listened to Percy; most tuned him out after the first or second word left his mouth because he was one of the most negative people around. Instead of looking for the gold lining, he looked for the mold, and as far as Percy was concerned he always found it.

Although Michael never got any seeds whatsoever from a Monsanto rep, it seemed this time there was definitely mold to be found, and he had found it. Or, more to the point, it found him.

CHAPTER 8

Before Michael knew it, the first rays of morning sun were seeping through pinholes in the fabric of the curtain near his desk. He peeked out the window and squinted. In a few more minutes a bright, daisy-yellow sphere would be hovering just above the ridge. The day was already starting to bloom. Normally by this time he'd have already logged at least an hour or more on the farm or at his store, but not today. He was way behind schedule, yet for once it didn't bother him because there were more important things to sort out.

Michael leaned back and yawned loudly. He was tired, but not totally spent. If he got a nap at some point during the day he could tough it out. After all, this wasn't his first all-nighter. He'd pulled more than a few working on his farm, even a few at the seed store, but this had been his first sitting behind a computer.

With the lawsuit hanging over his head like a freshly sharpened guillotine, Michael had to wonder, "How had Monsanto managed to change the rules without anyone having a vote?" He knew he certainly hadn't gotten one. It was as if there had been a coup and overnight Monsanto had placed itself in charge of agriculture. Now every farmer had to bow and scrape at the feet of the same company that secretly dumped tons and tons of toxins into the ground and water in Anniston—or risk losing their farm.

Another part of the lawsuit that had made Michael's head spin all night was the allegation that he—as proprietor of a seed cleaning business—had illegally cleaned Monsanto's GM seeds for a farmer. To confound matters, the conglomerate's lawyers insisted that was a big no-no simply because the farmer—*not Michael, the seed cleaner*—had entered into an agreement with the company not to save their seeds. Although Monsanto readily admitted that Michael had never signed one of their "technology agreements," it claimed he *should* have known it was illegal to clean their seeds.

There were several problems with the conglomerate's claim that no one could save their seeds. The most obvious was that farmers have been saving seeds since time immemorial. Telling them to stop was the equivalent of telling motorists to go on red and stop on green and expect compliance overnight. The second issue was that reps hawking Monsanto's technology had used highly questionable tactics to convince farmers to try GM seeds in the first place. A smiling sales rep would show up at a farmer's barn or his backdoor and offer to give him some seeds containing Monsanto's "technology." These GM seeds—a new concept to farmers, at least in Michael's area—were purported to produce higher yields than natural seeds. The rep would assure the farmer that he could use the seeds any way he chose. He could even plant them right along with the seeds he'd been using.

On the surface, it sounded like a win-win situation for farmers. Free seeds, especially ones allegedly superior to the trusty standbys they'd been using for years, decades, or even generations, seemed like a gift from heaven. And the reps weren't just handing out token samples, they were giving them away by the sackful—50-pound bags. The scuttlebutt was that some of the farmers in Michael's area got enough of the so-called free seeds—thousands of dollars worth—to plant several hundred acres with them.

Based on what several farmers told Michael, those free seeds came in "brown bags"—some in white ones. The term "brown bag" to Michael meant that there were no labels on them. To add to the confusion, the GM seeds distributed in brown bags looked just like natural ones. That alone created a disturbing set of questions: Exactly how were farmers and seed cleaners supposed to tell them apart? What if a batch of GM seeds originating from brown bags accidentally got mixed in with natural seeds? Did Monsanto really expect farmers and seed cleaners to have a scientist on staff with exorbitantly expensive DNA testing equipment at the ready to separate GM seeds from natural ones?

A truly troubling issue was the brown bags themselves. It bewildered Michael that the users of a product, one that arrives in a brown bag and is indistinguishable by the naked eye from the original version it was copied from, could now be sued because they violated a patent on the "new" product. The patent certainly wasn't stamped on the GM seeds.

Four or five years before Michael was sued by Monsanto, a fellow farmer, Aaron King, got some GM soybean seeds from a local rep, Lyle Rowe. King told Michael the GM seeds were not only free, but delivered in brown bags; Rowe even told King face-to-face he could do whatever he wanted with them. Naturally, King took Rowe at his word that there were no strings attached. After all, they were a gift.

Like a number of other farmers, King tried the free GM seeds. After harvesting his crop and mining the seeds, he brought them to Michael to be cleaned. As partial payment on his cleaning bill, King gave Michael some of the seeds, a common practice. Michael, in turn, planted them, and then did what farmers have been doing for thousands of years; after harvesting his crop he saved the seeds, cleaned them, and then replanted them in the spring.

In an effort to stay competitive in a very difficult occupation, Michael prided himself on trying new things, experimenting and looking to the future. Yet right away he noticed that the GM seeds produced lower yields than the natural seeds he'd been using. Still, he wanted to give them a fair shot, and one year was certainly not enough for that. So he planted them for successive years, even increasing the acreage he planted. He even sold some of the seeds to other farmers, a routine practice for a seed business.

After giving the GM seeds a fair chance—planting them for about four years, Michael concluded that they had been a bust on his farm. So he stopped using them altogether and went back to the dependable natural seeds he'd used for years and years.

Based on Michael's firsthand experience, Monsanto's genetically modified Roundup Ready Soybeans were over hyped and presented a step in the wrong direction. They made about as much sense to him as throwing away a sturdy and dependable ladder and replacing it with a gimmicky and flimsy stepstool that costs more and does less.

Another problem with Monsanto's claim was that it contradicted Michael's license to clean seeds, a bona fide license granted by Alabama's Department of Agriculture, which was governed by the U.S. Department of Agriculture. Unlike the GM seeds that were given away in plain brown bags with no writing on them, the rules for his license were spelled out in detail. Among the many 'do's and don't's', Michael was told he could not refuse to clean anyone's seeds. The real kicker was: Michael's license had been granted many years before Monsanto ever sold—or even gave away—the GM seeds they made in their labs.

Michael was convinced this situation was the epitome of audacity: a multibillion dollar company with all the advantages and the deck completely stacked it its favor expected cash-strapped, overworked, and underpaid farmers and seed cleaners to accommodate it. Never mind that when it gave away its 'unmarked' GM seeds that action created an "implied license." The implied license, a staple of law and common sense, grants the recipient of a gift the right to do whatever he chooses with it, so long as there are no visible signs of a copyright, patent or other mandates that would limit those rights.

One particular aspect of Monsanto's legal action had piqued Michael's curiosity. Given that he was told by people he trusted that the local reps for Monsanto had misled farmers in Jackson County, Alabama: Had reps in other areas done the same? Using his computer, it took Michael only a few key strokes to discover that lawsuits had been filed in a number of states and even across international borders. Farmers in Canada had been sued, as well.

Michael reasoned that if farmers in other states and Canada had the same complaints that he and some other local farmers had, then odds were the problem wasn't confined to a few rogue seed reps in rural Alabama.

Michael stepped into the bathroom near his desk and splashed cold water on his face. He wanted to be wide awake. There was too much important information to digest to be anything less than 100 percent alert. As he dried off his face he took a long, hard look at himself in the mirror. He wondered what Monsanto saw when they looked at him, as well as other farmers. Were they valued customers? Or something else entirely?

It wasn't easy to find a dishonest farmer. To be sure, they were out there. Michael knew a few. But they were the exception to the rule. Gullible farmers, however, were as common as pig tracks on a hog farm. Michael knew lots of them, and to a degree he considered himself one, as well. Michael kept the keys to every tractor he had ever owned right in the ignition, and they were always parked in such a way that they were easily accessible. This wasn't done to test the honesty of his neighbors. It simply came with the territory. There was an unwritten rule among Michael and his fellow farmers that if anyone was in the middle of planting or harvesting, or any crucial endeavor, and his tractor broke down he could simply go borrow one from his neighbor. If no one was around, he didn't even have to ask permission. The only stipulation was that he bring it back in the condition he found it.

Unlike the supermarkets and stores that sell the food farmers grow, farmers have rarely seen themselves as competitors with one another. The vast majority of them recognize that they're all in the same boat— at this point a lifeboat—and that everyone has to paddle, bail, and steer together as a team to keep it afloat.

Michael deduced that Monsanto had made it their business to get inside the heads of farmers and find out what made them tick. The company figured out that farmers were honest, decent, trusting people who would hand over the shirt off their backs and then ask if there was anything else they could do.

Staring long and hard at his own reflection in the mirror, Michael felt he knew what Monsanto and its reps saw when they sized him up, or any farmer for that matter. They saw a guileless bumpkin who could be easily manipulated. They saw him as a gullible, trusting mark, easy and ripe for the picking, and he was convinced that the conglomerate was exploiting that trust in the worst way imaginable.

As he toweled off his face, Michael contemplated the notion that it was now 'illegal' for a farmer to save certain seeds. Unlike the seeds Monsanto gave away back in the 1990s in plain brown bags, they now had labels on their bags that contained a small novel's worth of legalese dictating what farmers could and couldn't do with the seeds. To Michael, the most unsettling part was that the label proclaimed that whoever opened the bag agreed to follow all of Monsanto's stifling terms and conditions, and it was printed in type the size of ant tracks. A magnifying glass was needed to read it, and a lawyer to decipher it.

No signatures were needed or required to finalize the agreement: simply by opening a bag of seeds the conglomerate decreed that each farmer instantly became one of its 'seed police' and was expected to turn in anyone suspected of violating the agreement. It was a heavy-handed dictum that could very well pit farmers against one another. Worse, this entire notion went directly against the American way of farming, a system that had worked quite well and kept the nation fed for more than two hundred years without Monsanto's involvement.

Michael was especially concerned about arbitrarily abandoning the tried and true practice of saving seeds. It had been standard procedure among farmers since records were kept. It predated the incorporation of Monsanto by several thousand years. Michael felt strongly that it was woefully unwise to suddenly abandon all that simply because a conglomerate wanted to increase its market share. After all, this wasn't simply a step in the manufacturing of some widget or gizmo. The food supply was hanging in the balance—the most basic need required for survival.

Consulting his Bible, Michael came across Genesis 1:11–12: "And God said, Let the earth bring forth grass, the herb yielding seed, and the fruit tree yielding fruit after his kind, whose seed is in itself, upon the earth: and it was so. And the earth brought forth grass, and herb yielding seed after his kind, and the tree yielding fruit, whose seed was in itself, after his kind: and God saw that it was good." It spelled out that God had given seed to mankind to sustain life. Seed being "in itself" meant not only that it could reproduce, but that saving seeds to perpetuate the genus and provide food was exactly what man was supposed to do to with it. A bit further on in Genesis—chapter 47, the last portion of verse 19—Michael found an ominous dictum, " . . . and give us seed, that we may live, and not die, that the land be not desolate." Without seeds, land becomes desolate; Michael knew this to be true, as did every farmer and gardener the world over. And saving seeds was the utmost essential part of the equation for sustaining life.

For Michael, this was proof enough that this was something far bigger than him and even a conglomerate the size of Monsanto. Even those who didn't share his religious beliefs would find it impossible to argue against the fact that seeds are required for sustaining human life - - - and always have been. Without seeds you have no crops, no trees, no plants, no bushes, not even grass or weeds. Without them there can be no yield to feed humans, nor any source of food to sustain the lives of countless animals. And animals that are carnivores would starve because their prey that eats plants would be gone. *Seeds are the very essence of nature and the world we inhabit.*

Michael could draw a parallel with a mechanic buying a lug wrench only to find out after the fact that every time he changed a customer's tires he had to replace the lug nuts, even if they were in good shape. But that wasn't all, he'd have to buy the new lug nuts from Monsanto, and only Monsanto, or he'd get sued into bankruptcy. The outlandish requirement would force an unnecessary expense on the mechanic's customers every time they had a flat, a brake job, or rotated their tires. And without competition, what assurance would there be that Monsanto's lug nuts would be even half as good as the ones they replaced? If the mechanic was forced to use a possibly inferior product he could be putting his customers in danger without even knowing it, just as a farmer could 'possibly' be passing such a risk on to consumers with GM seeds.

* * *

One day while running an errand for work, an incident kept replaying like a loop of film in Michael's mind. It had taken place at his seed business a year or two earlier, perhaps even three. Looking back on it, the episode now stuck out like a mottled buzzard amidst a flock of graceful swans.

One day a farmer Michael had never seen before—an uncommon sight in a rural area where everyone knows each other—had pulled up to White's Seed with a truckload of soybeans. The farmer claimed to be from a town about eighty-five or ninety miles away, which was extremely odd. It meant he had driven past several seed cleaners to give Michael his business. It was no secret that White's Seed had a good reputation, but with the high price of fuel and the razor thin margins farmer's battle to turn a profit it would have taken more than that for someone to drive all that extra distance.

Michael could distinctly remember asking the stranger why he'd driven such a long distance to have his seeds cleaned. The man's answer was not only plausible, it seemed genuinely sincere, but Michael still felt something was off-kilter. So he asked the stranger point-blank, "These ain't those Monsanto soybeans, are they? The ones some people are saying a fellow can get into trouble for saving?" Rumors were already swirling around, even then, that some farmers in other states were having problems with Monsanto.

There was no hesitation whatsoever in the stranger's voice when addressing Michael's concern about Monsanto. It was a clear and emphatic "No." Finally, Michael was satisfied that the man was what he seemed.

The entire job took several hours. When it was complete, Michael did what was customary, he provided a receipt for the work he'd done. That's when everything changed. A sinister smirk took hold of the stranger's face. He hopped into his truck and just as he peeled out of the parking lot with the freshly cleaned seeds neatly loaded onto the back, he sneered and waved the receipt out the window like a victory flag as he shouted.

"Thanks, Michael White, for cleaning them Monsanto Roundup Ready Soybeans for me!"

Now Michael was coming to terms with something he should've realized long before. The stranger hadn't been a farmer with a perverted sense of humor. He was apparently a spy Monsanto had sent to entrap him; *a Benedict Arnold in overalls*.

CHAPTER 9

After several hours in Huntsville, Alabama, spent taking care of some business and running errands, Michael was headed home. Driving with the flow of traffic in his big dually truck, he was traveling east on Highway 72 and leaving the city behind. He made no secret of the fact that city life would never suit him. The best part of the trip was when the city was finally disappearing in his rearview mirror. But today there was something else clouding the mirror in addition to the Huntsville skyline. A gray Ford F-250 pickup truck was following him.

It wasn't riding his bumper, but it was following him, nonetheless. By this point in time he certainly knew a tail when he saw one—on occasion he had had as many as two different ones before dinnertime, and this was most definitely a tail.

Although Michael contemplated pulling over on the side of the road to see what would happen, instead, he drove for about fifteen miles or so, waiting until he came upon a gas station with lots of customers, just in case he needed eyewitnesses, and then pulled in. The Ford did likewise. But instead of pulling up to the pumps like Michael, it parked way over by a vacuum and tire inflator, about the furthest most point at the station from Michael.

Michael topped off his tank, and then purposely wasted some time by fiddling around under the hood of his truck, pretending to check his oil, brake fluid, power steering fluid, you name it. He used this opportunity to look at the spy through the gap between the top of his dash and the bottom lip of the raised hood.

Whoever was driving the Ford was staying put, and because its windows were heavily tinted it was impossible to see the driver's face. While clandestinely watching the strange truck Michael had an eerie and almost certain feeling he was also being watched. The thought only added to his frustration.

Slamming the hood of his truck closed, Michael hopped in and roared off down the road. He decided that if this stranger wanted to tail him, then he'd better have plenty of gas and little regard for the speed limit. Pushing his truck well past 80 mph on a stretch of deserted road where the speed limit was only 55, Michael forced the stranger to either keep up or drop out. No big surprise, the Ford stayed with him all the way back to Dutton, even when he momentarily hit 90 mph.

One thing was certain, the stalkers were becoming more frequent, and brazen.

* * *

A few days later, Michael drove into Scottsboro to keep an appointment with his lawyer, Don Word. The quaint, tree-lined streets leading to the town's courthouse square brought back memories of another era, albeit one aspect of that supposedly kinder and gentler time still stains this otherwise idyllic village. More than eighty years earlier, two white women accused nine black youths, ranging in age from 12 - 20, of rape. Tragically, the times being what they were, the youths were convicted on weak and contradictory testimony by an all white jury. The convictions were appealed and the case made its way to the U.S. Supreme Court not once, but twice. In the end, it changed American Jurisprudence forever, i.e., it established the principle that all defendants are entitled to effective assistance by counsel and that no one can be excluded from a jury solely because of their race. Nevertheless, all these years later, the mere words 'The Scottsboro Boys' is a vivid reminder of the town's worst days and painful past.

The storefronts Michael passed were all occupied and looked ready for business. Unlike far too many small towns in the area, Scottsboro showed no signs of drying up and dying. It actually looked quite healthy, robust even. But finding a parking space was rarely a problem, and Michael was able to park just a little way down Market Street from where Don's office was located.

Don was a country lawyer and made no bones about it. He had tackled his share of complicated cases and had an excellent track record doing so, but he was a country boy at heart. On occasion, he still took goods in exchange for his legal services because a number of people in the area simply couldn't afford a lawyer. Luckily for them, Don had no qualms about getting a home-cured ham, fresh eggs and fried pies for drafting a will or contract. It didn't matter whether the value of the items actually covered his bill or not. Don was too much of an idealist to deny someone his help over a few dollars. More often than not he even gave the food items away to someone who truly needed them. In a cynical world where lawyers are too often thought of as heartless vultures and money grubbers, Don was a shining example of a genuinely good guy in pinstripes.

Michael had given Don a head's up about a possible lawsuit not long after he was advised that Monsanto would file suit against a number of farmers in Alabama, but Don had found the notion of a Fortune 500 company suing Michael extremely unlikely and told him so in no uncertain terms. And when Michael told him what Monsanto's spies had been doing, well, that's when Don went from being merely skeptical to thinking that Michael had slipped off the deep end; he truly thought Michael had gone crazy. He went so far as to consider having professionals intervene and provide Michael with the psychological help he felt he desperately needed.

More than once after hearing Michael recount the 'alleged' espionage at his farm and home, Don had mumbled to himself, "Spies tailing a farmer in rural Alabama? Snapping clandestine pictures day and night of him and his family? Genetically modified substances in the food supply?" It sounded like the plot for a dime store spy novel dipped in science fiction . . . fiction being the key word.

However, once Michael showed Don the lawsuit he decided it was time to do a bit of research. After doing his homework—much to his chagrin and alarm, Don realized that Michael was anything but crazy. He even found himself apologizing profusely to Michael for having doubted him. But Michael didn't need an apology; he needed an attorney he could trust and count on implicitly. And as far as he was concerned there was no better man for the job than Don Word, an avowed skeptic who'd now become a true believer in his cause.

Although their meeting on this day was relatively brief, Michael appreciated the fact that Don was already formulating an excellent strategy and was treating his case with the utmost importance. He no longer felt as if he was battling the conglomerate on his own; now he had a partner.

Feeling better about his situation than he had in weeks, Michael walked out of Don's office just as the sun was disappearing into the horizon. The little town, already closing down for the evening, was bathed in the sunset's orange glow and augmented by a purplish gray sky. For a brief moment Michael paused to appreciate the peaceful postcard-perfect view before making his way back to his truck.

Michael, driving very slowly because pedestrians were present, was halfway around the courthouse square and about to exit Scottsboro by way of a side road when something caught his eye. Parked in an alley, tucked away from prying eyes, was a gray Ford truck.

Stopping his own truck in the middle of the street, Michael slowly turned around and stared at the Ford. Was it the same one that had followed him only days before? It certainly looked like it.

A deep sigh of frustration seeped out of Michael. No wonder Don had initially been skeptical, and had even thought he'd gone stark raving mad. It was even hard for Michael himself to believe he had gotten tangled up in this convoluted web of spies and stalkers. It was as if he was having a terrible nightmare all day long, except there was no escaping it, not even when he slept . . . because it haunted him there as well.

CHAPTER 10

Arriving at his seed business around 6 a.m., Michael turned on the coffeepot and began assessing just how much work there was to be done. His in-box alone was piled to the height of a toaster. But he was actually amazed the stack wasn't larger. He hadn't completely abandoned his duties during the past few weeks, but he had been forced to cut way back on them. The lawsuit had a voracious appetite for his time.

In the past he had often burned the midnight oil to keep his farm and seed business afloat. Now he was burning the candle at both ends doing research in preparation for what was sure to be a contentious legal battle. Naturally, whether he wanted to admit it or not, both his farm and seed business were suffering as a result, to say nothing about his family life.

A few nights ago while working into the wee hours, the notion had struck Michael that the people at Monsanto who'd set this legal tsunami in motion against him were probably punching out at five each day. And he doubted any of them had been awake to hear a rooster crow in recent memory. Pulling out his old fashioned ledger, Michael pushed Monsanto and its horde of nine-to-fivers out of his mind and got down to business.

Like many business operations, Michael's farm and seed company had a busy season and an off season, and if he didn't make his money during the busy season and manage it wisely, he wouldn't be around for the off season. Small businesses are susceptible to many pitfalls that can strike in an instant. But cash flow—specifically the lack of it—strangles the life out of more small businesses than any other culprit. Michael had learned that invaluable lesson while watching his competitors collapse all around him during tough times because they weren't taking care of business.

Fortunately for Michael, he usually had enough reserve cash to get him through the dips and potholes that swallowed lesser businesses. Still, he shuddered to think what could happen if he got waylaid by a complicated and protracted legal battle and had to hire someone to take over the job of running his businesses. He couldn't think of anyone locally who could handle the load who didn't already have a full-time job. And even if he did find someone qualified he couldn't begin to pay them what they were worth, much less a salary to compensate them for the long, backbreaking, and thankless hours the jobs entailed.

Suddenly, the phone on his desk rang to life. Michael had turned the volume down on the ringer years ago so it wouldn't disturb him during his bookkeeping chores, but it could still be jarring, especially when he was lost in his thoughts. Plus, he was jumpy, what with all the stalking, spying and picture taking.

Michael glanced at his watch. It wasn't time to open yet, but he tried to be available for his customers whenever possible. "White's Seed," he answered in a casual and friendly tone.

"Is this Michael White?" a voice asked. The question came out slow and thick, as if the caller was disguising his voice. Michael stiffened in his chair. Since the suit began, he'd had more than a few crank callers. Some of them simply stayed on the line for a few moments and then hung up. Other calls, however, were filled with heavy breathing, long silences, occasional mumbles, and even some talk in the background, yet nothing intelligible was ever said.

Michael was tempted to hang up right away, to slam the phone down without giving the caller any satisfaction. But until he knew for certain that it wasn't a legitimate business call, he had to treat it as such. While most could ignore an inconvenient phone call, a small-business owner like Michael simply couldn't afford to risk running off potential customers.

"Yeah, this is Michael," he answered. "How can I help you?"

"Help me? Shit," the caller snapped, aggression pouring through the receiver. "You better be helping yourself, son. And quick-like. Know what I'm saying?"

No question, it certainly wasn't a business call. Michael could've hung up and been done with it, but something in the back of his mind told him he'd better hear what the caller had to say. Remaining calm, Michael replied, "I don't know what you mean, friend."

"Bullshit," the man spat into the phone. "If you don't, then you're a bigger damn fool than most folks already think you are."

Instead of allowing the caller to get a rise out of him, Michael used a strategy he had learned from his father. When a troublemaker wants to babble, let him. If fact, encourage him. You never know when he might show one card too many without even knowing it. Keeping his voice composed, Michael proposed, "Well, if I'm doing something foolish, why don't you help me get on the right track?"

"If you don't watch it, boy, you're gonna lose your fucking farm, and your business, and even that house of yours." With each word the caller's bravado increased, and his tone grew darker.

"Is that so?" Michael replied matter-of-factly.

The anonymous caller was livid. "You're damn right it's so, you stupid motherfucker! And the same goes for your old man, too," he hissed. Up to that point, Michael had endured the crude and profane remarks without getting rattled. But bringing his elderly father into the mix cut him to the quick. Michael tried not to tip his hand, but the caller must have sensed his distress. "Guess you don't give a shit if your old daddy and your sick momma gets throw'd out into the street. Do ya?" Then, as if he held some kind of moral authority, he snapped, "You is one sorry bastard, Michael White, putting your folks through all this bullshit. You ought to be ashamed of yourself. You ain't nothing but a piece of scum-sucking trash!"

There was a click on the line, then nothing. The caller had hung up just in time, because Michael was furious. How dare this perverted goon—a coward too afraid to identify himself—try and browbeat Michael with guilt and scurrilous lies.

Michael's gut reaction was to call the sheriff. But what could he do? It was far too late to try tracing the call.

Spying a clock on the wall, Michael realized that although the intensity of it made it seem much longer, the call had lasted only a couple of minutes at most. Most likely, the caller had purposely cut it short because a lifetime of watching detective shows had ingrained the American brain to believe that a criminal only has a short window of opportunity to talk if he suspects a line is tapped. For Michael, that reinforced what he already knew. From the bogus license plates to the incessant stalking, he was dealing with criminal minds.

Suddenly, something far worse than anger and frustration hit Michael in the pit of his stomach. What if this malicious caller was already dialing his father's number? What if he was filling Wayne's ear full of this reprehensible garbage? What if at that very moment he was trying to frighten the eighty-year-old retiree and his wife to death?

Although quite awhile had passed since the day the young process server gave Michael the envelope addressed to Wayne, the thought that Monsanto was going after his father was still paramount on his mind. With the authority to conduct business for his parents, Michael had opened it and read it. Yet each time he thought about sharing it with his father he became physically ill. It was so upsetting to Michael that he had simply put off telling him about it. But now Michael could no longer protect his father by keeping him in the dark. The sleazy and demented caller had just forced his hand.

Without even taking time to lock his business, Michael raced to his truck, jumped inside, and roared off down the road toward his parent's house. Michael tried desperately to ignore the caller's malicious taunts and verbal abuse, but the horrible words played over and over in his head like a bad movie with a tragic ending.

Arriving at his parent's house with a screeching halt, Michael thought about his mother, suffering unmercifully with terminal cancer. Although she was a fighter, both he and his father knew she wouldn't win the battle. Odds were she wouldn't see her next birthday. The most they could do was make her comfortable, which they tried their best to do at every turn.

Michael had seen his mother the day before and she was not in very good shape. If she got wind of the anonymous caller's malicious intent it could be a shock that would kill her. Michael prayed that if the caller had gotten through to his father he'd simply hung up on the animal. But his daddy's hearing, like the rest of his health, was failing. In the past he sometimes asked Virginia to listen on the phone for him because her hearing was still fairly decent, even if the rest of her body was failing.

As he hoped out of his truck, Michael said a quick prayer that he'd beaten the reprehensible caller to the punch. Running from his truck to the house, he opened the door and let himself in without bothering to knock.

Quickly making his way down the small hallway, Michael found his mother and father together in the room she had occupied since the illness made her bedridden. It was a small room, tiny actually. Using generous terms, the house itself could be best described as modest. Yet it was this little house that the Whites had worked so very hard to buy some thirty-five years ago so that their children could have a better life than they had growing up in poverty on Sand Mountain.

As on so many other days, Wayne was sitting beside his dying wife

8192
and holding her frail hand in his, the hand he had taken in marriage some sixty plus years ago. Michael knew that sometimes hours could pass by and neither of them would speak. They didn't have to. Theirs was a love that was bigger and more profound than words.

Upon seeing his parents, now in the twilight of their lives yet holding hands as if they had only just begun, Michael found himself choking back a swell of emotions. Rather than let them see him all choked up, he tiptoed back into the den and regrouped. He knew saying what he had to say wasn't going to be easy, but there was no getting around it. He leaned back, took a deep breath, and exhaled slowly. He repeated this several times, and, once relaxed, acted as if he'd just entered the house. Knocking on the wall, he called out in a sunny voice, "Daddy? You here?"

"Michael, that you?" his father answered back.

Though it wasn't nearly as strong as it once had been, there was no mistaking Wayne's voice. Michael could pick it out of a crowd at a hundred paces. It was that distinct. "Yeah, it's me, Daddy," he replied.

"Come on back, son. I'm in here with your Momma."

Glancing down, Michael realized he had dirt on his boots. "Can you meet me out back?" he asked. Although the White's little house was anything but fancy, his mother had always kept it meticulously clean and even now, with Michael pushing fifty, he didn't dare track dirt through her home. He loved the woman more than life itself, and the last thing he would do was disrespect her. Besides, he was hoping he could speak to his father without his mother overhearing. There was no point in making both of his parents suffer with the news he had to divulge. "Be there in a minute, son," came Wayne's reply.

Father and son met beside the old barn that stood behind the house. Built back when Wayne was still farming, it now served as a storage facility for household goods, lawn and garden equipment, and various odds-and-ends.

Before getting down to the reason for his impromptu early-morning visit, Michael nodded back toward the house and asked, "How's Momma?"

Wayne cleared his throat and said, "'Bout the same." It was his way of avoiding the painful details of the cancer that was eating away at her body.

Even though their roles had been all but reversed—Michael was now the de facto guardian for his parents, Wayne was still his father. Michael knew when to ask a question, and when to leave a subject alone. It was understood that if there was anything he should know about his mother's condition, well, his father would tell him.

Michael desperately wanted to say what was on his mind, but he simply couldn't come up with the right words. As he searched, Wayne studied his face. The octogenarian still had a sharp mind and eyes to match. "Son, you're stalling. It's all over your face. Question is: Why ya stalling? And whatcha' trying to avoid?"

For a moment Michael dropped his head. It would be easier for him to say what he needed to without seeing his father's reaction. But he quickly remembered how Wayne had always told him to look people in the eye, even if he had bad news. This was certainly bad news, no question about it. Nevertheless, he'd given the process server his word that he'd tell his father about the suit, and now the time had come. Looking Wayne straight in the eye, Michael began, "Daddy, remember back when I first told you about my lawsuit?"

"Sure do." Wayne nodded. Thinking back, he remarked, "That was an awful dark day." Indeed it had been. Michael had not only told his father about his own lawsuit, but the spies and stalking as well.

"Well, I held back on part of it."

Not since Michael was a teenager had he come to his parents for even a dime. But Wayne sensed his son must be in financial straits because they'd always had an open relationship and never before had his son found it so difficult to discuss something with him. "Son, if you need money," he said. "Well, you know your Momma and I ain't got much. But what we got, it's yours. You don't even have to ask, and you don't have to pay it back."

Michael quickly shook his head, "That ain't it. I don't need your money, Daddy." He didn't have the heart to tell his father that he had been secretly augmenting his parent's meager fixed income for quite some time because of the exorbitant medical expenses associated with his mother's cancer. They didn't have any money to lend, not to Michael, not to anyone. But there was no need to burden them with that information, not now, not ever. Michael considered it a genuine privilege to help his parents.

With a heavy sigh, Michael finally spilled the beans, and they were rotten to the core. "They're suing you, too."

Wayne cocked his head like an old rooster that had just found out for the first time in his long life he has missed a sunrise. Partially deaf in one ear, and only slightly better in the other, Wayne pointed at the better of the two. "Run that by me again, son?"

Speaking much louder and very slowly, Michael announced, "Monsanto's suing you, Daddy, just like they're suing me."

If Michael had hit his father over the head with a bag of rocks it could not have been more of a jolt. "Monsanto's suing me?!" Fighting back indignation, he snapped, "What in the world for?"

Apologetic, Michael answered his father, "Stealing their technology."

Outraged to the point of war, Wayne bellowed as loud as his eighty-year-old lungs could muster, "I ain't never stole nothing in my life. Not from nobody, certainly not from some big old company." He was spitting lightning. "Boy, have they got some nerve!"

"I know you ain't stole nothing, Daddy. What they're saying is that you used seeds with their technology—saved 'em—and did it without their consent."

It was important for Wayne to restate what Michael had said, to put it in his own words just to be certain he had understood every word of what he had just been told. "Are you telling me that Monsanto is accusing me of using those abominations they cook up in some laboratory? They're saying I was farming with 'em, right?"

Michael nodded, "Yes sir, that's it, pretty much."

Wayne White was nobody's fool. He had served on the school board, worked for the TVA, and had a knack for numbers and logic. He also had an uncanny ability to pick a needle from a haystack. "When did Monsanto first start selling these, these, uh, soybean seeds of theirs?" he asked. He wasn't sure what to call them, although he'd often heard them referred to as 'Frankenstein-seeds.'

"I ain't a hundred percent sure," Michael replied. "But I think it was the mid-nineties. Probably '95 or '96 - - - about seven or eight years ago."

A sly grin slowly took control of Wayne's face as his anger melted away. "I stopped farming more than thirty years ago, way back in 1971. Everybody on this mountain knows it, and that includes the county agent that keeps crop records. And anybody wants proof, they can check with the IRS." Posturing, almost as if addressing a roomful of people, Wayne pronounced, "It's mathematically impossible for me to have ever used a single one of Monsanto's soybean seeds. Them things didn't even exist back when I farmed, so there's no way on God's green earth I could've used them—not that I ever would have." With that he symbolically dusted his hands off, because in his mind the matter had been settled. He looked at Michael and smiled. "End of story."

Michael hung his head. He couldn't look his daddy in the eye, not this time. "It ain't that easy, Daddy."

Wayne tilted his head; confusion was all over his face. "Why not? Don't the facts matter anymore? Don't the truth count for somethin'?"

Michael cleared his throat. "Not really. Not since Monsanto started suing farmers." He stared off into the distance for a moment, then locked eyes with his father once again. "If we ain't careful," he said, "they can wind up taking your land, your car, your bank account, maybe even your house."

Dumbstruck, Wayne stared at Michael as if he were an apparition, "They can take my house? The roof that serves as protection for your dying mother? They'd do that? They'd steal a house out from under an eighty-year-old man and his dying wife over some seeds?"

Michael nodded. "They can if we don't fight this thing."

Tears welled up in Wayne's eyes. He was having a very difficult time taking everything in. It wasn't merely that he was overwhelmed with too much information; it was that he genuinely feared for the safety and well-being of his wife. He had done his utmost best for more than sixty years to care for her. But now some giant corporation—certainly not something he could battle—was threatening to snatch everything he had like a thief in the night. He was frightened beyond belief.

Rather than allow his son to see him break down, this man who'd served in WWII headed for the back door of his house, mumbling in disgust along the way. "I thought this kinda garbage only happened overseas where they got dictators and such." Michael hung his head and fought back his own anger and frustration. With tears welling up in his eyes, he watched as his father disappeared inside the modest home he had worked so hard for so many years to buy—a home he now feared Monsanto might snatch out from under him in the blink of an eye to satisfy its outlandish demands for 'triple' damages.

The most galling aspect to Michael about the suit against his father was that he was convinced the conglomerate had filed it for one reason, and only one. He felt it was little more than a sleazy ploy intended to make him cry uncle.

CHAPTER 11

Michael's state of mind was midway between panic and rage. He genuinely feared the harassment that Monsanto's spies could rain down on the innocent people connected to him. In his own life it was now as standard as the rising sun. It was a rare day when he didn't spot at least one spy shadowing him, to say nothing of the ones he never saw. Often, the unknown was the worst part. That was certainly what made it all so difficult for his wife and children. They felt they had to constantly look over their shoulders, too.

Would the conglomerate's spies haunt his parents the way it had his wife and children? The stress could easily put them in early graves. The mere notion of his elderly parents being stalked made him so angry he could barely see, much less collect his thoughts. His immediate desire was to talk to someone who would recognize the gravity of the situation and understand his anger, someone who could offer wise council, if not a sympathetic ear. Normally, that person would be his father, but the lawsuit against Wayne had eliminated him as a sounding board.

Without even realizing it, Michael mumbled, "L. V.", as in Lucas Varnell "L. V." Dane, an old family friend. Michael knew he could count on L. V. to provide wise and thoughtful counsel. He also knew L. V. had an open mind and would not summarily dismiss his convoluted saga with Monsanto as the ravings of a man who had lost touch with reality . . . or worse.

L. V. was one of the wisest people Michael had ever known. He stayed abreast of current events and was a voracious reader with an encyclopedic mind for minute details. Nevertheless, he could just as easily sit and talk for hours about fishing for bass on a quiet country lake with the gaggle of geezers at the Reliford Cafe. But what he truly loved was American history, particularly the 19th and 20th Centuries, and could hold his own if tossed into a roomful of scholars and professors.

Another subject L. V. knew a lot about was Wayne White. They had been friends for a long time and he was well aware that his old pal hadn't farmed in more than thirty years. Yet of all the many things L. V. brought to the table, he also possessed something few of the world's high-powered lawyers could understand, something that was certainly foreign to the people behind the suit filed against Wayne White. L. V. was a man of integrity who knew and respected the law back when it had the power to determine the truth, to right wrongs, repair damaged people, and even help balance the precarious scales of justice between the haves and have-nots—before it was hijacked by lawyers who put money ahead of principle. For a selfless man like L. V., it was a tragedy of epic proportions that greed had undermined so much of what he and people like him had stood for all their lives.

With Michael looking on, L. V. studied the suit Monsanto had filed against Wayne White.

Finally, after carefully reading through the document, L. V. delicately combed the few remaining strands of hair on his head into place and then pronounced in a hushed voice, "Michael, multibillion-dollar companies that operate around the globe don't send their high-priced shysters in three-piece suits to Podunk, Alabama, to file suit against an elderly man with no assets to speak of. Unless, of course, there's a whole heckuva lot more at stake than just a few bags of seeds." His eyes drifted back to the document. "I'd be mighty surprised if these folks don't know exactly when your daddy stopped farming, and that your momma is bedridden and suffering something terrible from cancer." Using his thumb and index finger for a gauge, he surmised, "Why I'll betcha that somewhere, some-place, there's a file on your folks this thick." If the gap between his thumb and index finger had been the thickness of a steak it could've fed an entire family.

"Ain't there laws against this kind of lowdown mess?" Michael all but pleaded.

"If Monsanto—or anyone for that matter—files a suit when they have prior knowledge that it's groundless, yes," L. V. replied. "It's not only against the law, it undermines the very foundation of our justice system."

That was just what Michael had wanted to hear. "Well then they oughta get in a pile of trouble for filing this bogus lawsuit, right?"

L. V. could remember a time when no self-respecting company, large or small, would have dared drag a frail and elderly retiree into court, even if they'd had an iron-clad case. However, to do so when their suit had no merit would have been decried as a mockery of the entire system and made them an outcast in the business world. But a lot of things had changed in his long lifetime, and it would be hard to explain to Michael, a simple and decent fellow with only limited exposure to the legal system, that the likes of Harper Lee's Atticus Finch resided only within the pages of fiction. Now it seemed that, too often, the high octane lawyers that represented big companies were little more than jackals, hyenas and serpents motivated, inspired and fueled by money and greed.

Rather than offer a long and tedious explanation as to exactly how he believed the American system of justice had been hijacked and corrupted by sleazy lawyers, slimy lobbyists, and gutless politicians, L. V. instead asked Michael a question. "Son, you ever heard of Agent Orange?"[3]

Soon after graduating high school in 1972, Michael had gone in for a military physical. Had they not cut back on the draft at the proverbial

---

[3] In 1962 the U.S. Military began a plan known as Operation Ranch Hand in which it sprayed the jungles of Vietnam with a herbicide. The main objective was to eliminate the cover used by enemy soldiers. However, the use of Agent Orange turned ORH into a catastrophic nightmare for countless U.S. soldiers, as well as Vietnamese civilians, because they were exposed to TCDD, an ultra toxic contaminant in the defoliant.

eleventh hour, he probably would've wound up in Vietnam. Some of his friends, primarily those who were a bit older, had been drafted—while a few had volunteered—and for that reason he'd heard a horror story or two about Agent Orange. So Michael nodded. "Yep. Sure have."

"So you know it was a highly toxic chemical used during the Vietnam War?"

Again, Michael nodded. "Yep."

"Did you know that tens of thousands of U.S. troops were exposed to Agent Orange without ever being told it was extremely dangerous?"

Michael was taken aback, "I didn't know the number was that high."

"And did you know that thousands and thousands of soldiers have suffered horribly and died needlessly because they were exposed to Agent Orange?"

Stunned by the enormous number, Michael replied. "I wasn't sure how many it was, but I sure didn't know it was anywhere near that many."

L. V. continued, his voice taking on the somber tone of someone who realizes he must spill some awfully rotten beans. "The worst part is that this horror story is still unfolding. As we speak—*right this very moment*, scores and scores of former U.S. soldiers are suffering and dying because they were exposed to Agent Orange. And that's not counting the thousands and thousands of Vietnamese civilians that got exposed—a lot of 'em when they were just little children, infants even. And they got thousands and thousands of people with birth defects cause of it, too. They're all suffering and dying."

That startling and appalling information caught Michael flatfooted, so much so that L. V. let a few moments pass in silence. And he didn't even mention that the link between exposure to Agent Orange and spina bifida is so compelling that the U. S. Department of Veterans Affairs provides lifetime benefits for any and all children born with that horrendously debilitating congenital birth defect if a parent served in Vietnam where the toxic herbicide was present.

Only after L. V. was absolutely certain that Michael understood the implications of what he had said did he finally drop the real bomb on him. "The lion's share of Agent Orange used in Vietnam was produced by none other than Monsanto."

Michael's eyes looked as if someone had blinded him with a 10,000 watt Klieg light. He had no idea Monsanto was part of the equation behind the infamous, toxic defoliant. "You telling me Monsanto made Agent Orange?"

"Not only did they make it," L. V. replied. "But Monsanto has been battling people suffering and dying from Agent Orange for decades, doing anything and everything they can to deny those people justice!"

In Michael's mind this revelation made the cigarette companies look like a bunch of Sunday school teachers and Good Samaritans. He could only imagine that Monsanto's executives had gone to extraordinary lengths to make sure their own children were no where near Agent Orange during Vietnam - - - assuming any of their offspring served in the military.

Realizing he had just dropped an anvil-load of information on a man who had come by for some counseling and consolation, L. V. relaxed his tone and summed things up. "Sorry to be so blunt, but now you know why I think Monsanto doesn't give a damn about your parents. All they care about is money. You ask me, they're driven solely by greed; they'll do anything for a buck, and they don't care who they hurt."

On his drive home, Michael was struck by the harsh reality that—instead of getting the answers he so desperately sought—he was now haunted by a highly disturbing and dread inducing question: 'What will become of the world if Monsanto, a company that made Agent Orange and PCBs, gets control of our food supply?'

CHAPTER 12

Several times during the course of a long day Michael had seen a red truck following behind him that was outfitted for a plumber. For the life of him he couldn't recall any plumbers in the area with a red truck. So instead of going straight home, he took the long way. It added another ten or fifteen minutes to an exhausting day, but it was crucial for him to know if he was being tailed or not.

The first turn Michael made in his detour was onto a regularly traveled road, but the second one was onto a little-used dirt road so bumpy that no one would use it by choice. Sure enough, the red plumber's truck kept a respectable distance yet stayed on his tail.

Although it was getting dark and hard to see, by the time Michael got to his house there was zero room for doubt he was being followed. To a casual observer his tail may have looked like a plumber's truck, but the only thing it had remotely in common with any "plumbers" Michael had ever heard of were the ones associated with disgraced former President Richard Nixon and the Watergate burglary back in the early 1970s.

Parking beside his barn, Michael stayed in his truck just to see what the red truck would do. It sped up and took off down the road. Michael watched until its taillights completely disappeared into the twilight. But he figured this wasn't the last he would see of it. So he sat for a few more minutes. And, sure enough, less than five minutes later the truck came back, cruising by his driveway at a very slow pace. Michael was no plumber, but he knew there was absolutely no way the driver of the red truck could have possibly had time to make a service call and now be headed back to his shop.

It dawned on Michael that it was one thing to spot a tail on Sand

Mountain where a dozen cars and trucks on a lonely stretch of backroad within a half hour's time constituted heavy traffic. But on a city's harried highways and streets a plumber or electrician's truck could blend into the scenery like a tree in the forest. He now wondered if he had been followed while in Huntsville or other towns and didn't even know it?

Suddenly, Michael realized he was allowing this highly frustrating ordeal, once again, to consume him. It was destroying his life, family life and mental well-being. With a considerable amount of effort, he pushed every thought that pertained to Monsanto, its GM seeds, its spies, their stalking, out of his head . . . at least for the moment.

* * *

A few weeks later, the red truck nowhere in sight, Michael found himself pulling into his driveway on a beautiful star filled night. Getting out of his truck, a quick glance up at the heavens let him know there was little or no chance for rain. That was a very good thing because he had a crop in the field that had already gotten enough of a soaking.

Walking from the barn to the house, Michael heard the muted roar of a small plane overhead. He glanced up and quickly spotted the plane, its white belly standing out against the night sky. Student pilots occasionally used the airspace over the mountain for practice. Years back, long before he had a family and a slew of obligations, Michael had toyed with the idea of learning to fly. The notion of soaring high above the earth and touching the clouds had been appealing to him. But now he saw it as a young man's dream. That time for him had passed.

Mounting the back porch, Michael took one last look at the small plane as it gently banked overhead, making a circle around the mountain top. Putting himself in the pilot's seat, he imagined the breathtaking panoramic view of the mountain, to say nothing of the star-filled sky. He let out a deep sigh. It was a peaceful thought.

Reaching for the back door, Michael watched as it flung open before he got his hand on the knob. Suddenly, he was face-to-face with Debbie, and she was not smiling. Lately, that wasn't out of the norm. Smiles at their house were harder and harder to come by, especially between Michael and Debbie. What had once been a wonderful marriage—one he often thanked God for—was slowly coming unraveled, and it seemed as if many of their problems stemmed from the lawsuit, particularly being stalked by Monsanto's goons. Some days he felt like they were drowning, side-by-side, and there was no one who could throw them a life preserver. "You need to go check on your momma," Debbie said.

Her words hit Michael like a brick in the face. Not only did he feel as if—lately—he'd been less than attentive with his family, but he also hadn't been to see his mother since yesterday. And with her cancer, missing even one day was simply unthinkable.

"I'm on my way." Michael said, his voice half moan, and half shout as he turned and raced back toward his truck.

Never in his life had Michael's mother let him down. Now he felt so utterly selfish, so cruel and insensitive to her needs. He had let a lawsuit, along with a bunch of sleazy spies, manifest itself into somehow being more important than the love and caring she had showered on him all his life. Michael's truck could not get him to his parent's house fast enough. The entire way there he kept praying that she was still alive.

* * *

Wayne met Michael at the door. Without a word, he motioned his son inside, and Michael raced to his mother's sickbed.

Once a strong, vibrant woman, Virginia's body had been ravaged to the point that she was now little more than a skeleton covered with skin. She barely weighed seventy pounds; about half of what she weighed before the cancer hit her. She could no longer feed, bathe, or dress herself. She had to wear diapers, which her devoted husband changed throughout the day to make sure she was dry and comfortable.

Virginia's breathing was shallow and unsteady. Her skin was a pale, sickly white that made her all but disappear amidst the white bed sheet. On the rare occasion when she could summon the energy to speak, her words were difficult to understand.

Michael put his hand on his mother's. Never before had he noticed how much larger his was than hers. It was tiny by comparison, almost like that of a small child. "Momma, it's me, Michael. How are you?" He gently put his ear beside her mouth. He had learned that if she wanted to speak that was the only way to hear her. It usually took a while for her to drum up the strength to talk. So Michael waited. And he waited.

A few moments passed, then a few minutes. Soon a half hour had gone by, but she hadn't said a thing. But it didn't matter. Michael was content just listening to her breathe. Weak as it was, it provided a comfort he could not explain.

A hand touched Michael's shoulder, which made him jump. It was his father. Although he said nothing, he gestured for his son to join him outside.

They met in the small carport where there was no chance Virginia could hear them. Although quite fragile himself, Wayne lamented about his wife's health. "When she can speak, son, and that ain't too often, she always asks for you." Michael nodded. He knew his mother loved him dearly. "She asked for you late this afternoon, otherwise I wouldn't have bothered you."

Michael's words came out haltingly. "I know I haven't been a good son, I —"

Wayne interrupted and waved off Michael's concerns. "Don't beat yourself up, son. You're carrying a load, a mighty big one. She knows that, and I know it, too."

"It don't matter," Michael said. "My family's gotta come first."

Wayne countered. "Son, that's why you're neck-deep in this lawsuit, 'cause your family does matter more to you than life itself."

Michael was caught off guard. Up until that moment, he hadn't been sure if his own father understood the turmoil and personal agony the lawsuit had wrought. For a while, father and son just stood and stared, with Michael savoring this revelation. Since Monsanto and its goons came to roost on Sand Mountain, times like these were rare indeed.

CHAPTER 13

Although Wayne and Virginia White married young—both were just teenagers, first they had a proper courtship, the kind that would seem utterly archaic now. But in their day, anything less would've been frightfully wrong. And they lived in a world where right and wrong were not only clearly defined, they were etched in bedrock.

The vows the young couple took were no different. Love, honor and obey, for richer or poorer, and in sickness and in health, were far more than merely words for them to recite, they were the cornerstones of a lifetime commitment together. In a world where some people seemingly divorce without a second thought, the mere notion of not staying together for the rest of their lives was unfathomable.

They certainly faced their share of bumps along life's road, though neither of them were complainers. Besides, hard times were part of life on the mountain. To be sure, all was not rocks, hills and valleys. Wayne and Virginia had their share of good fortune, though good fortune on the mountain could have a different meaning than other places; it could be as simple as 'you have food on the table,' to 'you have shoes on your feet.'

Good times or bad, Wayne and Virginia's love and admiration for each other only grew with time. It was in many ways a storybook romance, albeit without the castle. Even when Virginia's cancer confined her to a bed and robbed her of many basic faculties, it only doubled Wayne's resolve to love and care for her even more.

The only thing on earth that could break the vow they made to always stay together was death. And it came on a spring day in March of 2004—Virginia's 81st year of life, thus bringing to a close a loving marriage that had spanned sixty-two memorable years.

CHAPTER 14

The first few weeks following the loss of his mother were a haze for Michael. There were days when he would pull into his father's driveway intending to visit her, only to remember after he saw wilting wreaths of flowers out back taken from her grave that she was gone. That would prompt him to go by the cemetery and visit her. There was no tombstone yet; he was told it would take months to have one erected. Nevertheless, he didn't need a marker to tell him where she was. He could have found it at midnight with a starless sky.

Michael found it comforting to sit beside his mother's grave and talk to her—get things off his mind, or just talk about life in general. And sometimes he didn't talk at all, not a word; he just sat there and thought about her. It provided calming reassurance for him, especially given all he was going through.

But one day the tranquility he found at the cemetery came crashing down like an avalanche. The peace, privacy and calm were shattered when he looked up and spied one of Monsanto's goons slowly cruising past the cemetery. Just the sight of them made him almost physically ill; but stalking him at the cemetery while visiting his mother's grave? It was beyond nauseating; it also said more about the ghoulish spies than he could ever put into words. Worse, they may have been shadowing him at the cemetery all along, but because he was overcome by grief he hadn't even noticed until now.

Furious and more than ready for a confrontation, Michael hopped up and trotted toward the goon's truck, which was moving at a crawl. But as soon as the driver realized Michael was coming toward him he sped off, stealing away with something Michael cherished dearly: the peace, sanctity, and solitude of his visits to his mother's grave.

Michael seriously contemplated jumping in his truck and pursing the heartless thug. But what good would it do? The sleazy stalker was most certainly using a bogus tag, and he would no doubt speed away with reckless abandon . . . perhaps racing away at 100 mph to keep Michael from catching him and finding out his identity and that of his patron. The interloper might not give a damn how many lives he put in jeopardy blasting around the mountain at more than double the speed limit, but Michael certainly did.

Not long after that Michael and Troy Dunham, an old and trusted friend he had known for decades, had a chat. Their talks were good for Michael's soul because Troy not only understood him far better than just about anyone, they shared a remarkably similar faith in God. More than a few times they had some heady conversations about religion that kept them up into the wee hours of the morning. And sometimes they would talk for hours and hours and the word 'Monsanto' would never even come up. Yet when it did, Troy never tried to overload Michael with advice; he realized his friend was under enormous stress and strain and sometimes simply listening trumps advice a thousand times over.

On this warm evening after both of them had gotten comfortable and they had dispensed with small talk, Michael more or less announced. "I'm having a tough time trying to get over losing Momma."

Troy understood better than most. "It's been years since I lost my mother, and it still hurts. I figure it always will."

"I guess the worst part is that I actually thought these thugs would've backed off just a bit, maybe have some compassion, maybe a smidgen of decency, given me some time to grieve and mourn in private. But they didn't. Nothing ever changed. They're like leeches. All they know how to do is suck the life out of you."

"You ask me, they're worse than leeches. A leech acts out of instinct. These people know that what they're doing is just plain wrong." Then Troy switched the subject. "I guess you heard that Solutia filed bankruptcy?"

Michael perked up. "Solutia? Ain't that the company that's taking the fall for Monsanto down in Anniston?"

"Yep. It's supposed to pay several hundred million dollars on that settlement." He grimaced. "Fat chance getting it now. I'll betcha Anniston's at the back of a long, long line of people they owe money to."

"I wouldn't be surprised one bit if they had planned to file bankruptcy before they ever got sued down there." Michael lamented. "But I guarantee you not one executive at Solutia is gonna miss a paycheck, and certainly not any of 'em at Monsanto."

"Or their big fat oversized bonuses." Troy added.

Michael nodded in agreement, then sighed as he felt the effects of sleep deprivation catching up with him. "Maybe if I was to get a good night's sleep I could clear my head enough to think through some things. But I haven't sleep mor'n three hours on any given night for the past two or three weeks. Some nights I don't sleep at all."

"Sounds like you need a break. Maybe a vacation?"

Michael shook his head. "Ain't got the time, and sure ain't got the money."

Troy understood Michael's predicament all too well. Although the conversations they had were therapeutic for Michael, he wanted to do more to help his old friend. And Troy got the chance when Denny Stinson, knowing Michael and Troy were best friends, reached out to Troy to set up a meeting with Michael.

Although he wasn't particularly close with either Michael or Troy, Denny was the sort they both could trust.

To protect everyone involved, much like his meetings with Buddy Jim,

Michael met Denny at a remote location so that no one would be the wiser. Although Michael had no idea why Denny wanted to meet, he understood that meeting with him in public could possibly draw the wrath of Monsanto's henchmen, something he wouldn't wish on anyone, certainly not someone trying to help him.

After only a minimal amount of small talk, Denny put a cardboard box directly in front of Michael and said matter-of-factly, "Here ya go. It's a gift for you."

Given that Christmas was a long way off, and the same went for his birthday, Michael simply stared at the box—about one foot square—for a long moment, not sure what to make of it. He finally said, "Little early for Christmas, ain't it?"

Denny reached down and pushed the box closer to Michael. "Call it whatever you want, but it's yours."

Gingerly, Michael took the box and just held it, almost as if he wasn't sure what to do with it.

"Go ahead, open it." Denny urged Michael.

Slowly, Michael began tearing at the box, but with little success. Grief and a lack of sleep were obviously wearing on him. Denny produced a pocket knife but warned, "Don't cut deep." Michael nodded, then slowly and gently sliced through the packing tape securing the box.

After carefully folding back the lid, Michael bent his head down until he was looking directly inside the box. Meanwhile, Denny watched intently for his reaction.

Michael put his hand inside the box, then came up with a large handful of photos. Even though he knew exactly what they were, he stared at them in stunned silence for a long time. Taken clandestinely by Monsanto's spies with high-quality cameras and telephoto lenses, they looked like something straight out of a spy movie. Michael's amazement at seeing them firsthand grew with each new picture he saw, each seemingly more invasive than the one before. He couldn't possibly pretend that having access to these secret photos was anything less than monumental.

It occurred to Michael that one of Monsanto's spies who had been stalking him simply had a bout of conscience and flipped. Or, at the very least, thought he would even the playing field just a tiny bit. It might even be a bigwig in the corporation's executive offices who was fed-up with the way Michael was being treated. And, of course, it might very well be a low to midlevel employee at the conglomerate; someone who had been there a long time and had seen one too many people get steamrolled by the company. Even after all he'd been through, Michael wanted to believe there were decent and honest people at Monsanto, ones who did not condone what it had done to him and his family. And if they wanted to remain anonymous, for whatever reason, so be it. Michael would gladly protect their identity till the end of time.

At this juncture, how Denny obtained the photos—or even from whom—didn't matter nearly as much as the fact that he had them. They were a gift from heaven, and that's the way Michael saw them.

Digging down into the box Michael rummaged through the photos a moment, then paused and asked, "How many of these are there? Looks like the stack's about a foot deep. Must be a thousand of 'em , maybe even more."

If ever a man had a poker face, it was Denny. And he used it in response to Michael's question. Recognizing that Denny was not only a man who could be trusted, but that he was also the type who could be the sole of discretion, he said, "I think it's best that you hold onto these photos for me 'cause I don't know of any place I can put 'em where Monsanto might not find 'em. That is, if you don't mind?"

Without saying anything, Denny simply nodded. He'd serve as the keeper of the photos.

Exhaling a deep breath, Michael had to ask a question that was weighing heavily on his mind. "Any pictures of my wife and kids in here?" Denny contemplated how he would answer this, but before any words came out Michael held up his hand. "On second thought, don't tell me. I don't wanna know." Denny had a family. He understood Michael's situation. There were times when it was better not to know certain things. Peace of mind was far more important, even if it was rooted in ignorance.

Using great care, Michael carefully put the pictures he had seen back in the box, then locked a steady gaze on Denny, "If there's any pictures of me at Momma's grave in here, promise me you'll destroy 'em, every single one of 'em. I don't ever wanna know they're so despicable, lowdown and vile that they'd take pictures of me at my Momma's grave, 'cause if I knew . . . " His voice drifted off without finishing his thought.

Without confirming or denying their existence, with a simple nod of his head Denny let Michael know he would personally take care of any such barbarically invasive photos.

Moving slowly and methodically, Michael re-closed the box, handed it back to Denny, then spoke directly from his heart. "You're a darn good man. Ain't many like you, not even close; not ones that would do what you've done for me. I thank you straight from the bottom of my heart."

Like Michael, Denny didn't need or even expect a pat on the back for doing the right thing. It was more or less part of their DNA. Nevertheless, like Denny, Michael always showed his appreciation for those who helped him, especially now.

CHAPTER 15

It had been a long, muscle pulverizing morning on the farm, and now it was almost noon. So Oren hinted to Michael in a not so subtle fashion that it was time to get their lunch at the Dairy Bar. Given that Oren worked better when his stomach wasn't growling, Michael didn't waste any time getting into his Jeep and then onto the road.

The ride to the Dairy Bar along sparsely traveled farm roads took Michael right beside his most productive cornfield. Several people had complimented him by saying they thought it was one of the better looking crops in the county. Still, he was ever mindful that a heavy rain—or none at all—could turn it into an eyesore and a money loser. But for now, it was about as close as could be had to a picture perfect crop in Jackson County.

Although he had checked on the cornfield earlier—not long after sunrise, Michael was still filled with anticipation when he rounded the gently curving farm road that led to his pride and joy. The field provided him with the kind of good feeling that had been hard to come by of late.

But as the field came into view a scowl—rather than a smile—crept onto Michael's face. "What the hell?" he snarled, uttering a word that almost never passed his lips as he simultaneously jerked his Jeep off the road and onto the shoulder beside his corn field.

There, prominently displayed directly in front of his field, was a large sign proclaiming that his postcard-perfect crop owed its pedigree to a specific brand of genetically modified seeds. They were not Monsanto seeds, but seeds that relied on Monsanto's technology; the conglomerate's logo was even featured on the sign beneath the name of the seed company. Michael had planted the field himself. He knew beyond all doubt that it contained only natural corn. There were no GMOs in his field . . . unless someone else put them there without his knowledge.

It wasn't unusual to see a sign for a seed company fronting a farmer's field. Seed companies encouraged their sales reps to put the signs in a prominent place near the best-looking crops in their territory so other farmers would see them. It was the most cost-effective and valuable form of advertising the reps had. Of course, the field *actually* had to have been sown with the company's seeds, or it constituted a violation of several laws. In the case of Michael's field—given all that was going on behind the scenes—it was far more than merely a matter of breaking the law, he saw it as a flagrant act of contempt.

Michael grabbed his camera and quickly hiked over to the offensive sign, a feeling of disgust and bile rising inside his throat. He closely examined the soil around the sign's post. It was obvious that someone had only recently rammed it into the ground. There were fresh footprints everywhere. He took a shot of the freshly disturbed earth for documentation and then dialed up a local seed rep, Jeb Raymer, the man who sold the seeds promoted on the sign. Although Michael knew Raymer, they were at best acquaintances, not friends.

It was difficult for Michael to keep his anger in check, but he did the best he could. "Raymer, this is Michael White. Did you put a sign up in front of my cornfield over near Dutton?"

Raymer sounded genuinely surprised. "Naw, not me. I ain't put a sign up anywhere in two weeks."

Michael let out a deep sigh. Perhaps someone else, maybe one of Jeb's flunkies, had put the sign up by mistake. "Well, there's one over here and I need you to take it down. Where are you now?" Raymer gave Michael his location. Michael cleared his throat. He wasn't the sort to make demands, but this wasn't an average day, not by anyone's yardstick. "It shouldn't take you mor'n twenty minutes to get here. I'll give you thirty."

With that, Michael hung up. He wasn't about to give Raymer the chance to say he was busy or couldn't make it. If he didn't show up, Michael would call the law and swear out a warrant against Raymer for trespassing. That way Raymer, his flunky, or whoever put the sign up, would have to explain to a judge why they did it.

But no warrant was needed. In no more than twenty minutes Jeb Raymer came driving up in his nice, shiny company truck. As soon as he parked Michael turned on his video camera and held it up so there was no question as to what he was doing. "Jeb, I'm filming this," he announced. "And I already got the sign on film." Pointing at the offending sign, he said in no uncertain terms, "I ain't gonna have no signs in my fields with Monsanto's name on 'em . . . not with all that's going on." He didn't even have to explain to Raymer what he meant by 'all that's going on,' the salesman knew all too well.

Raymer was all smiles and apologies. "Michael, I'm sorry as can be about this," he said as he hiked over to the sign promoting his seed company and Monsanto, "I meant to put this one up at a field just down the road, one grown with our seeds."

On the outside Michael was wearing his best poker face, yet on the inside he could feel his blood boiling. Raymer had just lied to him pointblank, completely contradicting what he had told him on the phone only twenty-odd minutes earlier. Not only that, he was also admitting he had put the sign up himself, yet simultaneously trying to pass it off as a trivial mistake. Michael saw a big problem with his newly concocted story. There wasn't another cornfield anywhere near this one. Plus, Raymer had lived in the area long enough to know whose fields were whose. Posting the sign had been no mistake.

Instinct told Michael to call Raymer out on his lie. But if Raymer denied his earlier story, the whole thing could escalate into a war of words. And since Michael was angry, he might very well look like the bad guy, especially if Raymer kept up his sugar-and-spice act. He decided not to push the issue, at least not for the time being.

Raymer plucked the sign out of the ground—easy to do since he'd put it up only hours earlier—and then stuck it in the back of his truck. He couldn't apologize enough for his 'faux pas.'

It was obvious that as long as Michael's camera was aimed at Raymer he was going to be on his best behavior. So he lowered it to his side and walked over to his Jeep. Taking great pains to act nonchalant, he set the camera on the roof of his vehicle. Then, just as casually, Michael walked back to the front of the Jeep. Exactly as he had hoped, Raymer assumed that the camera had been turned off and could no longer record his image or voice. Raymer's big grin vanished almost instantly. Walking directly up to Michael, his sugar-and-spice act morphed into fire-and-ice.

In a low voice, and with his eyes fixed on Michael, Raymer said. "Michael, you got no idea how big this thing is and what you're getting yourself into. This thing involves big money . . . millions, even billions of dollars." Then he invoked the name of one of the wealthiest and most prominent farmers for hundreds of miles. "Mitchell Scruggs has already had a partner killed under mysterious circumstances all because they was battling Monsanto in court and was close to beating 'em ." With that bone chilling statement he had garnered Michael's undivided attention.

Raymer's eyes burned into Michael's like a noonday sun in July. "They found that man stretched out dead in his office with choke marks on his neck." Then Raymer summed up in a foreboding tone. "You had better be careful!"

With that, Raymer stomped off, got back in his truck, slammed the door, and roared off down the road, kicking up a cloud of dust in his wake and leaving Michael in stunned silence. Raymer's last words hung in the air like an ominous storm looming on the horizon, the kind people here in tornado alley take deadly serious.

For a long moment, all Michael could do was stare with utter disbelief at how quickly his world had been shattered. After all, this wasn't some big city street corner where people from the neighborhood routinely shout sociable insults and benign threats (the kind considered terms of endearment) at old friends and acquaintances as they pass by. This was hill country, the foothills of Appalachia, a place where men were prone to few words. Yet when they do speak, their words count mightily because there is a personal honor tied to backing them up. Toss in the furtive stalkers financed by Monsanto that were lurking around every corner—interlopers who routinely hid their identities behind stolen tags, and Michael would be an absolute fool to interpret Raymer's words as anything less than a death threat.

Gazing over at his corn he noted that the usual pride and peace he felt standing in his field had been replaced by feelings of fear, uncertainty and dread. In the wake of the threat it was as if a layer of top soil had been scraped back to reveal something sinister, something positively evil.

CHAPTER 16

Plopping down behind the desk at his seed business, Michael was still reeling from the encounter at his cornfield. His heart was pounding, he was tense, and his hands were shaking. It was hard to think straight, much less focus on business.

If he hadn't heard Raymer's threat with his own ears he wouldn't have believed it. Terrorists made death threats. The Mafia made death threats. But this warning had come from a man who went around posting signs touting the technology of a Fortune 500 company, a man authorized to sell seeds with Monsanto's technology. It was unconscionable that this had happened in rural America, the heartland, generally thought of as one of the safest places in the country.

Michael was no fool. In the grand scheme of things he knew he wasn't even a gnat on the radar screen of life. That's what made Raymer's words all the more chilling, 'You got no idea how big this thing is and what you're getting yourself into.'

What had he meant? Without knowing it, had Michael stumbled onto something the average Joe couldn't even comprehend? And what about Raymer's ominous claim that Monsanto had already killed a prominent man who had apparently gotten in its way? What had that man done to make Monsanto so mad that it would send thugs to murder him? Was it really because someone was on the verge of besting the conglomerate in a court of law? Was there a hit list? Was Michael on it? Was anyone else in his family on it? Once again he was besieged with a million questions, but no answers.

Answers or not, Michael knew he needed some insurance, though not the kind sold by New York Life. He took out a pen and paper and wrote a note to his father that outlined exactly what had happened with Raymer. It would've been much easier to type it on his computer, but he figured it was better to have it in his own handwriting . . . just in case he turned up dead with a bogus 'typed' suicide note lying near his body.

The last thing Michael wanted to do was upset his family. Monsanto's spies had already done that many times over. So he put the letter in an envelope, sealed it, put a piece of duct tape on for added protection, and then placed it in a special location where only his father would know to look. He could only hope that his eighty-year-old father would never have to read what he had just put down on paper. The mere thought of getting him involved upset Michael to no end. He was an elderly man who had spent his life living by the Golden Rule. At this point he deserved some peace and quiet, not this insanity of being bullied by spies and a seed peddler who seemingly had no conscience.

* * *

Supper for the Whites was not some pseudo family hour, the kind with fast-food or frozen pizza and little or no time for talk. Many nights they had an honest-to-goodness home-cooked meal complete with fresh vegetables and plenty of conversation. It was the kind of get-together most families only have on special occasions, if ever. Skipping supper would have raised a major red flag, so instead Michael went home and ate with his family just like always and tried to act as if nothing unusual had happened. Even so, his daughters were already on edge because of the spies who had been lurking around and snapping photos. Try as he might to shield them, Michael had been unable to keep his family at arm's length from this sordid mess. Everyone in the house was affected by the stalking. This frustrated and angered him mightily. Whatever Monsanto's beef was, it should have been solely with him, not his wife, and certainly not a couple of young girls, one of them only six years old. He wanted desperately to spare them from as much of this nightmare as possible, so he certainly didn't mention Raymer's threat.

Although Michael tried to pretend all was well, he knew he wasn't that good of an actor. Still, no one asked him pointblank during supper if anything was wrong, though he did notice several side glances from Debbie. Only after the dishes were cleared from the table and the children had left the room and gone to do homework did his wife finally address the obvious. "What's wrong?" she asked, consumed by a look of concern and anxiety.

Rather than tell her the whole unnerving story, Michael simply said, "All those spies we've been seeing taking pictures, well, next time you see 'em, bring the girls inside, and quick-like."

Debbie knew there was something terribly wrong that Michael wasn't telling her, but she also knew him well enough to know that he often went overboard trying to protect his family, going to great lengths to shield them from harm. Sometimes that meant keeping them in the dark. She sensed this was one of those times.

Even though it went against Debbie's nature, she demanded to know what was troubling Michael, primarily because it concerned the welfare of their children. "You can't keep this to yourself, not this time. Not if our children are involved. I gotta know what we're up against."

'Torn' did not begin to describe Michael's predicament. The safety of his family was paramount to him, yet so was insulating them from the cold, cruel and heartless elements of the world. That placed him in a serious and troubling quandary. How could he shield their innocence and, simultaneously, protect them? Truth is, it was impossible to do both completely, and he knew it. So he compromised. "What I'm about to say, you can't tell the girls." With a nod of her head, it was obvious that Debbie understood the gravity of the situation, and so she waited with bated breath for Michael to speak. Several moments passed with Michael simply starring at his wife, trying to figure how to break the horrible events of the day to her. After all, she was already extremely upset by the interlopers, telling Michael only days earlier, 'I don't want those creepy strangers taking pictures of our children. I don't like it one bit.'

Michael understood exactly what she meant. His own thoughts on the subject had been even more troubling, "I worry about child molesters, especially with all these strangers slithering around here like a bunch of snakes." It was, perhaps, that horrific notion that allowed Michael to tell Debbie the awful truth. She was right. She had to know what was going on; he owed it to her. And so he told her about the shocking encounter with Raymer, concluding with his cryptic and ominous words, ones he had construed as a death threat.

The look on Debbie's face said it all. In a single moment, everything had changed. A degree of innocence had been shattered and lost forever. The comfort zone they'd worked so hard to build for their children was stolen. And their lives would never be the same.

CHAPTER 17

After staring at the computer screen in his office for hours trying to get a handle on just what had motivated Raymer's dire warning, Michael finally decided to take a break. Googling had produced a vast amount of information about Monsanto, and practically everything Michael read had been disparaging. There was so much negative information—a lot of it vehemently negative—that if Michael had read it the day before he would have simply written some of it off as the rants and raves of disgruntled people with a grudge. But now he felt he knew better.

Based on what Michael had read, Monsanto seemed to be doing its damnedest to frighten and silence farmers. Still, he couldn't quite pinpoint exactly why the conglomerate was after them. Why had Raymer warned him "you got no idea how big this thing is"? The words kept echoing in his brain.

Leaning back from his computer and rubbing his tired eyes, Michael realized his head was pounding. It felt like someone was using a jackhammer on his skull. He needed a breather. Walking over to the window he saw there was a dense haze in the air—it had just rained—that made it impossible to see more than a few feet outside his office window.

If only a fraction of the many allegations he had read online were true—and after his recent experiences it would've been foolish to doubt them—Michael just didn't see how all these things could be happening with so little about it in the papers or on TV. If Monsanto was really out to get farmers then why wasn't it all over the news? The media always found ample ink and airtime to cover the escapades of the latest trailer-trollop turned pop star. *At the very minimum, wasn't the fate of the people producing the nation's food supply at least equally important?*

Michael felt certain that if doctors, pro athletes, politicians, movie stars—or God forbid, lawyers, were under attack as a group there would be an immediate congressional investigation and public outcry. The news media would be clogged and saturated with the story. But since it was farmers, anything but a flashy profession, it seemed that no one really cared . . . save for the farmers themselves. The irony, of course, was that what happens to farmers affects everyone; *no exceptions.*

Staring out the window and trying to clear his head, Michael squinted in an attempt to see through the night's opaque haze. But it was no use. He couldn't see a thing. Yet even though he couldn't see them, he knew that just outside the panes of glass there were hoppers filled with seed, and a bit further along there were elevators chock full of grain. Beyond that there were thousands of acres in cultivation. It all added up to food, simple, necessary, life-sustaining food. And the amount of effort and the means required to produce it was extraordinary, although no one except farmers ever gave any of this a second thought. The vast majority of people never even consider how precariously balanced the entire system is and its numerous vulnerabilities.

For most people, food is something that simply shows up neatly packaged and in abundant supply in their local grocery store or served up just like they ordered in a restaurant. Where their food comes from and how it gets to them isn't important to the average consumer as long as it gets there. When most people think of farmers—if they think about them at all—they imagine them living in another time and place, completely separate from their own world. In effect, farmers are invisible, and since they're invisible no one pays any attention to them.

The most frightening aspects Michael had become aware of were how widespread the issue appeared to be, and how the odds were stacked against him. But what he had also discovered was that he wasn't alone.

Tired of being ignored, other farmers had taken to the Internet in droves. These normally quiet and unassuming souls would not sit idly by while Monsanto made an all-out push to change their way of life and how the food supply worked. That's why they were furiously beating the online drums to make a case for themselves. Because they knew no one else would.

Michael knew if he didn't do something he would be just another statistic, just one more 'hayseed' who'd been plowed under. He also knew that if he failed he wouldn't be the only casualty. With his livelihood gone, his family would be placed in peril, as well. Now he understood exactly why so many farmers were outraged. The conglomerate had made things extremely personal.

CHAPTER 18

Sleep deprivation had finally caught up with Michael. Instead of rolling easily out of bed a couple of hours before dawn, he groggily forced himself to get up just before sunrise. Even so, he was still the only person awake in the house.

He padded softly down the hall, leaving the lights off and operating on memory as he navigated through the dark house until he reached the kitchen where he flipped on a light and then the coffee maker. His mornings started with a pot of full-strength coffee, and most nights ended with a cup of decaf. Coffee was one of his only vices.

The house was quiet at this hour, and so was Michael. He didn't want to disturb his family, especially his wife. Like him, she had been under enormous stress. The constant creeping about of Monsanto's spies would leave anyone on edge, but doubly so for a mother with young children. It was beyond unnerving to think that at any moment a stranger might be lurking in the shadows, watching you and, worse, snapping photos of your children. It could make anyone paranoid - - - especially so after Raymer's threat.

Michael tried to clear his head of Monsanto's spies and the lawsuit. Thinking about it was what had kept him up all night, and it was not a good way to start the morning.

Without a sound, he made his way into the dining room and took a seat and bowed his head. The quiet, early hours of the morning was his time to connect with God, to pray for guidance and direction. For Michael, starting the day without first speaking with God was unthinkable.

Lately, Michael's prayers had often taken on the form of a question. He had been asking God over and over for months, "How important is seed?"

So far he hadn't gotten an answer. But he was undaunted. During his darkest hours it was his faith that sustained him and gave him the strength to face each new day with confidence and purpose. And now when doubts and fears tried to creep into his mind it also provided him with a sense of conviction that what he was doing—standing up to Monsanto—was more than merely justified, it was the right thing to do.

After his prayers, Michael surveyed his front yard, land that he'd cleared by hand. Some years he planted a garden, and some years—like this one— he let the weeds have their way. The weeds weren't all bad. They helped prevent erosion. And he didn't have to get Monsanto's permission to grow weeds . . . at least not yet.

The first rays of sun were just beginning to peek over the horizon and chase away the darkness. The dew would be the next to go, but for now it glistened on the field of weeds like a vast collection of tiny, white Christmas lights.

Carefully observing natures' glory, Michael knew if he was patient he could see all kinds of wildlife. It wasn't uncommon to see a raccoon or opossum, a few rabbits, dozens of song birds, or even a deer or two in his yard. He especially enjoyed seeing a doe with a young fawn grazing. The thought put a gentle smile on Michael's face. He never tired of seeing white-tailed deer, one of the most graceful animals on the planet.

Waiting and hoping to see a few rabbits or even a deer, it occurred to Michael that nature requires a fine balancing act. And it doesn't take much to throw things way out of whack. He'd heard that bears were once fairly plentiful on the mountain, but now even a sighting was big news, and often written off as a "mistake" or "gossip." It was as if the bears had evaporated into thin air. Michael felt that if Monsanto had its way farmers who chose to use conventional methods and natural seeds would also go away.

A lifetime of farming had taught him that the food chain has always been a very small and tight circle, and that seeds are the engine that powers it. They are the main ingredient in the plants which supply fresh produce for people, and the feed needed for livestock, from cattle to chickens to goats to pigs. With the lone exception of seafood harvested from the ocean, the food people eat either comes from seeds or is dependent on them - - - that means every single bite of food. And for those who would look offshore for a savior, there aren't enough fish and crustaceans in the ocean to feed the entire world's population on a daily basis for more than a scant few weeks without greatly endangering the source and forcing countless species into extinction.

Michael picked up his Bible and opened it; it's where he went when searching for answers to difficult questions. Sifting through it, he found a passage and began to read. Out of nowhere, he felt an eerie sensation, almost as if he'd been shocked or stung. Then something clenched in his gut. He raced to the bathroom, Bible still in hand, and was violently ill, vomiting again and again.

After several minutes, breathing heavily and exhausted from being sick, he leaned against the wall of the bathroom and went back to the passage he was reading. Before he could finish it he became violently ill again. This time he had the dry heaves because he had already lost the contents of his stomach.

With sweat running down his forehead, Michael had an epiphany, which he attributed to the verses he had just read: If Monsanto forced farmers like him out of business, in short order, it was possible that it could eliminate natural seeds all together. If someone wasn't around to save them each year and replant them they would eventually become extinct. And once they did, GM seeds would be the only game in town.

With limited competition, Monsanto could control the food supply—every last bite, from a box of cornflakes to dinner at a five-star restaurant.

Simply by dictating how much of each variety of seed could be planted each year—or not—the conglomerate could manipulate the supply of food the world over. Michael was convinced it could even create artificial shortages designed to jack up the price merely to line its overstuffed pockets.

A parallel could be drawn with energy, specifically gasoline. But there's a drastic difference because there are alternative forms of energy: coal, natural gas, wind, solar, etc. If GM seeds displaced natural seeds—which Michael felt was Monsanto's grand plan—*there would be no alternatives.* Also, while people can in fact live without cars, no one can survive without food. The power Monsanto could wield if it controlled all crop seeds, or even half of them, could make OPEC look like a bunch of schoolboys dealing penny-ante poker on the playground.

As Michael finally slipped the pieces into place, his blood went cold. Now he finally understood why Jeb Raymer had warned him of the dire consequences of getting in Monsanto's way, 'You got no idea how big this thing is and what you're getting yourself into.'

It seemed abundantly clear to Michael that Monsanto's ultimate goal was control over the food supply - - - all based on what he termed a 'seed cartel.'

Once and for all, Michael had finally gotten the answer to the question, "How important is seed? . . . *there is nothing on the planet more important because it is the key element required for sustaining life.*"

CHAPTER 19

One thing that really got under Michael's skin like a bad rash was the fact that he had to sneak around to meet with people, especially old friends and allies, all in an effort to avoid the prying eyes of Monsanto's spies. It was beyond obscene that honest people had been forced to slink around like sleazy criminals planning a bank job. How and when, Michael wondered, had it gotten to the point where decent people had to hide out merely to have a frank and open conversation?

As much as Michael detested having to sneak around to meet with people, he understood it was a necessity because it seemed that fewer and fewer people were willing to meet with him in the light of day. Some were brutally honest and told him so up front, others danced around it, and in some cases he insisted on secrecy himself to keep his friends and confidants from winding up on "Monsanto's enemies list." Michael, of course, didn't know for sure if such a list existed. But he felt certain there was one - - - in one form or another.

During one of these secret meetings Michael found out about the "terminator technology." And he was told that Monsanto was hell bent on acquiring it. Described as nothing short of a "doomsday formula," Michael was told that it would allow the conglomerate to conjure up seeds in its labs that were incapable of reproducing. On the surface, the manufacture of sterile seeds certainly didn't sound like the end of the world. But if Monsanto were to apply the formula to a specific kind of seed and then distributed them in key locations around the country there could be a real possibility the genetically modified offspring could cross-pollinate with organic plants and cause them to be sterile, as well. In short order an entire species of plant, such as tomatoes, could be totally wiped out . . . except, of course, for the GM variety. The resulting loss in crop diversity could lead to limited supplies and choices at the supermarket—including all products made with and from tomatoes, from ketchup to salsa to spaghetti sauce. Even more important, a loss of adaptability for the remaining GM plants could result in an extremely vulnerable supply line. Michael wondered what would happen if the crop created in the lab could only survive under ultra restricted conditions, such as a hothouse or very specific climate? What if this GM version was susceptible to a particular disease or insect? . . .one that no one would know about until it was out in the wild. An entire genus of plants could be suddenly wiped out.

Michael soon formed a hypothesis that the most frightening and irreversible aspect of the "terminator technology" was what might happen if it was unleashed in the wild, either on purpose or by accident. It had the 'potential' to affect far more than just crops. It could impact all plant life— including animals and indigenous people that depend on them, and possibly even devastate an entire ecosystem. What would happen if even ten or twenty or thirty percent of the plants in a given ecosystem became sterile? Knowing the interdependence plants have on one another, the deforestation of the rainforests could seem almost tame by comparison.

It certainly didn't escape Michael that in the wrong hands the 'terminator' could be as dangerous as some weapons of mass destruction. After all, Michael was convinced that a GM plant can cripple the integrity of an organic plant, yet it doesn't work the other way. To top it off, he certainly had reason to distrust the company that was salivating to get its hands on the 'terminator.'

Michael wondered how the development of the "terminator technology" had all but slipped under the news media's radar. How could something like this—something with the potential to wreak cataclysmic devastation— go all but unnoticed? Was it because reporters mindlessly discounted it as something only farmers, gardeners and environmentalists should concern themselves with? What would happen if this highly sensitive technology fell into the hands of terrorists? Would they use it to undermine our food supply and starve us to death? By the time it made the six o'clock news would it be too late? Would it already be entrenched in the environment to the point where it was impossible to reverse or even contain?

As a fourth generation farmer who'd spent his life tilling the soil and operating a seed business, Michael understood the potential for catastrophe with the "terminator technology" far better than most people, even a lot of so-called experts, ones who knew their way around the most sophisticated labs, yet wouldn't know the back end of a jackass from the front unless it brayed quite loudly. The questions he raised were not idle thoughts; they were genuine and legitimate concerns of a man who had farmed for decades. [4]

---

[4] In 2007, Monsanto acquired Delta & Pine Land Company for $1.5 billion dollars. Prior to the acquisition, D&PL experimented with the 'terminator technology' and planned to use it in commercial applications. Before acquiring D&PL, Monsanto made a pledge in 1999 that it would not use the technology commercially. Prior to taking that pledge, Monsanto attempted to acquire D&PL in 1998, but the deal was thwarted at that time by federal authorities.

CHAPTER 20

Try as he might, it had been impossible for Michael to concentrate on his work. How could he? Every seed he saw reminded him of what was happening right under his nose, and when you're in the seed business you see a lot them during the course of a day.

He couldn't stop thinking about the haunting reality in which he believed that one day Monsanto could dictate the supply of food simply by rationing out how much of any given seed it would let farmers grow. By that same token, the conglomerate could also manipulate the commodities market and, in essence, the price of all food.

Michael thought back to 1972, the year he graduated high school. Gas had been plentiful and cheap, selling for about 30 - 33 cents a gallon. He could still vividly remember him and his buddies filling up the tank of an old hot-rod, giving the station attendant a five-dollar bill, and getting change back.

Then the following year all hell had broken loose as a result of the Arab Oil Embargo. Gas prices skyrocketed, almost doubling overnight. And to compound matters, not only was the price exorbitant, there was also a shortage. Drivers were lucky to find a station that actually had gas, or that would sell them more than a few gallons, even if they could afford it.

It created an economic tsunami, one that some people never truly got over. Michael remembered that many families had to choose between filling up their tanks and filling up their grocery carts. It was not a good time for people living on the edge, or anywhere near it. It wasn't much better for those who earned higher wages, even professionals because the double-digit inflation triggered by the astronomical rise in fuel prices hit everyone hard.

Michael tried to envision the nightmare of what would happen if every item in the grocery store doubled overnight, or even tripled. Add shortages to the mix and there would be nothing short of panic. It could make the gas crisis back in '73—an economic nightmare that all but brought the country to its knees—look like nothing more than a hiccup on Wall Street by comparison.

Would people hoard food the way they had hoarded gas back in the 1970s? Would food become a sacred commodity to be traded for other goods? More than a few people had used gas to rip off others back then. A lot of gas stations closed on Sundays during the shortage, even stations on interstates, in order that they would have fuel to pump on Mondays. Horror tales circulated that a motorist, dangerously low on fuel, might pull into a gas station right off the interstate only to find it closed and, instead, encounter a black marketer parked in the shadows. With a trunk full of 5-gallon cans, one of these human leeches could easily demand twice the going rate for a few gallons of gas from desperate motorists who were a long way from home. Their victims often had little choice except to pay double the pump price—which was, of course, double what it had been only a short time ago. Gas at quadruple the recent price—and acquired from a shady profiteer—added up to a grim picture of life.

In the overly comfortable world we've built for ourselves, Michael saw an entire generation or so of people who had no concept of shortages. They were so accustomed to an overabundance of everything—food, cars, clothes, gadgets, fuel—that most thought a shortage was when the latest and greatest Christmas toy was on back order. He had seen news reports about overzealous parents getting in fistfights at stores over who would have the privilege of buying the last remaining "gotta have" over-hyped, overpriced toy or computer gizmo available on the shelf. What would these same people do if they hadn't eaten in a few days? Would they fight other people over a loaf of bread? What extremes would they go to for food if their kids hadn't eaten in days?

Michael took out a notepad and pen. He wasn't exactly sure why, but he felt the need to keep a record of his thoughts and recent events. Maybe putting them on paper would make it easier to understand. At the very least he could try keeping it all in order.

Later on, after having some success with paper and pen, Michael got on the computer to look up something he had heard about farmers in India. Although there was a haze of dust on the screen, one of the downsides of operating inside a business that cleans the dirt and debris from seeds, it was clear enough to perform a Google search. And it only took a few seconds to find there was a slew of articles, information, and blogs referring to the abominable plight of farmers in India.

A number of bloggers have an agenda, as do some web sites associated with certain organizations, yet there was enough information from reliable news organizations to eliminate any suspicion that the horror story he found had been concocted.

For quite awhile Michael read articles and eyewitness accounts that chilled him to the bone. The truth, it seemed—based on what Michael had read—was that farmers in India, primarily those in the states of Andhra Pradesh and Maharashtra, were the victims of cruel, heartless, and unmitigated greed.

With farming roots that often went back ten generations or more, these Indians were anything but novices at the world's "toughest profession." They weren't the sort who didn't understand the inherent risks that came with farming. They were people toughened by pestilence, poverty, and droughts, i.e., people who did not expect much from life other than a fighting chance to make an honest living using their hands and the sweat of their brow.

Primarily cotton growers, most of these farmers made do with a small patch of land that had been handed down from generation to generation. And just like the land, most of the seeds, too, were generational; some of them were thought to have been around for hundreds and hundreds of years, if not longer.

These farmers planted their seeds, carefully tended and nurtured their crop, performed the back breaking labor of picking their cotton by hand, cleaned it by hand, and with the seeds they mined from the harvest they had more than enough to plant a crop of equal size, if not larger, the following year, a tried and true process that had worked for eons. That is, until giant corporations came along and told them that they had developed seemingly 'magic seeds' that would not only grow faster and produce higher yields, but they would no longer need to use pesticides. For trusting peasant farmers, this was a Godsend. The promises of higher yields coupled with the notion that they would not have to buy costly pesticides conjured up a scenario that could provide them with the equivalent of a few extra pennies per day to lavish on their families. Hard as it is to imagine, those pennies would be a monumental increase for them. And so, they fell in line like trusting souls do, eagerly taking out loans to buy these new 'magic seeds.'

But the GM seeds were not magic; they were anything but. The prices farmers paid for the GM seeds were, in some cases, a thousand percent more than conventional seeds. That alone meant they faced a staggering uphill battle just to make a profit. Even worse, much to their dismay, the farmers discovered they could not save the GM seeds and replant them, a practice that had served them well since time immemorial. For eighth-, ninth-, and tenth-generation farmers who'd been saving seeds all their lives, the new dictum was extremely difficult to comprehend. To compound matters, saving the GM seeds was illegal.

For impoverished farmers living in third-worldesque conditions who can barely feed and clothe their families, the mere notion of hiring a lawyer to battle a giant seed company is beyond absurd. Yet the problem that many of them faced was the fact that in order to buy new seeds they would first have to pay off the debt they owed on the GM seeds they had already purchased and used. But that was impossible for many of these farmers because the GM seeds, for a number of them, had not panned out. They were drowning in debt, and had no way out, in part because the claims of greater yields did not materialize, and in some cases the GM seeds failed completely.

Farmers the world over are a proud people because theirs is a noble profession. No one can deny that. But in India they are even more so. It is part of their culture, part of their heritage. "Losing face" is a very real thing, and to lose the land that's been in a family for a thousand years or more or fail to provide for one's family can do far more than merely break the spirit of even the toughest of farmers.

The utter hopelessness of going from a landowner to slave labor or a beggar, and with no way of ever getting their land back, was simply too much for many of these noble people to bear. Despair hung in the air of the villages like a dark and angry storm cloud. No one had any answers; they felt doomed. And so thousands of these decent and honorable people took the darkest exit of all . . . a number of them did so by ingesting the very pesticides that GM seed advocates told them they would no longer need.

It was impossible for a decent human being not to get angry, frustrated and upset when blindsided by this kind of horrific information, so Michael took some time to compose himself, then finally stated the obvious in a reasonably controlled voice. "If it was ten or twenty of 'em committing suicide, even fifty or so, you might could chalk it up to a sad coincidence. But when you got hundreds and even thousands of people taking their own lives, and they all live in the same area, with the same occupation, and they're all in the same leaky boat, well, coincidence ain't got nothing to do with it."[5]

The astronomical number of suicides among these farmers was so high that it was past the point of being even an epidemic, some people referred to it as a form of greed induced genocide. To Michael, anyone who saw it differently was either in denial or on someone's payroll that had a monetary stake in this abomination. And, from what Michael had read, one of the primary companies responsible for the despair wrought upon these simple and honest people was Monsanto.[6]

For a man who saw life in the starkest terms—black and white, good and evil, right and wrong, Michael felt he had just been handed more than enough justification to fight this monster. He now felt a *responsibility* to wage this battle, to fight for those who couldn't do so themselves.

---

[5] Monsanto disputes that the mass suicides of farmers in India were connected to GM seeds.

[6] In 2006, Prince Charles, heir to the British throne, upon seeing the tragic plight of farmers in India, not only spoke out against this injustice, but he also established a charitable organization, Bhumi Vardaan Foundation, to address this troubling matter and assist the farmers so they could grow sustainable organic crops.

CHAPTER 21

"Farm ornaments;" the quaint euphemism described expensive farm equipment—tractors, combines, cotton pickers—that simply gave out before their time and were left to rot beside a field. Unlike lawn ornaments, which have no functional purpose, farm ornaments served as stern reminders for farmers. Every time Michael saw an abandoned tractor, rusting and caught in a tangle of weeds, vines, and spiderwebs, he was reminded of what happens to valuable equipment when it's not properly maintained.

Maintenance was the bane of all farmers. There was never enough time to do it all, but if you didn't, you'd spend half your time fixing the things that broke down way too soon due to lack of maintenance. And replacing an expensive piece of equipment before its time was often the last straw for a struggling farmer. It could easily be enough to force him into bankruptcy.

When Michael was a young boy and worked for his daddy on their farm, Wayne had drilled maintenance into his head. Wayne was a wise and thrifty farmer. He could make a tractor last twenty years that another farmer would be lucky to keep running for ten. Keeping a piece of equipment operational for a few extra years often meant the difference between a profitable year and a loser. Thanks to Wayne, Michael learned at an early age to stay ahead of the curve on equipment maintenance.

So instead of sneaking over to Lake Guntersville and throwing a hook in the water, Michael spent the morning pulling maintenance on his oldest tractor.

Exiting the barn for a much needed break, Michael was surprised to find that the sun was gone and replaced by storm clouds. Scanning the ominous sky for signs of bad weather—something farmers must always be on the lookout for, he instead spotted something small, white and yellow moving in the distance. It was a stark contrast against the dark and turbulent sky. Naturally, his eyes were drawn to it.

Having spotted a similar plane flying over his home more than a few times in recent weeks, Michael kept a sharp eye on this one as it circled the area. He had a feeling deep down in his gut that this might very well be yet another one of Monsanto's spying tactics. Even so, there was something else about the plane that bothered Michael, yet he couldn't quite put his finger on it. After watching the plane for the longest time it finally came to him: *the aircraft didn't have any letters on its tail, and it didn't have any numbers, either.* "My sweet Lord," Michael muttered with astonished dismay. "An unmarked plane, completely untraceable! Guess I shouldn't be surprised. Not by this, not by anything these thugs do."

* * *

Over the next few weeks there was a noticeable increase in the air traffic over Michael's home and farm, particularly helicopters. Although none of the aircrafts had tail numbers, the primary unit appeared to be one of the most venerable and reliable workaday helicopters on the planet, a Bell 206. More commonly known as a JetRanger, the sleek, multi-passenger copter was perfect for darting in, around, over and through the mountains many nooks and crannies.

Sporting a distinctive blue and white paint job, in no time the JetRanger was buzzing Michael's house at all hours of the day and night. Yet there was no discernable pattern for the flights. Some days the sorties started around daylight, other days they didn't show up until noon. Occasionally the copter would fly over, then a plane, then the copter again. Regardless, the effect was always unsettling, especially for a husband and wife with young children.

One afternoon while watching the unmarked blue and white chopper fly repeatedly over his farm, it occurred to Michael there was a possibility that it was operating legitimately. Much like whiskey stills a generation or two ago, marijuana was grown surreptitiously on Sand Mountain, and had been for quite some time. Pot had long ago supplanted white lightning as a prime source of revenue among those who routinely operated outside the law. And they certainly weren't beyond using other people's property, especially parcels out in the hinterlands. Hardcore pot growers rarely used their own land, even if they owned a considerable amount; it was but one of many ways to avoid detection and getting arrested. Although Michael had never caught anyone red-handed growing pot on his land, he knew other farmers had.

Like most farmers, over the years Michael had seen a number of helicopters flying around Sand Mountain that he was reasonably certain were manned by the Drug Enforcement Agency. Although some felt the flyovers were an invasion of their privacy, it didn't bother Michael one way or the other. He wasn't doing anything wrong, and had absolutely nothing to hide.

The DEA's helicopters were almost always dark gray or black, and they tended to use Sikorsky Black Hawks, military grade choppers that were easily distinguishable from the blue and white JetRanger that had been buzzing Michael's home and farm relentlessly. Nevertheless, the DEA's choppers did share one trait with the blue and white copter; they often didn't have tail numbers either. Of course, the difference was that they were officially sanctioned by the U.S. Government.

To eliminate the possibility he was seeing DEA choppers and mistaking them for ones manned by Monsanto's henchmen, Michael contacted the sheriff's office and explained the situation. The sheriff's department told him that although the DEA wasn't required to let them know they were in the area performing surveillance work, more often than not they knew when they were operating on Sand Mountain. And they were not on the mountain on this day, nor had they been the previous day, or even the day before that.

After that initial conversation with the sheriff's department, from time to time Michael would check in with them when he spotted one of the unmarked aircrafts. He was merely double-checking to be certain he wasn't making a mistake as to who was behind the sorties.

It was around this time that Michael bumped into a friend—actually more of an acquaintance, Jake Perkins, while filling up his truck one day. Jake was an EMT on a medivac helicopter, the kind that rescues people with catastrophic injuries and rushes them to a trauma center while their lives hang in the balance.

Taking off with only a moment's notice, flying in terrible conditions—from bad to downright stormy weather, they sometimes fly with almost no visibility. These Good Samaritans of the sky routinely push the envelope to get to the scene of an accident or catastrophe as swiftly as humanly possible, and then rush the victim to the hospital when minutes and seconds count. It's a herculean task, and extremely dangerous; the crew members of airborne ambulances routinely risk their own lives to save their critically injured patients.

Jake had heard through the grapevine about the unmarked sorties targeting Michael's home and farm, so he took advantage of their chance encounter to share some information. First and foremost, Jake pointed out to Michael that the medivac chopper he worked on was clearly marked and easily identifiable as an emergency aircraft. It even had several large red crosses on it; there was no mistaking the purpose of the helicopter.

During a recent flight, Jake and his crew had encountered an unmarked chopper that fit the description of the blue and white one that had been buzzing Michael's property unrelentingly. It matched the unmarked copter right down to its highly visible and distinctive paint job. Jake recounted that while flying a safe distance from the blue and white helicopter—yet close enough to maintain constant visual contact, the pilot of the medivac attempted to raise the unmarked aircraft on the radio. There was no response, just dead silence. That was extremely disturbing because pilots are required to respond to other aircraft; its one of the surest ways to avoid mid-air collisions. Another reason for grave concern: the medivac might have needed emergency assistance. For all the pilot of the unmarked helicopter knew, the medivac could very well have been in serious trouble and desperately needed its help. Failing to answer the call of another pilot while in flight was a serious violation in and of itself, but ignoring the calls of a medivac was tantamount to ignoring an ambulance's siren on the highway and then intentionally blocking its path.

Then Jake lobed an even bigger bombshell at Michael. The pilot of the unmarked chopper apparently didn't like the fact that the medivac's pilot tried to raise him on the radio, or that he flew parallel with him for a considerable distance, because he soon peeled off and attempted to hide behind a large structure. Michael was on the edge of his chair, especially since there wasn't a single building he could think of in all of Jackson County for a helicopter to hide behind. "What building could that be?"

Jake leveled a serious gaze on Michael for a long moment, and then finally said in a whisper, "Bellefonte."

Michael felt his heart skip a beat. This took things to a new level, a level he considered to be way beyond serious, because there was only one thing named Bellefonte big enough that a chopper could hide behind . . . *a nuclear reactor in the shadows of Sand Mountain!* The unmarked chopper had used the giant inverted cones at Bellefonte for cover! Although Michael was no expert on aviation, he was certain that flying too close to a nuclear facility was an egregious violation on a number of levels, and with multiple agencies . . . to say nothing of using the facility to hide behind, and worse, hide from a bona fide emergency medical aircraft!

After letting the enormity of that sink in, Jake told Michael that in all his time working on air ambulance flights he had never seen such a blatant disregard for an emergency aircraft, as well as flight safety procedures and aviation rules in general.

Right before departing, Jake tossed out one last piece of information about the unmarked helicopter. While riding with a buddy one night they spotted it parked in a field behind the Jameson Inn. Located on the outskirts of Scottsboro, it was far from being the only motel in the area. However, it was the only one that Michael knew for a fact was a destination for at least some of Monsanto's spies; he had conducted inverse-surveillance more than once to confirm it. They may very well have stayed at other motels, perhaps even in other towns, but there was no questioning that— from time to time—some of them stayed at the Jameson Inn near Scottsboro.

With all the dots now connected and verified, as far as Michael was concerned any shadow of a doubt about the origins of the unmarked chopper had been eliminated. In his mind, it might as well have had Monsanto's logo emblazoned on its sides in giant red letters - - - *right where the missing tail number should have been.*

Michael felt a genuine debt of gratitude to Jake for having the courage to come forward; not many people would. It proved that Jake was a man of principles.

The priceless information Jake provided bolstered what Michael had already surmised: he and his family were under siege, right on Sand Mountain, a place the Whites had called home for generations. There was simply no other way to characterize the effects of the sorties, ones seemingly designed to induce maximum frustration, high anxiety, and absolute fear that his family might very well be harmed.

Sometimes late at night Michael would wake up in a cold sweat with the sound of an aircraft engine roaring in his ear, only to realize it was part of a bad dream. More than once he had tiptoed out of his bedroom so as not to wake Debbie to clear his head. But sometimes even that backfired, because once or perhaps even twice he discovered that a plane or chopper was buzzing around outside his house. It was a nightmare come to life.

The situation was getting out of hand because Michael genuinely feared that one of the pilots might crash into his house, either accidentally or on purpose, and kill his entire family. A good pilot could parachute out of his aircraft long before it came tumbling down and crashed into a ball of flames; Michael suspected it could be easily covered-up as an 'accident.' Given Monsanto's abominable deeds in nearby Anniston, plus the bold presence of spies on the mountain and Raymer's death threat, Michael truly feared for his life and the lives of his family. And he felt anything less would have been foolhardy.

CHAPTER 22

Collectively, there were probably a couple dozen private airstrips and small municipal airports on and around Sand Mountain, but Michael nixed visiting any of those. Given all the rumors and gossip that were swirling about regarding him and the sorties targeting his farm and home, he certainly didn't want anybody on the mountain to know just how much it was actually bothering him. That information might very well make its way right back to Monsanto and cause an increase in the number of flights. It was better to go someplace where he wasn't known, because he definitely did not want the information he sought to fall into the hands of his enemy.

After driving for a very long time on a series of back roads to shake any tails, Michael finally made it to an out-of-the-way airstrip that offered crop dusting, sky diving, flying lessons, and scenic tours. Michael had been advised by a trusted friend that the man who ran the place was extremely knowledgeable about flying both planes and helicopters. And, odds were, no one here would recognize Michael.

The airstrip, it turned out, was little more than a sliver of well-worn asphalt running through a field consisting primarily of Johnson grass and wildflowers. In another life it was probably a hay field, or maybe even a cow pasture. Perched atop a narrow pole was a tattered windsock gently blowing in the breeze. The lone building on the premises was a hangar shaped like a Quonset hut, the kind of structure that harked back to another era. Frequent flyer types would be sorely disappointed, if not appalled, by the rustic and minimalist facilities, yet it was more or less what Michael had expected. The airstrip was a small commercial venture that paid its own way, not an overbuilt municipal facility subsidized by taxpayers.

From the outside the old hangar didn't look particularly big, but inside there was probably enough room for three or even four small planes if they were arranged in just the right order. At the moment, though, there were only two in residence, both single-engine models that carried no more than four or five passengers tops. And a mechanic, dressed in coveralls spattered with oil and grease, was working on one of them.

"Hey bud, you run this place?" Michael asked as he walked up to the mechanic.

Without taking his eyes off the delicate job at hand, the mechanic shook his head, then pointed toward a door at the rear of the hangar. "You want Wiley. He's back there in his office."

"Much obliged," Michael replied, then made his way to the office where he knocked on the door. "Wiley? You in?"

A hearty, booming voice that sounded eerily reminiscent of a radio announcer from a bygone era declared, "I'm not only in, door's open."

Michael turned the knob, pushed the door open, and found himself inside another world. The office was a museum, if not a shrine, to aviation. The quality and quantity of artifacts, mementos, and memorabilia that had been collected and squeezed into such a small office was amazing. They all added up to a life well-lived that centered around flying.

The walls were blanketed with photos, yet two stood out above all the rest. The first, a faded and grainy black and white, featured a bullet-riddled Huey on a makeshift landing pad in Vietnam with a foreboding jungle for a backdrop. A tall, lanky pilot—probably no more than twenty-one or twenty-two—with a thick head of dark, unruly hair was standing beside the helicopter. Wearing fatigues splattered with mud and soaked with sweat, he had a half-smoked cigarette dangling from the lips of his young, unsmiling battle-hardened face. Just beneath that stark, gripping image was a fading color photo of the same young man smiling from ear to ear.

Attired in an immaculate dress uniform and sporting a crew cut, the proud young Marine had movie-star good looks and was wearing what appeared to be his newly earned wings. The contrast between the two images could not have been more dramatic . . . or telling.

Wiley Kemp, a tall, heavy-set man, was kicked back with his old scuffed-up cowboy boots propped on a battered metal desk that looked like a reject from a military surplus store. He was smoking a well-crafted corncob pipe, similar to the kind made famous by Gen. Douglas McArthur. Time and a life of hard knocks had robbed the once dashing Marine of his youth, innocence, and good looks. From his mottled gray hair, which was receding and had thinned considerably, to the lines chiseled deep into his cheeks and around his eyes, his face told his story better than any book ever could.

Like most people who came face-to-face with their own mortality at a young age, Wiley saw life differently from the general populace. He joked more, laughed louder, and played harder, yet he instinctively knew when to be serious and could be far more intense than most. Eyeing Michael, the old war weary aviator quipped, "Friend, you here to fly a plane or jump out of one?"

Michael couldn't help but grin. "On the first option, I'd have to say 'not today'; on the second, 'not in this lifetime.'"

With a wink and a puff on his pipe, Wiley snapped, "Then you're in the wrong place."

"Wouldn't be the first time." Michael replied, matching Wiley quip for quip.

It was obvious that Wiley enjoyed this kind of friendly give-and-take banter, so he motioned for Michael to have a seat in an old La-Z-Boy, the most comfortable seat in the room. Wiley pointed at a large, stainless steel coffee urn that was all but hidden amidst his mementos and memorabilia.

"Want a cup? It's fresh."

Michael shook his head. "No thanks. Just need a bit of information."

"If it's about women, you're out of luck. And if it's about making money, you're not even in the right state. But if it's about flying, I might can help you."

The last thing Michael wanted was to have to explain to Wiley the nightmare Monsanto had wrought on his family. So he couched his question as a hypothetical. "Let's say somebody was out in their backyard, maybe just mowing the grass, and they spied a plane or helicopter flying around, an unmarked one, and —"

A no-nonsense type when it came to his profession, Wiley cut Michael off in mid-sentence. "Sorry, pardner, that didn't happen, and it won't."

Taken aback, Michael cocked his head. "What do you mean? How can you know that for a fact?"

The old ace shot back. "9/11" That hung in the air a moment, then he added, "If you'd come in here a year before that, or a week, or even a day before, and said you'd seen an unmarked aircraft I'd have said, 'Sure, it happens.'" Wiley shook his head, "But not now."

"Why's that?"

"The world changed forever on September 11th, but nowhere did it change as much as is it did with aviation. A pilot gets caught now flying an aircraft with no tail number he'll never fly again, to say nothing of the accommodations he'll have for years to come."

"So you're saying it's illegal?"

Wiley sighed at Michael's naïveté. "It's a lot more than just illegal. No pilot in his right mind, hell, even in his wrong one, would even consider it. There's a whole helluva lot more to it than just laws and punishment. Civilized people don't need laws telling them certain things are wrong. Same goes for pilots. Flying without a tail number after 9/11 is something you just don't do." Although Wiley didn't say it word-for-word, even the small planes that populated his tiny airstrip could—in the wrong hands—become a lethal tool for terrorists. Filled with explosives or chemical weapons or both, a benign looking four-seater could wreak absolute havoc if crashed into a heavily populated area.

"So you're telling me," Michael said slowly and haltingly, "that if I, uh, I mean if someone saw a helicopter with no tail number, and, uh, they saw it again and again—a blue and white one—and it was flying right over their house and farm and — "

Just like before, the old pilot cut Michael off. "Friend, I don't doubt that you *thought* you saw a chopper with no tail number. It happens all the time. Somebody looks up, spies a small aircraft, the sun hits it just so, and all they see is white."

Locking eyes with Wiley, Michael pronounced in a low, deep, and tortured voice that left no margin for error. "I've seen this helicopter way too many times for it to be the sun blocking the tail number. Fact is, it ain't got no tail number. And I can even tell you what kind it is: it's a Bell JetRanger. And I ain't the only person that's seen it."

Suddenly, there was a marked change in Wiley's demeanor. Something in Michael's face, perhaps his eyes, maybe his voice, though probably a combination of all three, convinced Wiley that Michael was not just killing time or wasting his; he was deadly serious. "You really have seen an unmarked chopper, haven't you?"

Michael nodded. "Yeah. A lot. And it's got me worried, real worried. I'm worried about the safety of my family 'cause of it."

Wiley recognized that Michael was a tortured soul, and he must have felt Michael was on the up and up. Otherwise, he wouldn't have dared said what he did.

Using cryptic language and speaking in the most general terms possible, Wiley explained that the most vulnerable component on most choppers is the tail rotor. It provides the stability necessary to keep the aircraft flying. Without it, the chopper will spin out of control and crash. Military choppers are designed with reinforcements around the tail rotor to protect them against enemy fire and shrapnel. Civilian choppers are not, which means they can be highly vulnerable if someone knows their weak spots.

Without saying it pointblank, Wiley told Michael how to bring down a chopper with a high powered rifle if he really and truly felt his family was in grave danger. Coming from a battle hardened vet, it was heady information indeed, the kind that Michael fervently hoped and prayed he would never need.

CHAPTER 23

No one would ever call Ider, Alabama, a metropolis. With only 644 residents, it's far more likely to be described as a small village. But once a year the tiny hamlet's population explodes and it's standing room only. That's because the annual Mule Day Festival, held over the Labor Day weekend, draws people from hundreds—and in some cases—even thousands of miles away.

Most of the people who flock to Ider on Mule Day are other small-town folks, or at the very least those who wish they were. But that's no accident. Devoid of gimmicky fads and overblown hype, the festival celebrates the traditions and local flavor of the area and a simpler time. Attendees can mill around the antique car and tractor show or admire the work of talented, undiscovered artists, and of course food is always in abundance. Old-fashioned gospel singing can be heard here and there, and traditional games keep the children happy and busy. The most popular events at the festival, however, the ones that draw the biggest and nosiest crowds, feature mules and horses. They are the main reason Michael White, who often took part, made the trip to Ider every year.

Although Michael came for the mules—to watch them, talk about them with other mule aficionados, show off his own mules, and occasionally even trade for one, another highlight of the festival for him and his family was the Mule Day parade. Like the festival itself, the parade reminded people of a gentler time in life. There was always a high school band or two, a smiling queen and her court, cowboys and cowgirls on horseback, a battalion of clowns and, of course, lots of mules.

Of all the things the White family did together away from home, none was more of an annual tradition than attending Mule Day. And this year, given the spying, harassment and intimidation they had endured at the hands of Monsanto's relentless spies, they needed a break more than ever. So they got to the festival early, and planned to stay late. They didn't want to miss a thing this year, especially not the parade.

Seeing the parade from the sidelines was a real treat. But actually being a part of it was a genuine honor, and this year Michael was a participant. Guiding a rustic buckboard wagon led by a pair of his prized mules, he was accompanied by Debbie and their youngest child. Tiny for her age, six-year-old Emily was freckled faced, cute as a button, smart, polite and curious, yet very shy around strangers. Understandably, a shy six-year-old and spies lurking in the shadows was not a good mix . . . not for the child.

With Michael serving as muleskinner—*the person who guides the mules*, Debbie and Emily shared friendly waves with the spectators as they made their way down the parade route. This was no small accomplishment for Emily. Her parents were elated that she was doing so well, almost at ease, amidst a sea of strangers.

The White family quickly realized there was an unexpected benefit to being a prime attraction in the parade. They had a panoramic view of all the people watching the event, and that was a treat in and of itself. Many of them dressed in old-style clothing, going to great lengths to make their outfits appear authentic, which meant it was like having a window into the past.

Positioned between a woman wearing an early 1900s style dress—complete with parasol, and a man in full Civil War battle regalia, Michael spied a man and woman dressed as Uncle Sam. They both had on iconic red, white & blue costumes, along with theatrically tall top hats; the man even had on a long white beard. Although they weren't part of the parade, dressed as the old "I Want You" poster of Uncle Sam they were easy for Michael to spot from his catbird's seat. Stepping off the curb and into the street—a bit too close to his wagon for safety's sake in Michael's opinion, the woman, a redhead, gave him a great big exaggerated wave and shouted, "There's Michael White!" all but making it a proclamation. Then she and the man both pointed at Debbie and Emily and roared. "There's Debbie White! There's Emily White!"

Michael shot them a friendly smile and waved back; Emily and Debbie did the same. It was the kind of old fashioned, down-home, country greetings that were so much a part of their world. In rural Alabama, out on country roads, it was even customary to wave when you met an oncoming vehicle, whether you knew the driver or not. It was the neighborly thing to do. Besides, you never knew, you might very well know someone in the vehicle, even if you didn't know the driver.

As their wagon slowly moved along the parade route, Debbie and Emily kept waving and greeting the spectators with big, warm, happy smiles. Some of the people they knew well, others were nodding acquaintances at best, yet many were complete strangers. The man and woman dressed as Uncle Sam fit into the last category.

Any other time, Michael wouldn't have thought twice about the fact that the man and woman knew his name, and even that of his wife and youngest child. After all, there were people in the area that Michael knew on sight, yet he had never spoken with them. Still, there was something about the man and woman that set off the parent radar inside his head. Was it their matching Uncle Sam costumes? Their over-the-top waves and shouts? Or the tone of their voices? - - - in hindsight, Michael realized they were downright sarcastic, and even bordered on nasty and mean spirited.

Michael had noticed that a number of Monsanto's goons displayed American flag stickers and emblems on their trucks, as well as patriot bumper stickers. He had a gut feeling they used them to blend in, as well as a smoke screen to hide their true intentions. Before 9/11, finding a vehicle with an American flag sticker, even here in one of the most patriotic regions of the country, required a keen eye. There was a time when they were found almost exclusively on vehicles owned by members of the local VFW. But that was no longer the case. Now it seemed that 'not' having one made you stick out.

Michael turned around, glanced at the man and woman in the red, white & blue costumes, then looked at Debbie. "You know those people dressed like Uncle Sam?" Debbie just shrugged and shook her head; she had never seen them before. Michael collected his thoughts, then whispered to Debbie as quietly as possible, so as not to upset Emily, "I think they might be spies for Monsanto."

Debbie tensed up, yet made a point not to show her true emotions. She was an excellent mother, and the last thing she wanted was to add to the stress and strain her family was under, what with all the strangers lurking in the shadows and unmarked aircraft buzzing their home. She simply nodded that she understood, then put on a forced smile for the crowd, but more so for Emily. She wasn't about to let her baby be robbed of this golden moment in her childhood by a bunch of sleazy, slimy reprobates dressed in patriotic garb to shield their true objective . . . which is seems was harassing and intimidating the White family into submission.

* * *

Later in the day, Michael gave a large crowd of spectators a demonstration with his prized mules, showing off their ability to move logs on command, much like the way pioneers used them to clear homesteads on Sand Mountain in the 1800s. Michael took great pride in his mules. They were far more than a mere hobby to him. If he had lived in an earlier time, he was certain he would have spent his days working with mules, from farming to logging. He had an amazingly special kinship with these noble and eccentric creatures that even people who knew nothing about them recognized.

After putting his mules through their paces for the better part of the afternoon—ever mindful of their well-being, Michael decided it was time to head them to a trough for water. Moving parallel with the crowd, the pair of large, muscular mules was a sight to behold. Naturally, they caught the attention of more than a few people. Yet even when surrounded by strangers the mules were docile, including when people reached out and petted them. This was because Michael had spent years patiently working with them.

Out of nowhere, a loud, grating and annoying voice called out above the din of the crowd, "There's Michael White." A few moments later, it was repeated.

Looking all around, at first Michael couldn't pinpoint where the voice had come from. Then, about thirty or forty yards away, standing beside a gate where a mass of people were exiting the festival for the day, he spotted the redhead. Her partner, standing a few feet behind her, was stealthily operating as her lookout.

Since the day began, this was the third time the man and woman had found Michael, staked him out, then took turns shouting his name. And they made a point of staying just far enough away so that they were out of reach. On the surface it didn't seem like much. Nothing more than a silly prank; the kind of thing impish teens do for kicks. But these were anything but aimless kids. They were adults, probably in their forties, and they knew exactly what they were doing. Worse, they were being paid to do it.

When you added up how long the spying had been going on, plus the fact that the goons used bogus tags, unmarked aircrafts, and costumes to hide their true identities, the thinly veiled taunts directed at Michael and Debbie were enough to upset anyone. But when they aimed their insidious scheme at a six-year-old child there was no avoiding the obvious question, 'What kind of twisted and depraved barbarians drag a small and helpless child into what's supposed to be nothing more than a civil suit?'

The look on the woman's face said it all. This was no prank. This was no game. Far from it. She wore a cruel snarl stretching from ear-to-ear that said she meant business. It didn't take much for Michael to presume that the man and woman had been trained well, because they knew just how far to push the envelope—right to the absolute edge.

If Michael tried to get a restraining order—assuming he could actually ferret out their identities—a slick lawyer with no concept of right and wrong might very well make Michael look foolish in the confines of a sterile courtroom simply by having him repeat what the pseudo Uncle Sam's had said, i.e., little more than his name. He might even come off as someone who was over come by paranoia, while the Uncle Sam's lawyer would probably portray them as victims of a witch hunt. To top it off, Michael had never seen them before, so he faced an uphill battle trying to tie them to the incessant stalking, the unmarked sorties, bogus tags, or even the constant picture taking.

Suddenly, Michael realized he didn't know for sure where Debbie and Emily were. His mouth went dry and his face felt flush. At this very second were his wife and child being subjected to this same type of thinly veiled harassment by more goons dressed up as iconic patriots?

Knowing all too well that a pair of full-grown mules, no matter how well trained, could wreak havoc if they stampeded into the crowd, Michael quickly moved them over to a safe area and then lashed them to a post beside the trough. They could rest and drink water. But Michael had no intentions of resting. He was long past being fed-up with the sordid antics of the Uncle Sams; he could take no more, so he took off running as fast as he could toward them.

Seeing that Michael was coming for them, the woman shot him a haughty sneer before she and her accomplice slipped off their hats and then deftly melted into a large and congested crowd. By the time Michael maneuvered his way through the throngs of people and reached the point where they had been standing it was as if a magician had waved his wand and made them vanish. Needing a better vantage point, he jumped up on a nearby fence, balanced himself, and then scanned the crowd. The extra three feet of height made a world of difference. He could now see the heads and shoulders of nearly everyone in the crowd, at least the adults. But the redhead and her accomplice had obviously ditched their flashy red, white and blue jackets, leaving them with inconspicuous t-shirts, because he didn't see them anywhere. They were lost in a sea of other similarly attired people. It was quite obvious that they knew what they were doing and were skilled at it. This was not their first rodeo.

Michael didn't want to give up so easily, but his mules needed tending. He knew it, and he knew his tormentors knew it, and they knew him well enough to know he would never neglect his animals. Reluctantly, he gave up his bird's-eye view of the crowd and went back to where he was needed.

As he slowly made his way back to his mules, Michael muttered to himself, "What kind of company hires stalkers? What kind of monsters taunt a six-year-old child?"

* * *

A few weeks after Labor Day, Michael was in Scottsboro sitting in a friend's truck. He and Nick Henderson were talking about harvesting some timber when, suddenly, out of the corner of his eye, Michael realized that the passenger in a vehicle that was driving slowly past them was taking his picture.

Interrupting Nick in mid-sentence, Michael said in a hushed and serious tone, "Real easy like, pull out and follow that truck. But stay back a'ways. I don't want 'em to know we're following 'em."

Nick knew just enough about Michael's troubles with Monsanto's henchmen not to ask too many questions. Yet at the same time he figured there was a chance this could escalate into a serious situation. "We gonna have any trouble with these folks?"

"I sure ain't looking for none." Michael replied with total candor. Knowing Michael was a man of his word, that was good enough for Nick, so he began following the late model Ford pickup.

It wasn't hard to spot the Ford, a shiny new high dollar rig. Michael couldn't help but notice the stark contrast to Nick's well-worn work truck. Trying not to draw attention to himself, Nick stayed a quarter-to-a-half-mile behind the fancy new truck. And he must have done a good job of staying incognito, because in a short while the Ford casually pulled into a hardware store.

When Nick pulled into the lot a minute or so later, he found a spot that provided them with a clear view of the truck, yet far enough away so that they wouldn't be easy to spot. As Michael carefully wrote down the tag number, double checking each number and letter of the license plate from Georgia, Nick realized that the truck's passenger was missing and must have gone into the store right before they arrived.

With more than a little trepidation, Michael got out of Nick's truck and cautiously made his way toward the store. Once inside, Michael gave the impression he was searching diligently for a few items, yet he was actually scanning to see who was there. Fortunately, there were only a few customers, and he recognized all of them . . . except for a woman near the checkout counter. That had to be the truck's passenger.

Browsing his way through the merchandise, Michael made it past the checkout counter and then, unintentionally, found himself standing almost directly behind the woman. And that's when he felt his heart skip two beats . . . because it was the exact same red-haired woman who had stalked him and his family at Mule Day!

Certain that she'd recognize him—after all, she was taking his picture only a few minutes earlier and had spent an entire day stalking the White family, Michael made a beeline for the manager's office and slipped inside. Luckily, Barry Tucker, the store manager, was an old friend. Without overloading Barry with details, Michael simply asked him to keep close tabs on the redhead, and said he'd be back as soon as she was gone to get the scoop. With that, he made a quick exit, hopped in the truck with Nick and they immediately took off. But they didn't go far; they hid out just down the road, waiting for the duo in the Ford to leave the store. And they didn't have to wait long.

Less than fifteen minutes later, Michael was back in the store getting a detailed report about the woman: It seems as soon as Michael exited the building she walked directly to the store's big plate glass windows and watched him like a venomous snake, never taking her eyes off him until he got in the truck with Nick and they drove off. Once the redhead was certain Michael was gone, she went back to the counter and asked to have a key made. That was no big deal; the store made thousands of them in the course of a year. But she insisted on paying with cash and did not want a receipt generated for the purchase. In fact, she made absolutely sure the transaction could be handled exactly the way she wanted before she would even give the clerk, Henry Dawson, the key she wanted copied. Henry obliged her because the store wasn't part of a big chain, meaning he had leeway to make such accommodations for a customer.

Michael fished a ring of keys out of his pocket, sorted through them, and then found one in particular. He showed it to Henry to find out if he had used the same blank to make the key for the redhead. "Is this the key she made?"

Technically speaking, Henry was not a locksmith, yet he made more keys in any given week than most people will own in a lifetime. He shook his head. "Nope. That's not it."

Flipping through his keys, Michael then presented Henry with a second one, holding it up for close inspection. "What about this one? Is this the key she had made?"

It only took a few moments for Henry to examine the key and come to a firm conclusion. With a confident nod he replied, "That's the key I made."

Michael's blood went cold because the first key he'd shown Henry was the one to his seed business . . . and the second was to the front door of his home.

With his nerves on edge, Michael raced out of the store, jumped in the truck with Nick and barked, "Head for the sheriff's office and floor it!" And floor it, he did; they got there in record time.

Leaping from the truck, Michael hit the ground running and sprinted toward the sheriff's office. But just as he got there, the sheriff drove up in his patrol car. Breathless and barely able to speak coherently, everything poured out of Michael like a broken levy as he told the sheriff about what had happened at Mule Day, then about the pictures the redhead had taken of him earlier, and finally the highly peculiar purchase of the key. "I think she's got a key to the front door of my house. I'm scared these people are gonna do something to my family. They might be plotting one of those home invasions!"

A veteran of many years in law enforcement, the sheriff knew it was crucial to do things by the numbers. First things first, he told Michael, as he tried to calm him down while he ran a check on the Ford's tag. Oddly enough, there was a time—not so long ago—when the sheriff thought Michael was totally off his rocker, what with all his talk about spies, stalking, clandestine photos, unmarked aircraft and all supposedly orchestrated by a

Fortune 500 Company. Toss in the fact it was taking place in rural Alabama and it sounded like the rants of a stark raving lunatic. But he'd slowly come to realize that what was happening to Michael was not a figment of his imagination; it was as real as the ground he was standing on.

In a few minutes the results came back on the truck's tag. It was classified as 'void'; it was illegal for it to be on any vehicle, car or truck. And before it was listed as 'void' it had been on a car—not a truck, a Pontiac sedan that would now be twelve years-old. The redhead and her accomplice had gone to extreme measures to conceal their identity by using a bogus tag. Firing up his radio, the sheriff issued a 'be-on-the-look-out' for the late model truck to all his deputies. The countywide BOLO was definitely not something a law enforcement professional like the sheriff used on a whim.

* * *

Although not for lack of trying, the Ford truck was never located by the sheriff's department. One law officer opined that the occupants of the truck were probably monitoring a police band radio and the moment they heard the BOLO they hightailed it out of state to avoid capture—Georgia's only 26 miles east of Scottsboro as the crow flies, and Tennessee's just 21 miles due north.

That evening, given some time to reflect, Michael surmised that he couldn't prove in a court of law beyond a shadow of a doubt that the key the redhead made fit his home. However, when he tallied up all that was going on—the spying, stalking and taunts, and all done with fake tags to avoid detection—only a fool would think otherwise. Focusing on the key, however, was like fretting about a sore thumb when you're battling cancer.

As Michael replayed the events of the day over and over in his mind, he came up with a theory as to how the redhead eluded capture, as well as a few questions that would weigh heavily on his mind for a very long time.

His theory was rather simple: he believed that soon after leaving the hardware store the redhead and her partner in crime put the 'real' tag back on their truck so that they could casually drive away without getting pulled over. His questions, however, were not so simple. Why had the woman brazenly made a key—perhaps one that fit his front door—right after he had not only been in the hardware store, but the manager's office as well? Surely the woman realized that whatever she did in the store would get back to him? Of course, that brought up another question: Was that her motive? Did she want Michael to know that she and her partner were so brash and fearless that they thought nothing about making the key right under his nose? And that segued into an even more troubling question: Was their intent to let Michael know that at anytime, no matter how often he changed his locks, they could obtain a key to his front door and there wasn't a damn thing he could do about it?

There's not a parent alive with young children who could sleep peacefully with those wretched thoughts ricocheting inside their head. Undoubtedly, the redhead and her partner knew this, and that led to the most troubling question of all: Was the couple's employer complicit in their abominable scheme and behavior?

CHAPTER 24

When he was a small boy, Michael loved to play in a pasture near his home. For a child who dreamed of being a cowboy, the lush, green wide-open spaces were perfect entertainment, enough to keep him occupied for hours on end. One day he might find a unique rock and the next a genuine arrowhead. His bedroom was overflowing with the treasures he had discovered.

Early one morning Michael happened upon a bird that was behaving strangely. So he crept a bit closer to investigate. And that's when he realized it had been injured.

Michael knew it was impossible to catch a healthy bird. He had chased enough of them to know that. But this one was obviously in bad shape. Its left wing was dangling precariously off to its side, and it was in distress, squawking loudly. Michael instinctively wanted to catch it, take it home and care for it, make it well, and then release it back into the wild.

Inching up ever closer until he was only a few feet from the bird, Michael made a quick lunge for it. But it moved just a tad faster than he had anticipated. He missed it by only a few inches, but missed all the same. So he regrouped. The bird could move quicker than he had figured, that meant he would have to run it a bit; tire it out. And that's exactly what Michael did. He ran as fast as his young legs would carry him, chasing all around the pasture after the wounded bird. Funny thing, though, the bird didn't seem any worse for wear. Michael, however, was soon exhausted from racing up and down the steep hills under the broiling Alabama sun while dodging stones, stumps and ditches. But he wasn't about to give up, he just needed to refuel. So he walked home to grab a snack and a glass of water.

Virginia was baking pies when Michael entered the kitchen. Nevertheless, she watched with keen interest as her son drank not one, not two, but three glasses of water. Normally one, two at the most, was enough. "You must have been playing hard." She commented.

Michael quickly shook his head. "No ma'am, I've been working." He said it with such conviction that his mother had to bite her lip to keep from laughing.

"Working?" She asked. "At what?"

"Trying to save a bird."

Virginia perked up. She was all in favor of her son saving an injured songbird. However, she was keenly aware that there were some birds on Sand Mountain that no one should go near, especially if they were wounded. A red-tailed hawk or a great horned owl, if unable to fly, could be extremely dangerous if cornered. The concern in her voice was unmistakable. "Exactly what kind of bird are you out to save?"

"A hurt one." It was a perfectly logical answer coming from a small boy.

Virginia went for a different approach. "What's this bird look like? Color? Size?"

"He's brown. Not too big." Michael thought a moment, then added, "And he's got some white on his belly, a couple of black stripes and some orange around his tail." He'd chased it long enough that he could pick it out of a police lineup.

Virginia was all but certain what kind it was, but one question would clear up any doubt. "What's wrong with this bird?"

"It's got a broken wing. Ain't no way it can fly." Michael declared.

"I'm guessing you tried to catch it, right? Chased it around the field a time or two?"

Michael came back with a vigorous nod. "Yes ma'am, I've been chasing him around that pasture for the longest time. Even with that broken wing, that's one fast bird!"

Virginia knelt down beside her son. "Michael that was a killdeer. And somewhere out there it's got some eggs or maybe even some chicks." Trying to be as diplomatic as possible, she smoothed his sweaty hair a bit, then added, "But it didn't have a broken wing."

"But I saw it! It does have a — "

Virginia gently shook her head and waved Michael off in mid-sentence.

"That bird was just pretending to have a broken wing. It does that on purpose."

Michael was stunned. "Why in the world would it do that?"

"To keep you away from its nest; to protect its eggs. That killdeer was using the instincts God gave it to care for its young."

There was a long pause as eight-year-old Michael tried to take this heady information in all at once. For the longest time he didn't say anything. He just sat there and thought. Finally, he asked, "So you're telling me I never could've caught that bird?"

"Not unless it let you. And they don't do that."

Although he was only a child, it made sense to Michael. "That's a smart bird."

"It sure is." Virginia said as she gave him a big hug and a kiss.

* * *

While spending an uneasy night sitting in his easy chair holding a 9mm, waiting for one of Monsanto's spies to try and use the key they had made in his front door, Michael had thought a lot about that day forty-odd years ago when he tried his best to catch that killdeer. He could still remember how the bird had taken him on a wild goose chase, up and down the hills, around and around. It was like being stuck on a hamster's wheel, only he didn't realize it.

As he drove to work that morning, his mind was working overtime, even if his body was protesting after twenty-four hours without so much as a wink of sleep. He simply couldn't shake the image of the redhead at Mule Day dressed like Uncle Sam. She kept popping up inside his head, and he could hear her sneering over and over, "There's Emily White! There's Emily White! There's Emily White!" Each time it got louder, and more snide and sarcastic.

In broad daylight and in a public place the redhead and her accomplice had not only made a thinly veiled taunt directed at Michael's six-year-old child, they did it right in his face. Coupled with Raymer's threat, Michael was convinced that things had escalated to the point where he had to do something drastic, and do it now, to protect his family. What father worth his salt would see it any other way?

By the time he sat down at his desk at White's Seed, Michael had made a command decision. In order to steer Monsanto's thugs away from his family he would have to be a killdeer. It was the only way he could protect them.

Taking out a notepad, Michael made a list of nine places—safe houses—where he could hide out and sleep at night. That was more than enough so that he could sleep at a different location each night of the week, the plan being to keep Monsanto's spies guessing as to where he was on any given evening. On Monday night he might sleep at location number seven, then on Tuesday he'd stay at location four, and on Wednesday he'd sack out at number one. In essence, there would be no pattern, no routine; there would be no way Monsanto's lackeys could know where he was without expending a lot of time, effort and energy. He would keep them guessing, keep them off balance. Most important, his 'killdeer nights' would mean they'd spend their time chasing him, instead of harassing his family . . . just as the killdeer had kept him on the run in order to protect its young.

* * *

Michael's safe houses all had one thing in common. He could come and go and there were no expectations from the owners of a visit, or even a perfunctory conversation with Michael. They understood that most days he was so worn-out and beaten down from working 14 - 16 hours, all the while being hounded and harassed by Monsanto's spies, that when he showed-up—usually late into the night—all he wanted and often could do was collapse onto a bed and try to get a few hours of sleep before the nightmare started all over again the next day.

Some of the safe houses were better than others, and some nights he would bounce from one to another, again, just to keep Monsanto's spies guessing and on the move. One night, when he wasn't being tailed, instead of going to a safe house Michael made arrangements to meet Buddy Jim. They hadn't talked in a while, and Buddy Jim was always a fount of information, if not a good sounding board.

For some reason Michael began spilling his guts about how he feared Monsanto's henchmen and what they might do to his family, something he had never done with Buddy Jim, even though he considered him a confidant. After all, he was the person who first warned him about Monsanto, and even identified Lowden Brown for him. Yet for the first time Michael saw skepticism in Buddy Jim's eyes. It hurt him deeply that Buddy Jim thought he was exaggerating or, at the very least, had an overactive imagination. Nevertheless, he understood. Who could possibly believe his story? It sounded so outlandish and preposterous that if it wasn't happening to him he would be highly skeptical, too.

Michael let out a deep sigh then said, "I guess there's only one way to prove all this to you."

Buddy Jim cocked his head with curiosity, "How so?"

"Let's take a ride."

About thirty minutes later Michael and Buddy Jim were standing on the sagging and dilapidated porch of Royce and Loraine Blanchard's small, run-down, wood-frame house. It looked as if it hadn't been painted in decades and a strong wind might topple it over, that is, if the termites didn't get it first. Michael knocked on the weather-worn door. A few moments passed, then a deep, throaty woman's voice barked, "Who the hell's knocking on my door at this hour?"

"It's Michael White."

Both Michael and Buddy Jim could hear some movement inside the house, some whispers, then the frayed and faded curtains on a window by the door parted ever so slightly. A pair of eyes hardened by life peeked through the crack just long enough for Michael to wave. Soon after the eyes disappeared, one by one, several locks on the door unlocked with loud mechanical clanks. Then the door slowly creaked open.

Loraine Blanchard was a sturdy woman in her sixties. But it was obvious she'd been pounded hard by life and the years had exacted a heavy toll on her. Standing in the doorway and staring at them with a stone-faced expression, she didn't have on any makeup and didn't look like the type who ever had time for such things. She glared at Buddy Jim while barking at Michael, "Who's this SOB?"

"A friend of mine, a good one . . . real good one."

"Can I trust him?"

Michael nodded, "You can."

"Can you swear on the Bible he don't work for Monsanto?"

Again, Michael nodded. "You know me well enough to know I wouldn't be standing beside him if he did."

Loraine nodded in agreement. "I'll buy that." Then she ushered Michael and Buddy Jim into her humble home. Wallpaper was peeling off in sheets, the rug was threadbare, and everything in it looked like a hand-me-down that had been thrown out by someone else, except for an antiquated but durable hospital bed perched over in the corner of the small, dimly lit room. The bed was for her husband, Royce. Once a robust man who could easily hoist a bale of hay over his head with one hand, he'd had a near fatal stroke a number of years ago that robbed him of even the most basic of motor skills. His mind was all but gone, he couldn't talk, and he was incontinent. Permanently stuck in a fetal position and wearing diapers his wife had been changing like clockwork for a decade, his bony knees were almost touching his chin. Saliva was oozing out of one corner of his mouth, and his eyes were wide open, giving the impression that he was staring at you. But it was doubtful as to whether or not he could even see. More than likely, Royce didn't even know he was in the world. In spite of this, he was existing—and not much more—in a room that had that sickly sweet smell of Lysol commingled with stale urine and feces. Filling every inch of the room was the painful sound of Royce's short, raspy, guttural, labored breathing. This was a grotesque snapshot of life down-on-the-farm when there are few assets to speak of, absolutely no health insurance, and there's a 900 lb. bogeyman out for blood and breathing down your neck.

Michael introduced Buddy Jim to Loraine and then prodded her, "Why don't you tell Buddy Jim what Monsanto's done to you and Royce?"

It was hard for Loraine to talk about Monsanto without getting boiling mad and cursing like a sailor on furlough. She was a God-fearing woman, but she was long past her wits' end. The mere mention of the conglomerate made her so angry that she could spit thunder. "We just plowed forty-eight acres of beans under. Good soybeans. We killed 'em dead." She waved her hand around the room, gesturing first at the peeling wallpaper, and then the living corpse that passed for her husband. "You think we can afford to plow under even one acre of good beans?"

Buddy Jim was no farmer, yet he knew the answer to her question.

Loraine roared, "Ya know why we had to plow them forty-eight acres of beans under? And I'm talkin' damn good beans!"

Buddy Jim could only shake his head. "No ma'am, I sure don't."

"'Cause of goddamn Monsanto!" she roared with righteous indignation, "Those SOBs sent us a letter and said we *might* have one of their stinking-ass Frankenstein seeds out there somewhere in our field and if we didn't plow 'em all under they was gonna file a goddamn lawsuit against us and snatch our farm right out from under us!" Loraine went from angry to outrage. "I ain't never bought so much as a single one of their goddamn seeds; wouldn't have 'em if you gave 'em to me! I can't even afford medicine for my sick husband. Hell, it's all I can do just to keep enough clean diapers for him so he don't get a rash." She got right in Buddy Jim's face, while her own was blood red and getting darker by the minute. "You think I can afford to pay some goddamn lawyer to battle that bunch of bloodsuckers in St. Louis?[7] You think I got money laying around for that kind of bullshit?"

Never in his life had Buddy Jim felt so much fury, frustration, and despair in one person all at the same time. Yet never in his life had he felt that someone was more justified in having all those emotions. Loraine had most certainly earned the right.

Powered by a gale force of pent-up rage and resentment, Loraine's entire body was shaking. With an old .38 revolver not far away on an end table, she used her index finger and thumb to pantomime the pistol in her right hand. An expert with firearms, she slowly lowered her hand until she had a steady bead on an imaginary fat cat executive in the corner. "If the president of that lousy company was to ever show his sorry ass around

---

[7] Monsanto's headquarters is located in Creve Coeur, a suburb of St. Louis, Missouri.

here I'd blow his goddamn brains out!" Loraine said as she pulled the imaginary trigger; the stark 'bang' sound she made sounded eerily like a muffled version of the real thing, one that softly echoed throughout the old dilapidated house.

Exhaling deeply, her arm went limp as she lowered her hand to her side, then Loraine all but cried with abject despair, "I'd have more peace of mind in a jail cell," as tears slowly washed over her tired, battle-scared and time-worn face.

* * *

Neither Michael nor Buddy Jim said a word on their ride back, most likely because Buddy Jim was in shock, and Michael realized his friend needed time to decompress after meeting the Blanchards and seeing their horrific plight firsthand. Still, Michael hoped that Buddy Jim understood that Monsanto hadn't just picked the Blanchards at random. Given all the private detectives the conglomerate had blanketing Sand Mountain, and its horde of high priced lawyers, Michael was convinced beyond a shadow of a doubt that the conglomerate knew full well that the Blanchards were living hand to mouth, and that Royce was little more than a vegetable. Targeting a couple in such horrifically dire straits sent a powerful and chilling message to farmers for miles and miles, one that no reasonable person could ignore.

Michael parked his truck and was about to get out when Buddy Jim finally broke the silence. "Michael, I'm so sorry I doubted you. It's just that I had no idea a company, any company, could be so greedy, so cold, so heartless, so damn ruthless." Michael nodded. He understood completely; witnessing the Blanchard's tragic plight firsthand had a compelling way of making believers out of skeptics.

CHAPTER 25

Although the leaves of autumn were already falling, there still wasn't much going on with Michael's case. Like most lawsuits, the preliminary rounds were uneventful and consisted primarily of requests for documents and various motions. But one really odd thing had occurred. Monsanto had an 'expert' calculate the 'alleged damages' Michael had caused the company.

The conglomerate's expert came up with the figure of $2.4 million. Michael wasn't overly surprised by the total; he assumed they'd cook up an outrageously high amount. But the truly unnerving part was just how close it was to Michael's gross assets. It was as if they had inventoried everything he owned, right down to the boots on his feet, to come up with that figure. Not even Michael's own banker had ever tallied up such a finely detailed inventory of his assets. Yet somehow Monsanto had come uncannily close to the true figure. Perhaps it had 'lent' its expert the countless clandestine photos its spies had made of Michael, his family, home, farm and business to assist with his assessment?

Even though Michael was a millionaire on paper, if Monsanto prevailed in its suit against him and got "triple" the outlandish amount it was claiming it was owed, Michael couldn't possibly pay it, not now, not in a hundred years, not in a thousand.

The multibillion dollar conglomerate's message was clear to Michael. It was out to ruin him; it wanted to turn him into human road-kill. The carcass that had once been a thriving farm and seed business would certainly put other farmers in his area on notice as to what could very well happen to even the best and most prosperous farmers if they dared even toy with the notion of standing up to Monsanto.

* * *

Fall on Sand Mountain is beautiful, yet busy. It's harvest time and, for farmers, there's little chance to stop and smell the roses, much less admire the brilliant colors of autumn leaves. But for a farmer who is also a seed cleaner, it was doubly busy. Normally Michael didn't have time to catch his breath until well after Thanksgiving. This year, however, was quite different. His farm was as busy as ever, but not so for his seed business. It was off by a substantial margin.

Normally, even a small drop in business was the kind of thing that would've given Michael fits. It's something he would've been on top of long before it became acute. But the lawsuit and the unrelenting harassment by Monsanto's spies had taken up so much of his time he wasn't nearly as conscientious as in the past when it came to his own business. And given that there were now definitely fewer customers he could really feel the pinch.

No question about it, there were fewer farmers each year. That trend had been in place long before Michael was even born. However, until now, it had never really affected his seed business. In fact, while some seed cleaners slowed down and others went under, he hung on and actually saw an increase in business some years. But this year was markedly different.

Most farmers went out of business for two basic reasons. Either they lost so much money they had to file bankruptcy and throw in the towel, or they could no longer farm because of health reasons. In the latter case, if there wasn't a son or daughter willing to take over, they simply had to close-up shop and auction off their equipment in hopes the proceeds would support them in their old age. Either way, Michael, like every farmer on the mountain, eventually knew who went out of business and why. Yet even if he tallied up all the farmers who had closed shop in the past year or two it just didn't account for the precipitous drop in his business.

Rather than fret about the loss of business, Michael hopped in his truck and drove to Scottsboro. He had some business he had been putting off and figured this would be a good time to take care of it and, simultaneously, serve as a much needed diversion. Besides, he would use the opportunity to ask around and find out if White's Seed was the only farm related business having a down year, or the downturn was across the board. Over the years he'd found it was always best to get the facts before declaring panic.

The drive to Scottsboro was quite pleasant. It was not only scenic, but almost devoid of traffic, and for the first time in quite a while Michael didn't have a tail on him. Plus, on this day it was neither hot nor cold, so Michael put his windows down and enjoyed the fresh air. Nothing compared with having the raw wind in his face. It was one of the reasons he loved horseback riding. Galloping along with fresh, clean air in his face made him feel so alive, so invigorated, so happy, so content. There was no better therapy on earth for him.

Even today with the windshield blocking most of the air, it was still a nice feeling to have the wind blowing in his hair. It seemed to push all the bad thoughts created by Monsanto right out of his head. Michael's only regret on this day was that the ride wasn't longer. A detour could make it longer and would be quite nice, but he simply didn't have the time. Besides, if he had some free time he wanted to spend it with his family.

The drive gave him the chance to think about what was important. And while his business certainly was on the list, nothing compared with his family. Michael anguished over the fact that the lawsuit with Monsanto had devoured so much of his time, to say nothing of the sleep he had lost from being stalked by their goons. He thought about his father. He'd given up farming to take a job with the TVA so that he could spend more time with his family, plus have the stability of a steady paycheck. It was no small sacrifice. Wayne loved farming. But his family came first, always. That was all Michael needed. His father, and the lessons he had learned from him, had never steered him wrong. Once he had taken care of things in Scottsboro, he made up his mind that he would spend some time with his daughters.

When Michael arrived in Scottsboro he had his pick of parking spaces. The town wasn't empty, but it certainly wasn't crowded. After parking his truck, Michael went straight to the revenue commissioner's office - - - *revenue commissioner* was Alabama speak for 'tax collector.' He had promised Clyde, an old and dear friend, that he would pay the delinquent taxes on his family's land. Now an ex-farmer, Clyde had lost everything. Once successful enough to live quite comfortably, now Clyde couldn't even scrape together the money to hang on to his land, acreage that had been in Clyde's family for generations.

Family heirlooms had been the first things to go. One by one they were sold off to cover this bill, then another. Often sold at fire-sale prices because antique dealers smelled Clyde's desperation, items that had taken several lifetimes to acquire were gone in a matter of months. Yet he still had a stack of bills to pay, and more kept coming.

Every farmer, no matter how good, lived with the haunting reality that he was only a bad crop or two away from Clyde's fate.

On the brink of losing his sanity, the land was the only thing that stood between Clyde and complete despair. Michael, recognizing Clyde might be suicidal, had stepped in and offered to pay the taxes until his old pal could get back on his feet. Of course, down deep Michael knew the odds of Clyde getting back on his feet were remote, at least not the level where he once had been. Still, he had to have hope, and that's actually what Michael was buying his friend. Eventually, the land—just like the heirlooms—would have to be sold. But better to sell it, even at a fire-sale price, than suffer the public humiliation of having it auctioned off on the courthouse steps by the tax man.

After taking care of things at the revenue commissioner's office, Michael went to the bank, and then Don Word's law office. Once all his business was concluded, he dropped by Variety Bake Shop, a gathering spot for locals that served fresh coffee and the best homemade pastries for miles. There were a few people milling around, but no one with any real connection to farming. So Michael didn't stay long, just long enough to have a quick cup of coffee and catch up on local news.

During the next few weeks Michael made several calls trying to get a better handle on the state of farming on and around Sand Mountain. Either his messages weren't getting to the intended people, or his calls weren't being returned.

Then one day Michael spied Daryl Ross, an old friend and fellow farmer. Daryl was just who Michael needed to see because he kept abreast of other farmers in a way Michael didn't have time for; he could fill Michael in on the state of the local farm economy.

Michael smiled and waved. "Hi ya, Daryl." For a fraction of a second, Daryl paused, almost answered back, but then instead made a beeline toward his old Ford truck, which was about seventy yards away. Michael was genuinely miffed. He was certain Daryl had seen and heard him, yet it was almost as if he had ignored him, if not purposely dodged him.

Daryl had always seemed like such a level-headed fellow. More importantly, Michael had always counted him as a good friend. With his teeth grinding, Michael began following Daryl. But as soon as he did, Daryl made a run for it. Pushing sixty and lugging at least forty more pounds than was healthy for his short frame, Daryl didn't exactly sprint in making his getaway. But he moved as fast as his pitifully out-of-shape body would carry him.

Lean and in decent shape, Michael had no trouble gaining on Daryl. As the gap between them got shorter and shorter, Daryl would glance over his shoulder and each time seemed genuinely surprised that he couldn't shake Michael and was losing ground. Even more odd, he looked more and more frightened each time he saw Michael gaining on him. At this point Michael didn't care if he was scaring Daryl or not. He was going to get to the bottom of this, even if Daryl was running as if escaping a rabid dog.

When Daryl finally reached his old Ford truck he hopped inside with the kind of agility Michael found amazing for a man of his girth. Without a doubt, Daryl was scared. But for the life of him, Michael couldn't fathom why. They'd been friends for more than thirty years, and in all those years Michael couldn't remember them ever having a real argument. Sure, they didn't see eye-to-eye on everything, but nothing in their past explained Daryl's bizarre behavior.

Michael could have let his friend make a clean getaway and go home. Odds were he would probably call Michael before the day was over and explain everything. But Michael was in no mood to extend the olive branch, not given the way he had just been treated.

"What in the world is going on?" Michael roared as he gripped the door frame of Daryl's truck.

A moment passed as tears welled up in Daryl's eyes, then he put his head down on the steering wheel. All but sobbing, he sounded a bit like a small child who'd lost his way. "Michael, you gotta get away from me— you gotta. And you gotta do it right now!"

Michael quickly shook his head. "I ain't doing no such thing, not till you tell me why you're running from me like I got the plague." It was obvious that he had no intentions of leaving, not until he got some answers.

Barely speaking above a whisper, Daryl cried, "If they see me with you they'll take my farm."

Michael was sure he had heard right, even if Daryl's words had been weak. But it made no sense. "Daryl, who is gonna take your farm? And why would they?"

Fighting back tears, Daryl sobbed, "You know who."

"The bank?" It was the most obvious answer. Practically every farmer, at one time or another, has been under a banker's thumb, some gentle, some not so gentle.

Instead of answering out loud, Daryl just shook his head.

"Well if it ain't the bank, then who?" Still, Daryl said nothing. A lot of local banks that once made farm loans wouldn't touch them now, and a number of farmers were dependent on a hodgepodge of alternative lenders for their cash. Finally, Daryl just shook his head. This guessing game had stretched Michael to the end of his rope, and he was unapologetic. "Damn it, you tell me who's after you and tell me now!"

Like most everyone on the mountain, Daryl knew Michael cursed about once every blue moon; it was totally out of character for him. With his voice cracking and barely at a whisper, Daryl finally spilled the beans. "Monsanto. They'll take my farm. They'll do it, I know they will. All they gotta do is see me doing business with you, even talking to you." Fighting back tears, he confessed to a sick, appalling and reprehensible act. "They told me they ain't after me. Don't give a damn what I do. Said all they wanna do is get the goods on you. Said if I'd help 'em they'd leave me alone."

Suddenly, it made sense to Michael why his business was way down, and his phone calls had gone unreturned. Monsanto was behind it. In the back of his mind he probably knew it all along but simply didn't want to think it was possible . . . not here, not in a place where people still genuinely cared about their neighbors, and went out of their way to help them whenever they could.

As the floodgates sprung open, Daryl wailed, "I'm just barely hanging on by a thread." Tears fell out of his eyes and ran down his cheeks like an open spigot. "I'm one missed payment away from disaster. The farm, my house, the furniture, even my truck; everything I got's on the hook. I didn't have no choice, Michael, I swear I didn't."

Daryl's voice disintegrated into babble. He could no longer speak coherently.

Without a word, Michael took his hands off Daryl's truck and stepped back, signaling that his old friend was free to go. Even so, Daryl wouldn't look at Michael. It was as if Daryl feared he would turn into a pillar of salt simply by looking at his old friend. Staring straight ahead, he drove off, effectively ending a close friendship of more than thirty years.

Michael was both angry and hurt, but the feeling of betrayal was by far the most overwhelming of his emotions. He had counted Daryl as a good friend, and he didn't use the term loosely. Before today he would have gone to the bottom of the well for him.

It was obvious to Michael that Monsanto—directly or indirectly—had threatened Daryl with financial ruin if he didn't sever all ties with him; worse, someone had pressured him to inform on Michael. Apparently, Daryl had been given two wretched options; get crushed . . . or help crush your friend.

Normally, Michael might have been able to temper his pain and anger with the fact that Daryl was under duress. However, up until now, Daryl had been more than merely a friend of Michael's, he had also been a confidant. Michael had taken him into his confidence about his trials and tribulations, from the incessant stalking and spying to the enormous toll it was taking on his family. That meant Daryl knew Michael was under extreme duress. And no friend, certainly not a real one, turns on you when you're down. But to consort with the enemy, that was an act of betrayal for which there was no forgiveness. It meant the gut kick he had just gotten from Daryl was one of the most painful he ever had.

As Michael watched the old Ford disappear from sight he realized more than ever that the conglomerate wanted a great deal more than even the outlandish $2.4 million it was claiming in 'damages' against him. Not only had he just lost a good friend, his life was changing forever. The way farmers treated each other was changing, and in ways he could never have fathomed—and it was all bad, very bad.

CHAPTER 26

Michael was doing what he loved, driving a tractor and planting a field. He would tell people with a wry grin, "This is my leisure activity." And to a degree it was. Although it was definitely work, and certainly not easy, it gave him time to think and even unwind a bit. Planting is a detailed process, but Michael had been doing it since he was old enough to see over the steering wheel of a tractor. His skills were finely honed by time and experience.

The tractor he was using was his favorite. It wasn't his newest, though. It was, however, his workhorse—an old John Deere that not only had good power, but was rather agile for such a large piece of machinery. Above all else, it was reliable. It had served him well through a number of plantings and harvests, and with only a minimal amount of downtime.

Somewhere around the midpoint of the field, Michael heard a very strange sound coming from his tractor. It was an odd sound, a loud 'whopping' noise he couldn't pinpoint. Then he saw a cloud of dust kick up. Based on experience, he figured the most likely culprit was that a hydraulic hose under extreme high pressure had cracked and was spouting fluid like a geyser. So he did what a lifetime of experience had conditioned him to do. He shut the tractor down immediately.

Even though the tachometer and oil pressure gauge were now both at zero—sure indicators that the engine was off—neither the dust nor odd sound had gone. If anything, they had both gotten worse. Summoning every thought on the matter in his head, he instantly shifted the tractor into neutral and locked the brakes. That would make it safe so he could jump down and disconnect the coil wire. Without a doubt, that would disable the engine. But jumping off a tractor that was already behaving oddly, even in neutral and with the brakes locked, was a harry undertaking. The massive vehicle could crush him like a flea if he wasn't careful.

As Michael prepared to leap down from the driver's seat, something caught his eye. But it didn't have anything to do with his tractor. Up in the sky, literally right over his head, there was a helicopter hanging in the air no more than ninety or a hundred feet off the ground, its rotor spinning at a high rate of speed. If it had any problems whatsoever, the outcome would be disastrous for Michael.

Michael's first inclination was to hop off the tractor and jump under it for cover, just in case the copter crashed. He had ridden out a tornado warning or two under the belly of a tractor, not that a tornado couldn't toss his 14-ton tractor around like a Tonka Toy. But in the open field, much like now, it had been the only source of cover available.

Before Michael could get off his tractor the helicopter made a jerky and unsound lateral move, then executed a busch league landing right onto his field. Michael smelled a rat, the kind of that's native to St. Louis. After all, this was same blue and white chopper that had been buzzing his home so often in recent months. He'd even caught it on videotape, right down to the missing tail number.

In the time it took for Michael to walk from his tractor to the helicopter, the aircraft's rotor had ceased turning. Even so, wary of the situation, Michael figured that thirty or forty feet was close enough for him. The pilot, still wearing a headphone and microphone, stepped out of the copter about the time Michael asked, "You OK?"

The pilot nodded. "Yeah. Just waiting for fuel."

Michael didn't believe that cock-and-bull story for a moment; he was certain this was a carefully planned mission. This particular area of the mountain had zero cell phone coverage, so Michael couldn't call the law or anyone for help. And the closest landline that he knew of was at least ten, maybe even fifteen minutes away. By the time Michael could report that the chopper had trespassed and landed on his property without permission the unmarked and untraceable aircraft would be long gone.

For several moments Michael simply stared at the pilot, waiting to see what his next move might be. But he didn't do anything. He just stood there beside his chopper with a smirk and an air of brash self-importance, as if landing on private property without permission and disrupting the operations of a legal business was the most normal thing on earth to do, not to even mention the damage the blast from the choppers' rotor had done to the all important topsoil on Michael's field. Michael could only imagine the immense trouble he would face if he simply hired a copter and had it land on the asphalt at Monsanto's headquarters without written permission. Even *with a tail number* he figured he would probably get charged with criminal trespassing, and anything else the conglomerates army of slick lawyers could cook up.

This staring match could go on all day, and Michael's crop would still have to be planted, so he decided going back to work was his only viable option. As he turned and headed back toward his tractor the pilot called out in a haughty and sarcastic voice, "Whatcha' planting?"

That loaded question stopped Michael dead in his tracks. Had the pilot asked him anything else, he probably would have at least been cordial. But this was the one question he didn't want to hear, certainly not from a pilot he felt certain was on Monsanto's payroll—directly or indirectly. Turning slowly until he was facing the pilot, Michael glared at the man and then snapped, "None of your stinkin' business!" No sooner had those words passed his lips when an idea hit, one Michael ran with. "Why don't you dig up some of my seeds and see for yourself?"

The pilot didn't say a word; he just stood there, staring back at Michael with an arrogant smirk on his face. Meanwhile, Michael had gotten his fill of this twisted game, and he made sure the pilot knew it. "I've got three more trips to make on my tractor to finish up this field, and one of 'em's right where your helicopter's sitting." Pointing at the pilot, he added in a voice that left no room for misinterpretation. "You don't need to be sitting there when I come back this way." With that, Michael headed toward his tractor.

Before Michael was a quarter of the way back to his tractor the chopper's engine fired up. Although he couldn't see it, Michael could hear the rotor slowly turning, then feel the rush of wind it as it built up speed. By the time he had gotten back on his tractor the helicopter was lifting off the ground. Out of the corner of his eye Michael discreetly watched as the chopper quickly disappeared into the horizon, then muttered under his breath, "Guess that fellow wasn't low on fuel after all . . . or lies."

* * *

Around nine that night Michael got a call from Ellis Burnett, an old and trusted friend. Ellis was part of a small and dwindling minority of people who weren't afraid to help Michael.

Ellis had heard about the trouble Michael had been having with Monsanto, so he was sharing information he felt his friend should know. "There's a blue and white helicopter sitting in your soybean field; saw it with my own two eyes just now." Michael didn't tell Ellis about the encounter he had earlier in the day with the pilot flying the blue and white helicopter, but instead thanked him profusely for the call.

Driving to his field using the back way, and cutting his headlights before he arrived, Michael could clearly see that the helicopter Ellis had described was not only parked right in the middle of his field, but it was also the same one from earlier.

The first thought in Michael's head was to walk to the copter and find out if the pilot was on board. And if he was, he would tell him to leave immediately. But something in the back of his mind said that's exactly what Monsanto wanted. The pilot, armed to the teeth, might be waiting for Michael to 'surprise' him; give him a reason to 'defend' himself. Or, they simply wanted Michael to put his hands on the chopper. As soon as he left they could sabotage their own aircraft and—using Michael's fingerprints for evidence—claim he had vandalized their million dollar helicopter. It would be a double whammy against Michael; a criminal charge against him they could twist around and use to allege that he was 'out of control' when, in fact, it was their henchmen who fit that characterization.

Michael had already tiptoed through enough of their malicious minefields to know better than to take a bite of this poisoned apple. Without ever getting out of his truck, he drove away and never looked back.

CHAPTER 27

Although Michael was a homeowner, business owner, and solid citizen, for months and months he'd been forced to lead a nomadic existence. Most every night he roamed Sand Mountain—constantly checking his mirrors for tails—before finally settling down at one of his safe houses for a few fitful hours of sleep. It wasn't uncommon for him to get settled in for the night, only to hear a strange sound outside. Taking great pains to go undetected, he'd slip out under cover of darkness and head for yet another safe house, all in a concerted attempt to keep Monsanto's spies off balance. It was imperative to keep them guessing in order to protect his family.

The toughest part of this chaotic and unpredictable life was being away from his family. His two young daughters were growing up while he was forced to dodge, hide and play cat-and-mouse with spies, as if trapped inside a Tom Clancy spy novel. But their safety was paramount. He willingly made the sacrifices and would make more if necessary. But the pressure was wearing on him and dragging him down. There were days when simply getting out of bed felt like an insurmountable chore.

Tonight Michael was not only headed home for the evening, he planned to stay the entire night. Normally, he would drop by for a quick visit, then slip off for a safe house before the spies had time to confirm his whereabouts. But it made him feel like a visitor in his own home. Still, he had no choice. He had to do everything in his power to insure that Monsanto's unmarked helicopters wouldn't spend the night buzzing his home and their spies clicking off more photos. The mere thought of his daughters in their bedrooms with the unpredictable aircraft zooming about and spies with prying telephoto lens was just too much for a father to bear.

More than anything, Michael wished he could have just five minutes to sit down with Monsanto's CEO, man-to-man, to let him know what it had been like to have his family under siege for so long. After all, the executive likely had kids of his own. Michael had a thousand questions for the man, but two near the top of his list were: "What would you do if this happened to you and your family? And what would you think about the depraved people who made it all happen?"

Of course, he knew those five minutes would never come. People who have others do their dirty work, especially those in positions of power, rarely ever have to answer for their sins, at least not on earth. And that's why they behave so callously; it seemed to Michael that there is zero accountability for fat cats fueled by unmitigated greed.

Even if Michael could talk with any of the executives, he figured they would use a classic cop out: they would deny any responsibility or knowledge of what the private investigators had done, and were doing. In all likelihood, they would use the 'monkey defense', i.e., see no evil, hear no evil, speak no evil. They would claim they had no earthly idea Michael's family had been harassed, much less that it had been going on for so long, and was still taking place. But in Michael's opinion, anyone who sought and was granted a multimillion-dollar compensation package for an executive job at a company should be held accountable for what goes on at that firm under their watch, especially illegal activities. After all, *Monsanto expected Michael to know the difference between a natural soybean seed and one of their GM seeds on sight, even though they looked alike to the naked eye.* And Michael certainly wasn't making even a fraction of the piles of cash that got dumped into the laps of Monsanto's top brass.

As he turned into his driveway, Michael tried to clear his head of all things related to Monsanto. He didn't want to be preoccupied with his problems tonight. He wanted to feel normal, even if it was only for a few brief and fleeting hours.

Entering through the garage door, Michael came inside, tossed his keys on his desk, and was about to kick his boots off when he realized he hadn't heard the usual sounds of his daughters scrambling around to come meet him. So he walked into the kitchen, only to find Debbie, and he could tell from her face that something was wrong, bad wrong.

Their conversation was one of the toughest they'd ever had, yet it was civil. The outcome of it, however, was tragic. After almost twenty-two years of marriage, theirs was over.

CHAPTER 28

As days dissolved into weeks, and weeks into months, Michael reluctantly reconciled himself to the fact that the life he once had—the married part, that is—was over. It was a tough pill to swallow that his marriage could not be saved, especially for a man who was opposed to divorce on both religious and personal grounds. But he was learning to accept it, just like he was learning to accept so many other things since Monsanto began its undeclared war on him. His life and been turned upside down in ways he never could have imagined, even when it came to the simplest things.

There was a time when picking up the mail from the P.O. box for his seed business was a pleasure for Michael. Often there was a check or two waiting for him from one of his customers. But that was no longer the case, and it hadn't been since Monsanto's henchmen began scaring off his friends and customers. Although checks were now a distant memory, bills, however, kept on coming, and they were beginning to pile up. Some days Michael was simply overwhelmed by the bills, especially since the revenue from his business had essentially been strangled off.

Only recently Michael had been told by Gary Dobson, a friend and farmer who had been a good customer of his seed business for years, that he had gotten a late night visit from one of Monsanto's goons. He told Gary in no uncertain terms, 'We don't care what you've done, don't even care if you've saved our seeds. We just want Michael White. And if you help us get him then you'll be in the clear.' The most troubling part of that highly disturbing story to Michael was the unknown, wondering out loud, 'How many other farmers has Monsanto's thugs gone to see? Ones I don't know a thing about? And how many of 'em have turned Judas on me to save their own hides?' He knew Daryl Ross had; he had admitted it. Even so, the mere thought that some of his oldest and dearest friends might have sold him out was more than enough to make him nauseated.

Although Michael felt Monsanto's strategy was beyond reprehensible, even he had to acknowledge it could be devastatingly effective. Farmers live to farm, so threatening to take their farm is equivalent to taking away a professional athlete's ability to play their chosen sport. Some farmers will, unfortunately, make a pact with the devil if it will keep them farming for one more year, even if only just one more season.

Those familiar with the nefarious machinations of the House Committee on Un-American Activities, particularly in the 1940s - 50s, might see a parallel with Monsanto's strategy. The HUAC, which trampled all over the very rights and freedoms it professed to protect for Americans, pressured and even steamrolled people to "name-names." Often the canary who sang the loudest went free, even if the information he or she provided was totally unfounded. As long as they "named-names," it seems that's all that truly mattered to the HUAC. It thrived for a long time on the blood of sacrificial lambs.

The reprehensible practices of the HUAC hit the entertainment industry hardest, not unlike a bombshell laced with toxins. Honest and decent people were turned into social lepers by the HUAC's deplorable government sponsored witch hunt. Lives and reputations were scarred, damaged and ruined forever. The infamous "blacklist" cost many talented and seasoned professionals their livelihoods; some never worked again or rarely did so, and some even took their own lives out of sheer despair. It was one of the darkest, most shameful and regrettable chapters in modern American history . . . all done in the name of protecting our freedoms.

Sadly, the turncoats and backstabbing didn't stop with Michael's friends and fellow farmers. Edwin Dobbs, an influential local politician he once supported, came to him one evening and tried to coerce him into "settling" with Monsanto "for the good of every farmer on Sand Mountain."

To add insult to injury, Buddy Jim had revealed to Michael that he was all but certain Dobbs was in Monsanto's back pocket. Worse, those 'secret' meetings Dobbs held for a select few farmers to privately air their concerns and grievances about Monsanto's spies, their illegal activities and nefarious "patent enforcement" tactics were most likely a complete and utter sham. According to Buddy Jim, he was convinced that Dobbs relayed everything the farmers said, including Michael, to Monsanto's lackeys. Upon hearing that, Michael was physically ill for days.

As Michael entered the post office, he ran into Sammy Joe Denton. Since Sammy Joe parked his plow a couple of years ago, they hadn't seen nearly as much of each other as they once did. After exchanging perfunctory greetings, Sammy Joe gave Michael a hard stare from his head down to the toes of his well-worn boots. His old pal was gaunt, pale and looked downright sickly. Although everyone else was too polite or reluctant to say anything—even Troy and L. V., two of his closest confidants, Sammy Joe did not fit in that category. "Michael, you sick? You don't look worth a damn." Sammy Joe was painfully blunt, but honest.

From the day his ordeal began, Michael had gone from a robust, muscular and healthy 188 lbs. all the way down to a sickly and haggard weight of about 135 lbs. His once solid 6 foot frame was now little more than skin and bones. The dramatic and woefully unhealthy weight loss was caused by a combination of working too much, sleeping too little, not eating enough, but mostly nerves. Michael's were shot. Being stalked, sued, harassed, the relentless sorties, and Raymer's threat had just about destroyed him mentally; the stress had wreaked havoc on his mind, body and spirit. Ironically, it seemed that Michael was the last to fully realize the horrendous toll Monsanto's incessant campaign against him had taken on his health and quality of life.

Michael heaved out a sigh as he unconsciously slipped off his hat and ran his fingers through his hair; it was a habit he did quite often, especially when stressed, which was more or less all the time now. Soon after the ordeal began, his hair turned from chestnut brown to a shade of unbecoming gray that made him old before his time, and it literally happened overnight. Answering Sammy Joe, he reluctantly admitted. "I've felt better." Then he came out with a profound understatement. "I guess this mess with Monsanto has taken a bit of a toll on me."

Sammy Joe scrunched his brow, "If you don't start taking better care of yourself, Michael, you ain't gonna be around long enough to battle those bastards in court."

His voice filled with angst, Michael replied. "I got a feeling in the bottom of my gut they'd like nothing better than that." Then added, "Might even be part of their plan."

Sammy Joe had never been the sort who feared speaking his mind, and today was no exception. "Michael, back around '97 or '98 or maybe even '99, I started reading stuff online about Monsanto, and heard rumblings about 'em, too. And none of it was good. Not for farmers; not for nobody. Hell, it was unbelievable and tragic all at the same time. I knew something was bad wrong, even if I couldn't connect all the dots back then."

Michael nodded emphatically. "I hear what you're saying." Then added, speaking in a hushed voice. "You were sure smart, getting out when you did. Farming's changed, and none of it for the good. They got farmers turning against farmers. Customers I carried on my books for years are acting like I'm a leper now. Heck, people I thought was my best friends are running in the opposite direction when they see me. Just thinking about all this mess makes me sick, I'm talkin' bad sick."

As a fourth generation farmer, the plight of fellow farmers ignited a wildfire down deep in Sammy Joe's soul the likes of which no corporate executive could ever possibly understand. He was snorting gasoline and spitting flames as he spoke. "Hell, they expect a seed cleaner to know the difference between one of their Frankenstein soybeans and a real one just by looking at it. I farmed forty years, and cleaned seeds near 'bout that long, and I can't tell 'em apart. And then there's that bullshit where they claim if a farmer opens a bag of their seeds he's gotta abide by all their rules or lose his farm . . . all cause they got some damn fine print on a fucking bag. That's nothing but pure horseshit." Using his hand for emphasis, he snapped, "I don't know about you, but I'll be goddamned if a bunch of greedy, lowlife, money grubbing SOBs in suits that don't know a plow from a pile of shit is gonna tell me how to farm."

Lowering his voice to a fierce growl, Sammy Joe concluded. "Folks gotta wakeup. This ain't just another big, bloated company trying to rip off poor, hardworking folks so they can cram more money into their overstuffed pockets. We're talking about the food supply here. We're talking about life and death. These sorry ass bastards could wind up starving people to death - - - millions of 'em."

Although Sammy Joe could be both obstreperous and virulently blunt when riled, any attempt to be polite and politically correct would have needlessly watered down his message. Besides, few had his gift for taking a complicated subject and boiling it down to its essence, and Michael for one appreciated his friend's courage and unbridled honesty.

For longer than he could recall, Michael had felt as if he was living under a dark cloud and it followed him everywhere he went, no matter how hard he tried to out run it. But the day he ran into Sammy Joe it went from a dark cloud to a full-fledged storm. From his P.O. box filled with bills, to Sammy Joe's candid assessment of his health and Monsanto's machinations, to a spy tailing him most of the day, to a helicopter buzzing overhead, to the realization that many of his once loyal friends and customers had abandoned him for fear they would be the next victims of Monsanto's witch hunt, Michael finally realized that his whole world was slipping away. To compound matters, the loss of his beloved mother and now the unraveling of his marriage both weighed heavily on him, the latter he felt was in no small part a result of the spies and their incessant stalking. Try as he might, he couldn't think of one thing in his life that was going right.

Of late, bleak, troubling and confusing thoughts had been gnawing at Michael's brain, ones he had no control over, the kind that made it difficult to function, much less think. It was a struggle to perform even the simplest of tasks. Most days merely getting out of bed was an ordeal; this for a man who had spent a lifetime springing out of bed hours before sunrise. Nevertheless, he couldn't call in sick, and taking a personal day off wasn't even remotely realistic. The exalted luxury of long weekends and multi-week vacations many executives consider their birthright aren't options for real working people, especially not farmers. Michael didn't have any minions standing by to fill in for him during an absence. Like most small businessmen, if he didn't show up for work the bookkeeping didn't get done, trucks weren't loaded, floors went unswept and garbage piled up.

Although Michael's seed business was on life support, his duties hadn't gone away. Actually, they had doubled—maybe even tripled—because he could no longer afford to pay employees. Honest, decent, hardworking people who had once worked for him suffered as a result. They, too, were casualties in the campaign Monsanto's spies were waging against Michael.

* * *

Standing in his office, trying to make sense of the insanity that had become his life, Michael finally came to the stark and painful conclusion that the business he had spent more than twenty years building from scratch and nurtured with the sweat of his brow had died. Murdered was more like it. As he surveyed the ruins of what had once been his pride and joy, Michael wondered if the people who'd destroyed it had ever built anything in their lives? Or had they devoted their existence on the planet to tearing down and destroying the hard work of others?

Staring at a small, plain black frame on the wall containing the first dollar he had made from the business, Michael could feel his chest tightening and his head getting light. It felt as if there wasn't enough oxygen in the room. He tugged at his collar for relief, hoping that would help. But his worn and faded t-shirt was not restricting his breathing in the least.

There was a distinct numbness in Michael's arms, and he had heard that numbness in the left was a sign of an impending heart attack. But the numb feeling wasn't confined to his arms; it went all the way to his toes. Sensing that he might be severely ill, he debated calling his soon to be ex-wife. It was not a simple decision. The spying and stalking had taken a toll on Debbie. And he couldn't blame her. What mother with young children wouldn't worry endlessly with a bunch of creepy strangers slinking around day and night? - - - especially ones who snapped pictures incessantly and hid their identities behind bogus tags? Nevertheless, there was still a bond between Michael and Debbie.

Almost as if in a trance, Michael stared at his phone, trying to decide whether to call Debbie or an ambulance. Before he could dial either number an odd notion struck him. He could very well be having a nightmare; he might actually be sound asleep. He had certainly had more than his share of horrific nightmares in the last year or so. Sometimes he could feel the breath of Monsanto's spies right on the back of his neck, only to wake up and find himself drenched with sweat. But the really terrifying part was that the nightmares didn't fade away with the light of day, they actually got worse because the spies were not fictional—not a figment of his night terrors. Given his state of mind, they were as real and dangerous as a man-eating crocodile submerged at the river's edge, patiently waiting to pounce and devour when least expected.

As he pressed the numbers on his phone, Michael not only felt his fingers were moving in agonizingly slow motion, but he realized that the room was turning dark. It looked as if the light bulbs were all slowly fading out, as if they were being manipulated by someone operating a dimmer switch. But there was no switch of that sort in his office, not to mention he was all alone.

It occurred to Michael that it could be a short; the light switch might be going bad. So he walked toward it—no more than 15 feet away, hoping a few quick flips might fix the problem, at least temporarily. But something tripped him up, and he found himself tumbling toward the floor. Eerily, almost as if detached from his own body, he saw himself falling. Even more strange, he was no longer in his office; he was being sucked into a giant whirlpool, and everything around him quickly went from dim to murky to dark. Swirling down into this cold, wet, miserable abyss—unable to breathe—he recognized it as the terrifying sensation of drowning. He tried to yell for help, but knew no one would hear him. Besides, nothing came out of his mouth when he cried out, so he said a silent yet fervent prayer as he prepared to die. Then he closed his eyes as he felt the life in his body slip away.

CHAPTER 29

Did Michael have a heart attack or a stroke? Or had he been hallucinating? Or did the part of his brain that serves to shield him from harm merely block out the last few hours of his life to protect him? That's what Michael wondered when he blinked his eyes and realized he was in the emergency room of a hospital. Yet before he could sort out the answer, he saw that Debbie was standing by his side. And all he could think to say was, "I'm so sorry. I shouldn't have stood up to Monsanto. I should've just let 'em have their way; let 'em have it all, the farm, the business, everything. Then maybe they'd have left us alone . . . wouldn't have ruined our lives. We'd still be happy."

Debbie gripped Michael's hand tightly and shook her head, "No, you did the right thing. I'm proud of you." Her words were immensely comforting for Michael, especially given that they would be divorcing soon. For the longest time he'd felt all alone, felt completely isolated, if not ostracized; he needed reassurance she was on his side. He genuinely wanted to say 'thank you,' but was so tired he didn't know if he did—or not—before he closed his weary eyes. He was desperately in search of some much needed rest; he wanted the nightmare that had become his life to simply go away.

* * *

The next few days were a blur for Michael. Doctors and nurses came and went, as did family members and his few remaining friends. People spoke to him, but he rarely heard what they had to say. He saw their mouths moving, he heard sounds, but the words were jumbled and incoherent. About the only things he could recall hearing were repetitive comments, such as "you need rest" and "time to heal."

Depression, at least when expressed in a "clinical sense," was foreign to Michael. Sure, he'd heard that people suffered from it, and that it was supposedly a debilitating malaise. But hardworking people like Michael didn't have time for such things. He'd always thought of it as a rich man's disease. But he was beginning to see things quite differently.

Another term that cropped up was "nervous breakdown." That one Michael had certainly heard of, though, again, he didn't think it was something that could happen to him or anyone like him. Yet he couldn't possibly deny that he was genuinely sick, even if he didn't have any broken bones or gaping wounds. There was no way he could pretend he wasn't ill. Something was definitely wrong. But he was too tired to think about it, or wonder why so many people—a number of them strangers—were drifting in and out of his room. So he went to sleep, and didn't care if he ever woke up again.

* * *

If anyone had told Michael a year ago—even a month ago—that he would be on the 'couch' in a psychiatrist's office he would have said that person was the one who needed their head examined. He didn't hide the fact that, prior to his breakdown, he didn't put any stock in analysis, and certainly not psychiatrists. Yet here he was in the office of Dr. Harold Gruen spilling his guts out, and it actually felt good. He could feel the healing process begin, albeit he was warned that it would be a slow one. After all, he'd been ill for a very long time and hadn't even known it.

As details of the relentless torment Michael and his family had suffered tumbled from his lips it occurred to him that Dr. Gruen might think he was crazy, a lunatic doing little more than babbling gibberish. Who ever heard of a Fortune 500 company coming all the way to rural Alabama to wreak havoc and create chaos for a simple farmer? To the casual observer it was beyond ludicrous; it was paranoia run amuck. Stopping himself in mid-sentence, Michael had to ask, "You think I'm crazy or paranoid or both. Don't ya?"

Dr. Gruen gently shook his head, "No, I don't."

Michael shot back, "You're just saying that 'cause I had a breakdown. You're just humoring me. You don't believe for a second that anybody's out to get me, especially not some giant corporation."

The doctor stopped taking notes, put down his pen and paper, then assured Michael that he believed his story was true. Nevertheless, Michael was more than merely skeptical. "Why would you believe me, doc? Even I know what I'm saying sounds nuts."

"Not to me." Dr. Gruen countered.

"Why's that?" Michael asked, wanting to find a reason to believe the doctor.

Using the broadest terms and generalizations, the doctor explained that he had worked with some people whose lives had been devastated because of the actions of a conglomerate; he knew first hand that some big companies—though certainly not all—are not the benevolent giants they proclaim to be. Ironically, it was Michael's opinion that Monsanto had spent untold millions over the years in a concerted effort to deceive the public and create an image that was anything but true, and he told the doctor as much.

When their session was over, right as Michael was about to leave, he felt compelled to say, "I hope those people—the ones hurt by that big company—are OK. What I mean is: I hoped you helped 'em."

Because of his strict adherence to doctor-patient confidentiality, Dr. Gruen couldn't possibly go into any detail about his patients, past or present. Nevertheless, the doctor pursed his lips, thought a moment, then ruminated that he had done the best he could, yet by the time he had started treating them their lives had already been devastated. In most cases the damage was all but irreversible.

Not long after Michael began seeing Dr. Gruen he found out through the grapevine why the psychiatrist had no trouble believing his story, one so many others had thought was a figment of a tormented and troubled mind, if not downright absurd. It seems the good doctor had treated some people in Anniston, simple, hardworking people who—just like Michael— had once thought psychiatry wasn't much different from voodoo, a pacifier for the rich, and that big companies never knowingly hurt anyone. But those people in Anniston, victims of the tons and tons of PCBs secretly dumped there for decades by Monsanto, now saw things quite differently.

CHAPTER 30

After his breakdown, some of the most peaceful moments for Michael were visits with his father. On this day—like many, upon entering Wayne's house Michael made a fresh pot of coffee and then poured a cup for both of them. It was part of a gentle routine, one that served them well, and helped Michael heal up, mentally and physically.

Although Wayne had been having a rough go of things lately—his own health was not good, he perked up noticeably during their visits. The time they had together was golden. Much of it was based on their special bond, one built on a solid foundation of love and respect. Wayne had always taught Michael the difference between right and wrong, though not with lectures or long winded speeches. His actions and deeds—guided by personal honor and integrity—over the course of a lifetime had provided the lessons.

Before their coffee had time to cool they were interrupted by the phone on the kitchen wall. It was hard to ignore because it was extremely loud. Wayne was losing his hearing and had it turned up loud enough to be heard throughout the house, even in the carport. "You want me to get it, Daddy?" Michael asked. Wayne nodded and pointed at the phone, giving Michael his blessing. "Hello." Michael answered. After listening for a moment, he covered the receiver and whispered to Wayne, "It's for me, Daddy. Business." Wayne understood implicitly. He knew that business covered a wide range of subjects with his son. Michael patiently waited until his father walked down the hall and disappeared into his room before speaking into the receiver with bated breath. "Yeah, you hold onto them varmints tight. Don't let 'em go nowhere. I'll be right there!"

* * *

Making the trek from his father's home to the Decker's farm in record time, Michael got to the front gate, pulled off onto the shoulder of the road, and parked his truck. Just as he had been told over the phone, there was a late model GMC pickup near the gate that was unable to move. It wasn't wrecked or broken down. It had been hemmed in.

Randy and Paul Decker, father and son, had seen the truck snooping around their property and, instead of letting the interlopers intimidate them like they had other farmers, they sprung into action immediately. Acting as a team, they used their own trucks as chase vehicles and pursued the spies relentlessly until they finally boxed them in just before they could get away.

The Decker's called the law. But they knew it would take them awhile to reach this rural location. They also knew Monsanto's henchmen had been pursing Michael relentlessly and felt they were out to ruin his business and disrupt his family life, not to mention what it was doing to his frail, elderly father. So they figured that Michael more than deserved the opportunity to question the thugs—at least until the law arrived.

Getting out of his truck, Michael walked straight over to Randy and Paul, both of whom were standing together by their trucks. Randy asked Michael what he wanted to do about Monsanto's spies. Michael replied, "I'd say we need to interrogate these folks. Mind if I take the reins?" Father and son nodded, giving Michael the go-ahead.

Moving slowly and cautiously, Michael walked around toward the driver's side of the white truck but kept quite a bit of distance. Even though Michael had two eyewitnesses, if Monsanto's goons opened fired on him, all the witnesses in the world couldn't help if he was dead. And they might just eliminate the witnesses, as well.

Keeping his distance, Michael saw that none other than Lowden Brown, the same man he had chased down in the black Toyota truck quite some time ago, was standing near the passenger side of the white GMC truck. A woman, the same one who had been with Lowden previously, was standing close by as well. Inside the truck there was a man seated behind the steering wheel with his head down.

For a moment Michael stared at Lowden, but he wouldn't look back at Michael. Then, in an odd twist, Lowden turned toward Michael and called out. "What are you doing here, Michael White?"

Michael wasn't the least bit surprised that Lowden recognized him; he had taken enough clandestine photos of Michael and his family to pick them out of a police lineup. Refusing to be intimidated, there was only one way for Michael to counter Lowden's brazen question. "Lowden, why are you over here spying on these people?"

"I ain't breaking no laws." Lowden shot back. Michael grimaced. If he had asked Lowden what time it was he probably would've given him the temperature. It was the kind of slimy avoidance tactic cops get everyday when interrogating hardened criminals.

Michael figured it was best to throw several questions at Lowden. He might slip up and actually answer one of them. "Is that your wife with you? Is she on Monsanto's payroll? And what about that man in the truck? Is he a spy, too?"

Lowden scowled at Michael and then growled as if he had the moral authority to pass judgment on others. "It's illegal for these people to block me in." Employing an exaggerated gesture, he shook his finger testily at Randy and Paul and their trucks. "You're breaking the law!"

It took every ounce of restraint in Michael's body not to blow his stack. Keeping his voice controlled, he shot back, "You were stalking these people, you were trespassing, you were —"

Pointing at the ground, Lowden cut Michael off in midsentence. "This here's the right-of-way. This here's public property, boy."

Shaking his head, Michael came right back at him, "No it ain't. You're past the right-of-way; you're on private property. I'll say it again, you're trespassing. And they got a right to hold you till the law gets here."

"Listen, boy, I used to work for the government and had a badge. I know the law. Understand? Don't you dare try and tell me nothing!" Lowden sneered; a sense of exalted entitlement clung to him like the stench of roadkill baking in the noonday sun.

Keeping his cool, Michael shot back, "If you know the law, why do you ride around all over the place with illegal tags?" He gestured toward the tag on the white truck. "Is that one of those fake tags you and your thugs are always hiding behind when you're out spying on me and my family?"

It was definitely not what Lowden wanted to hear. The sour look on his face told Michael he had touched a raw nerve and really ticked him off, even more so than he already was. With his face turning beet red, Lowden marched to the rear of the truck, leaned down and then yanked the tag off.

Unlike normal vehicles where the tag is held in place with screws or bolts, the one on the white truck was in a slot so that it could be quickly and easily removed by simply pulling it straight up, which is what he had done. Holding up the tag for Michael to see, Lowden snarled, "You don't like this tag?" With an air of defiance and self-importance that bordered on obscene, he pointed down at the license-plate holder which, low and behold, had a second tag affixed behind the one he had removed. Pointing at the second one, he snapped, "How bout that one? Ya like it?"

"Is it fake, too?" Michael asked.

Reaching down, Lowden yanked the second tag out, revealing there was yet a *third* tag already in the custom made holder to take the other one's place. Even at close range it was all but impossible to tell it from a legal license plate holder. Lowden tossed the two tags he had taken out of the holder into the back of the white truck with a double clank.

Randy and Paul were stunned. Michael, however, had suspected for a very long time that the trucks Monsanto's spies used had multiple tags that could be quickly and easily changed in a moment's notice. Now he knew it for a fact.

Pointing at the third tag, Michael asked, "It that one fake, too?"

"What if it is fake?" Lowden sneered. Then he hissed. "We'll keep runnin' 'em. We're above the law! We can do anything we want!"

Now it was Michael's turned to be stunned. If he hadn't heard Lowden with his own ears he would have said there's no way a sleazy goon representing a Fortune 500 company would dare make that statement, *even if it were true.*

Doing what he should have from the very start, Michael went back to his truck, grabbed his video camera, switched it to record mode and came back to see if Lowden would repeat that chilling statement on tape.

But if Michael had hoped to hear Lowden's outrageous declaration twice, he was sorely out of luck. Upon seeing the camera, Lowden just folded his arms across his chest and closed his mouth as if a zipper had been put on it.

With his camera rolling, Michael pointed at the tag on the back of the white truck and asked once again, "Is that a fake tag?"

Lowden might have been a lot of things, but he wasn't stupid. He didn't respond to Michael's question, not even with one of his carefully calculated non-answers. Realizing time was of the essence, Michael threw Lowden a curve and told him that the law was on its way and would be there soon.

Suddenly, Lowden must have realized that more than his pickup had been hemmed in. He leaned inside the truck, whispered something to the driver, then got the woman's attention. Lowden and the woman quickly stepped away from the truck and then walked down the road about fifty or sixty feet before stopping. Using hand signals, and going to great lengths not to say anything, Lowden motioned for the man inside the truck to meet him and the woman at their new location.

Executing a risky and dangerous maneuver, one that could possibly cause the white truck to flip over and injure Michael, Randy and Paul, the man behind the wheel blasted straight down into the ditch and then roared up a steep embankment on the opposite side. With his tires spinning wildly, he shot past the Decker's trucks and then raced back down through the ditch, bouncing up onto the road with a bang and a bone jarring rattle.

Michael and the Deckers realized that the confrontation was over, but it had definitely served a purpose. Randy and Paul had heard stories about how arrogant and obnoxious Monsanto's henchmen were. However, this was the first time they had seen it in person. Michael sighed. "Something's awfully wrong when a man thinks he's above the law, especially a man who claims he use to wear a badge for a living."

Randy and Paul nodded in agreement as the white truck drove down the road and stopped on the shoulder, right where Lowden and the woman were standing. Lowden opened the passenger door and the woman quickly got inside. But not Lowden. He simply couldn't resist turning toward Michael and sneering one last time. Only then did he hop inside the truck. As the trio roared off, escaping an encounter with justice, Michael shook his head with dismay and disgust. "Yep, something's mighty wrong."

CHAPTER 31

Although Michael was traveling along a deserted road, every so often he checked his mirrors to see if one of Monsanto's thugs was tailing him. An hour or so earlier he had shaken one in town and hadn't seen another one since. Still, that didn't mean they weren't tracking him from the sky.

Taking the long way to L. V.'s house was no mistake. Michael had legitimate concerns that Monsanto's goons would retaliate against those who helped him. And of all the people who had helped, L. V. was right at the top of the list.

Living where he did in a rural area, L. V. was a perfect target for Monsanto's thugs. Time and again Michael had seen them use subtle intimidation tactics, the kind that were hard to prove unless you were actually there—like at Mule Day, but they were intimidation tactics, nonetheless. So Michael felt compelled to keep his meetings with L. V. clandestine, even if it meant going way out of his way in order to cover his tracks. After all, their stalking had certainly taken a monumental toll on him. He wouldn't wish the breakdown he'd had on anyone, certainly not one of his most trusted friends and confidants.

It had become almost a ritual for Michael, going to L. V.'s practically every week—sometimes more than once a week—to discuss his case, pray, chat, and just clear his head. But this evening would be different. This would, in all likelihood, be the last time he would have a chance to meet with his friend and mentor before his deposition, something that had been weighing heavily on Michael.

When he sat down with L. V., Michael's mind was already racing. There were a thousand things he wanted to discuss, but he couldn't seem to keep his thoughts straight. L. V. poured them both a cup of coffee, then asked matter-of-factly, "How do you control pollen?"

Michael couldn't help but smile. "You're joking, right?"

"No, I'm asking a question," the old man responded. "How do you control pollen?"

"Nobody can control it. And if ya don't believe me, ask anybody with allergies." Michael, a longtime allergy sufferer, was living proof of his declaration.

L. V. leaned forward a bit, then pronounced, "I've heard one of Monsanto's Technology Agreements says that it's the job of farmers to control pollen."

All Michael could do was shake his head with dismay. "I've heard that, too. And I've heard that they say pollen only travels a few feet. I think they say ten feet or even fifteen; might even say fifty. Don't really matter what they say." Michael gestured as he spoke, "I've been up in the mountains in Colorado and seen big clouds of pollen drifting along pretty as you please. I'll guarantee you that pollen had already traveled a few miles by the time I saw it, and then I watched it travel a few more before I lost sight of it." Pointing out the window, he continued. "Heck, come spring you can see it floating around right outside your windows. You know good and well it travels mor'n ten feet, or even a hundred. You can no more control pollen than you can the wind."

Doing what he did best, L. V. was playing a calm yet firm devil's advocate. "So why would they claim it only travels a few feet if it actually blows for miles? Why insist farmer's control it if they can't? Why would a company with an army of lawyers say all this stuff if it wasn't so?"

"I guess they're trying to protect their patents. If the pollen from their genetically modified crops drifts over and contaminates an organic plant that tells me that they've got zero control over their product. And if it can't be controlled under normal circumstances, their patent probably ain't worth the paper it was printed on. They can't expect a farmer to police pollen just so they can keep their patent, especially since it can't be done." What Michael didn't verbalize was his strong held belief—one shared with many people, from farmers to horticulturists—that during the process of unintended cross pollination a GM plant can absolutely cripple the integrity of an organic one - - - yet it doesn't work in reverse, i.e., the GM plant is unscathed by the pollen from the natural plant.

L. V. sighed and then cocked his head, "So you wouldn't sign any of their Stewardship or Technology Agreements?"

Michael's agitation boiled over to the surface. "I never have and never will!" Exhaling, he paused a moment to calm down. "I'm no lawyer, but I always thought a contract was worthless if it required you to do something that can't be done, and it's impossible to control pollen." Then he added. "A lot of farmers are saying Monsanto's reps have forged their signatures on those Technology Agreements. There's a farmer in Iowa or Indiana—I think his name's Jim Winger, or Winiger, he wrote on a website that they forged his name and he knows the name of the Monsanto rep that did it. Said the rep testified that Monsanto told him to forge farmers' signatures on those agreements."

"I was taught that stewardship meant taking care of something for the good of everyone," Michael continued. "If Monsanto thinks stewardship and forgery go together they better buy 'em a new dictionary."

Before moving on to another topic, L. V. took a sip of his coffee. "What can you tell me about Monsanto's Bt (bacillus thuringiensis) crops?"

Michael had expected L. V. to give him a pep talk before the deposition. Instead he was grilling him with some highly loaded questions.

"I don't like 'em."

The old man gestured, "Why not? What's not to like?" Leaning back a bit, he surmised, "I read that Bt crops are genetically modified so that if a bug gets on the plant and takes a bite that bug will die, which means the plant won't get eaten up by bugs, which means it can produce a lot higher yield than an organic plant."

Michael snorted with disgust, "Yeah, that's kinda how it's supposed to work."

"Supposed to work? You're saying it doesn't work that way?"

"Yes and no."

L. V. cocked his head with dismay. "That's like telling me it's night and day."

"Well, the Bt crops do kill bugs. That's true. But I figure that means the plant has poison inside it to kill those bugs. I guess it's bred into it." Michael used his hands to demonstrate. "A lot of folks don't wanna eat fruits and vegetables that have been sprayed with pesticides. They say the pesticides can seep into 'em and contaminate 'em. Well, just imagine how much worse Bt crops are. The pesticides have gotta be inside the plants; they're in the genes, the DNA! It's gotta be part of the plant! Ain't no way on earth you can eat 'em and not be eating pesticides, if not outright poison! No way around it!"

Michael had just presented a solid case that should have given any reasonable person something to think long and hard about. Nevertheless, L. V. came right back at him with both barrels and snapped, "Well surely they've done tests? Surely they haven't just thrown these Bt crops out onto an unsuspecting public?" Michael fired right back. "Hand me that article I brought you the other day."

During the last few months Michael had given L. V. several articles to read, so he kept them in order of when he got them. L. V. picked up the folder where he stored them and opened it. He looked at the one on top, the latest one, then asked. "This one from the New York Times Magazine titled *Playing God in the Garden* by Michael Pollan?"

Michael nodded. "Yep, that's it. And that's a darn good title." L. V.

plucked it out of the folder and gave it to Michael. He stared at it for a moment, reading silently until he found the part he wanted. "Listen to this. This Pollan fellow really knows his stuff. He says he talked to Phil Angell, Monsanto's Director of Corporate Communications, and here's what old Angell told him. I'm quoting here. '*Monsanto should not have to vouchsafe the safety of biotech food. Our interest is in selling as much of it as possible. Assuring its safety is the FDA's (Food and Drug Administration) job.*'" Michael put the article down and then hissed. "If that's not bad enough, what old Angell didn't say is that there's a great big revolving door between Monsanto and the FDA. And I'm ain't talking about low-level worker ants. I'm talking about captains, colonels, and generals. The fox ain't just guarding the hen house, it's got a set of keys to the place."

Burning an icy stare into L. V., Michael pronounced, "Monsanto's trying to play God with our food supply. And I can tell you right here and now with one hundred percent certainty, Monsanto ain't God. In fact, I'd describe 'em as just the opposite!"

By this point Michael had gotten himself worked into a frenzy. He was on the verge of completely losing his cool; something he rarely did.

Suddenly, Michael realized what his old friend had done. He had gotten Michael primed for his deposition. It was OK for Michael to get angry or even lose his composure here, but things would be decidedly different at the deposition where a stenographer would be taking down every word he said. Michael would be facing Monsanto's top guns, seasoned pros whose job it was to trip him up, make him look stupid, get him confused, and make him angry so he would make a mistake, perhaps even say something that he would later regret.

As L. V. walked Michael out to the porch at the end of the evening, he put his hand on Michael's shoulder and said, "Son, you're gonna do just fine at that deposition. Just remember; no matter what, stay calm."

Michael nodded. "I'll sure try," he said, turning to walk down the steps. But halfway down he stopped. "Mr. L. V., do you know anything about Colony Collapse?"

The old man had to think a moment, then asked. "That's what they're calling the problem with the bees? The one where they're dying off for no apparent reason. Right?"

"Yep. Some scientists are saying they can't figure out why they're dying. But I believe they know mor'n they're saying."

Michael and L. V. had spent enough time together for the old man to know when something was bugging Michael. So he asked, "You got a theory on what's behind this Colony Collapse?"

"I do." Michael replied.

"Well, you gonna tell me or not?"

"A few years back, I heard that Monsanto's own literature said some *beneficial insects* might die 'cause of their Bt crops." Michael exhaled a deep breath. "I think the helpful insects they were talking about are bees, honeybees, the ones we gotta have to pollinate crops worldwide." After letting that sink in a moment, he added, "Without bees, there ain't no way to pollinate all the crops, not even with an army of workers. There's just no substitute for bees."

Without another word, Michael began walking toward his truck. And L. V. contemplated a world without bees. Could food prices double? Could they triple? Or was it possible that they could quadruple? After all, the enormous number of people needed to do the backbreaking labor that bees perform would be costly, perhaps exorbitantly so, and that's assuming there would be enough laborers willing to do the grueling work that bees gladly do for free.

As Michael got in his truck and drove away, L. V. realized that his friend was not only carrying the weight of the world on his shoulders, but also the safety of the food its people needed to survive.

CHAPTER 32

With the deposition looming just ahead, Raymer's threat was very much on Michael's mind. It was the reason he had been up most of the night, and was now brewing a third pot of coffee. But it wasn't for consumption in his office, it was for the road.

After contemplating the matter most of the night, Michael had finally come to the conclusion that he had to go see Mitchell Scruggs, the man whose partner Jeb Raymer said had been murdered. He had to have some answers, and he needed them now more than ever.

Although Michael didn't know Scruggs personally, he certainly knew the Tupelo farmer by reputation. Scruggs owned and farmed a substantial number of acres, far more than most of his counterparts in Mississippi, or any state for that matter. Thirty thousand acres was the number Michael had heard bandied about, though he didn't know if it was gossip or fact. But farming was just part of Scruggs's far-flung operation. He also owned a seed business, much like Michael's but on a far grander scale, and in addition he had a large John Deere dealership, a giant farm supply store, one of the largest cotton gins around, and extensive real estate holdings. By anyone's yardstick, Scruggs was a whale in a sea filled with tadpole, guppy and trout sized farms.

Michael was certain the highly successful entrepreneur wouldn't sit idly by while Monsanto ran roughshod over him. So with nothing more than a Thermos full of hot coffee and only a vague idea of what he would say or even how he would introduce himself, at around 3 a.m. Michael took off for Tupelo on the off chance that a very busy man he had never met would provide him with some much-needed information and advice. That is, if Scruggs would even see him without an appointment.

* * *

Using a vehicle that was not registered in his name to avoid being tailed by Monsanto's goons, Michael made quick work of the two hundred mile road trip, arriving at Scruggs's farm supply store in Tupelo right around opening time.

The enormous store was a smorgasbord of farm related items. Any other time Michael would've loved to browse around, searching carefully through the hard-to-find items that could only be purchased online in his neck of the woods. But he wasn't there for the merchandise. Surveying aisle after endless aisle, what he was looking for was a friendly face: specifically, one with a few miles on it.

It was a good bet that a man of Scruggs's stature didn't see anyone unless they either had an appointment or a damn good excuse for not having one, so Michael was hoping to find a retired or ex-farmer working there, someone who would hear Michael out and then appeal to Scruggs on his behalf.

It didn't take Michael long to find the person he was looking for. He was an older fellow, the sort who looked as if he had spent the better part of his life on a small farm. Greeting Michael with a smile, he asked, "Can I help ya with sumpin', mister?" It was a standard greeting common in any small-town store in the South, warm and cordial, but certainly nothing out of the ordinary. Nevertheless, sleep deprived and running way past empty, Michael must have read more into it because before he realized what he was doing his story was spilling out onto the stranger like water from a breached levee.

In response, the old-timer simply stared back at Michael with his faded green eyes. It was impossible to gauge his reaction to the deluge of information Michael had dumped on him. After a few moments of uncomfortable silence the old fellow excused himself and then exited through a door marked EMPLOYEES ONLY.

Michael wanted desperately to follow along and ask where he was going. For all he knew the old-timer was going to call the cops. He had no idea if he had conveyed his thoughts in a coherent manner, or if he had come off like a crazy man that should be in a padded cell.

For a moment Michael was frozen in place. He began to feel the walls closing in on him. Maybe he was losing it. After all, he had driven almost two hundred miles in the hopes of speaking with an incredibly busy and important man he had never even met, never even spoken with. "This was all a big mistake." he babbled to no one in particular.

Without wasting another minute, Michael turned and headed for the exit as quickly as possible, and took great pains to do so without drawing undue attention to himself. He sincerely hoped that he could simply get in the vehicle he was driving and head back home; pretend this episode never happened.

Only a few feet from the exit, Michael was certain he was home-free. That is, until he spied a man quickly approaching. Before he could even react the man had taken him by the arm and was steering him through a side door behind which he was certain there were cops waiting to haul him off to jail, if not the asylum.

He had made a reckless decision in the wee hours of the morning to take a leap of faith. There was nothing to do now but ride it out and see how he landed.

* * *

Mitchell Scruggs was an unassuming sort of fellow, the kind that few would pick out of a lineup as an extraordinarily successful multimillionaire entrepreneur. That's why when he stopped Michael at the exit of his store Michael had no idea that he was actually the man he had come to see.

Looking around Scruggs's office, Michael was surprised at how down-to-earth it appeared. There was nothing remotely ornate; it simply reflected a life of hard work and accomplishments, nothing more or less. Michael may not have been in the same tax stratosphere as Scruggs, but they were not so far apart in age, values, and occupation.

For the next couple of hours Michael White and Mitchell Scruggs had a long and in-depth conversation covering everything from Elvis—Tupelo's most famous son, to the price of soybeans, organic as well as genetically modified.

Back on the road and headed home to Alabama, Michael realized he had gotten a rare gift: a little peace of mind. That's because, among other things, Scruggs had told him that Raymer's story about Monsanto being involved in the death of his partner, or anyone else at his place of business, was not true; *it was a lie.*

A man who worked for Scruggs had died in one of his warehouses, but it was an accident; nothing more, nothing less. Monsanto did not play a role in the man's death.

In hindsight, it was now obvious from the beginning that Raymer's ominous story had been meant to unnerve Michael. And it had worked beyond perfection, in no small part because Michael was finding more and more evidence to backup the rest of Raymer's story.

The thing that gnawed at Michael more now than ever before was his belief that Raymer had not acted alone. Given Raymer's words, actions and behavior that day, it just seemed to Michael as if someone with a lot more knowledge about the inner workings of Monsanto—perhaps one of their spies?—had put Raymer up to the clash in his cornfield. Was it a scare tactic intended to force Michael into submission? Had it been used on other farmers? Or was it something they had cooked up just for Michael? Michael had no answers—and certainly no facts—for those troubling yet hypothetical questions; all he could do was speculate.

In the end, the saddest part of the whole debacle was that Michael had lived under a frightfully dark cloud for an agonizingly long year while believing beyond all doubt that Raymer's death threat was absolutely and unequivocally true. And no one could ever give him back the peace of mind he had lost, or his family, or that year of their lives.

CHAPTER 33

Troy never knew when Michael might show up in the middle of the night to crash in his extra bedroom. But that's the way it had to be. The safe houses that Michael used had to be available whenever he needed them, no notice required. Otherwise, he couldn't possibly keep Monsanto's lackeys guessing as to where he might sleep on any given night, a necessity required to keep them off-balance and from harassing his daughters and soon to be ex-wife.

But of all the nights when Monsanto's spies would've loved to have known his whereabouts and be a fly on the wall, this was indeed the night. Just hours after the conclusion of his deposition, Michael had pretended to stop at no less than two of his safe houses before doubling back and sneaking in through the back door of Troy's home.

Although Troy normally went to bed fairly early, whenever he heard Michael kicking around he stayed up a bit later than usual so they could talk. They didn't always talk about Michael's case with Monsanto, but on this night Troy wanted to hear all about Michael's deposition. Prior to the depo, it had pretty much consumed Michael. And now Troy was more than curious to hear how it went.

After almost eight hours of being grilled by Monsanto's high-octane legal talent, and their repeated efforts to coerce him to "name-names"—much like the infamous HUAC—of fellow farmers who might have 'wronged' Monsanto, Michael was ready to put the depo out of his head, at least for the night. But if Troy wanted to hear how it went, Michael felt obliged to give him a recap.

"It started out with basic information. My name. Where I was born. Who my parents are. How many children I have. That kind of stuff." He was about to move on when he remembered, "Oh, yeah, and they asked me if I saved seeds."

Troy cocked his head with curiosity. "What did you say?"

"I told 'em the truth. I sure do save 'em! Been saving 'em since I started farming, which was long before they ever cooked up any of those Frankenstein seeds in their laboratories."

Michael rubbed his brow, then leaned back and sighed. "They were hoping they'd rattle some bones . . . maybe even pull a skeleton outta my closet. But they must not know much about bones, or they'd know that most times they're best left alone."

"How so?" Troy asked.

"Take the job I got right out of high school." Michael shot Troy a knowing look. "Now that's a pile of bones a lot of people don't want anybody shaking."

Troy was only moderately curious about a job Michael had more than thirty years ago, "What kind of job?"

"Working at a textile mill."

"Use to be a lot of 'em around here. Lotta people worked at mills." Troy remarked matter-of-factly.

Michael nodded in agreement, then added, "But not no more."

"I guess they still make a lot of socks over at Ft. Payne," Troy surmised, "but not like they once did."

"They've been calling it the 'Sock Capital of the World' for at least thirty years or more," Michael stated, then added, "But I don't know if that's true now or not." With that, Michael drifted back more than thirty years to a chapter of his life he had never shared with Troy, one that took place right after high school.

With no real direction for his future, no concrete goals and only a vague idea of what he wanted out of life, soon after graduating high school

Michael landed a job working on a maintenance crew at a textile mill. It was his first full-time job.

The summer of '72 was a hot one, even by Alabama standards. It was made all the worse for Michael and his friends on the maintenance crew because of the conditions they were subjected to at the mill. But jobs were extremely hard to come by in the rural South, especially jobs with a steady paycheck for people with nothing more than a high school diploma. So they didn't complain, not openly.

The maintenance crew's main job at the mill was cleaning up a bunch of old pipes located in crawlspaces so cramped and confining that even the slim young boys had to put their hands and arms straight over their heads just to slip inside them. Once inside they had to clean the pipes while operating blind because it was not only dark, but their hands remained above their heads at all times; the crawlspaces were so small that no one on the crew was thin enough to get his hands down in front of him. To exacerbate this difficult and uncomfortable situation, the pipes were filled with boiling water, which meant they could fry the skin of these young men if they touched them for more than a second or two. Even a couple of seconds' worth of contact often resulted in some nasty burns. And to top off these miserable and dangerous working conditions, the heat inside the crawlspaces was staggering, more than 130 degrees, complete with enough steam blasting out of cracks in the pipes to melt a bar of soap right before their eyes. Although the young men were all in good shape— several of them weren't far removed from their days as standout high school athletes, none of them could work in the crawlspaces for more than ten minutes before being overcome by the heat and steam. To compound matters, the foreman at the plant didn't seem to care one iota about their safety or welfare, and with almost no standards in place to protect them, the crew members had to really watch each other's backs. There were no other lifelines.

"Surely you had gloves and a protective suit on?" Troy interrupted. "And a hardhat?"

"No, the crawlspaces were so small you couldn't get in there if you had a hardhat on. And they never gave us any gloves or anything like that."

Troy was stunned by the total lack of protective gear. "Why in the world did those pipes have to be cleaned in the first place?"

"It was an old plant. They were insulated with asbestos, and that was soaked with some kind of chemical, one that would burn your skin like acid. I think the government had told 'em they had to get all that asbestos and mess out of the plant or they'd shut 'em down." Michael gestured, "So that's what we were there for. To get all that junk out. Only they never told us it was toxic."

With his jaw on the floor, Troy said, "You were cleaning up toxic waste!? That ain't good, not one bit." Then he asked, "If you didn't have on any protective gear, how in the heck did you get the asbestos out?"

Michael shrugged, "We scraped it off the pipes by hand with screw drivers. Then we'd bring all that toxic gunk outside and dump it into steel drums."

Still reeling from the notion that Michael was handling toxic waste without protective gear, not even gloves, Troy's mind shifted to another thought. "I hate to ask, but what did they do with those drums?"

"They were supposed to send 'em to a place where they could be disposed of properly. But they didn't all make it. They paid off some of the truck drivers to falsify their logs to make it look like they'd driven the drums to another location a long way off. But a whole lot of those drums never left that plant."

Troy was on the edge of his chair. "What happened to them then?"

"At night they'd bury 'em right there on the grounds. Probably saved 'em a pile of money. That and the fact they were only paying us two bucks an hour."

Troy was now past the point of being shocked. "You only got paid two dollars an hour to clean up toxic waste!? And you did it without any protective gear!?"

"Actually, we didn't really make two dollars an hour. That's just what they told us we were making. 'Cause of the way they doled out the checks—which was real odd, we figured up at the end of the year that they'd only paid us for 48 weeks when, in fact, we'd really worked 51 or 52 weeks."

"So they not only worked you like slaves? They cheated you, too?"

Michael sighed and then nodded. "Yeah, that's about the size of it."

"I'm surprised none of y'all got killed doing that nasty job."

Michael thought back to that horrible time and place, recalling a sickening episode that took place one day on the job. One of the people in Michael's crew, Beau Livingston, got trapped inside a crawlspace. When he tried to extricate himself, his right hip got lodged against a couple of pipes. He screamed bloody murder at the top of his lungs as the pipes burned his skin like a blowtorch. The entire crew immediately went into action to rescue him, pulling and tugging with all their might to get him out. They even tried to bust the walls open to dig him out. But nothing worked. The whole time this nightmare was unfolding Michael and the others could smell and hear Beau's flesh burning as if was roasting over a barbecue pit, the gruesome sound commingling with the young man's blood curdling screams for help. It was beyond horrible.

By the time they finally got Beau out of the crawlspace his entire right hip had been grotesquely charred and he was near death. They rushed him to a hospital where he was taken to the ICU. Beau's condition was grave, and his family was told to expect the worst. He was unconscious when they said their final goodbyes.

Miraculously, Beau made it through the night, and the next and the next. Defying all odds, after an extended recovery, he finally left the hospital, albeit in a wheelchair. He had survived a harrowing nightmare, but he would never be the same and would have only limited mobility for the rest of his life.

"Whatever happened to Beau? Can he walk at all now?" Troy asked, interrupting Michael's thoughts.

A long moment passed before Michael responded. "Beau was a good fellow, a real good one. I liked him a lot. But after that awful day when he got burned up, well . . . he was just never quite the same again. Then to top it off, his girlfriend left him while he was sick. Or maybe she was his wife? I can't remember all the details." He let out a deep sigh and then said almost in a whisper, "I think he was about twenty-one or two, maybe twenty-three, when he took his own life."

For a long time neither Troy nor Michael spoke. The quiet gave Troy time to take in this sad and tragic story, and Michael time to reflect on the past.

Finally, Michael broke the silence, sharing some highly disturbing news that he rarely ever told anyone. "More than a few of those people I worked with back then, well, they've got a rare form of heart disease now and some of 'em have died from it." He heaved a loud sigh. "That's way too much coincidence for that many folks to have the same disease, especially a bunch that the only real link between 'em is that they all worked together way back when at the same mill." Staring off into the distance, Michael spoke as if consumed by his own worst fears, "I worry that it'll get me, too. That I won't see my kids grow up—that I won't be able to take care of 'em." Then he focused back on Troy. "We were just a bunch of naïve country boys. Some of us were just teenagers. We didn't know nothing about asbestos or toxic chemicals or none of that stuff back then. There wasn't no CNN or Internet. And not a single one of the managers at the mill ever told us we were working with dangerous chemicals that could make us sick, much less give us heart disease."

Troy felt terrible for Michael. His pain was palpable. "Michael, I know a lot of people in rural areas got exploited by big companies in the past. But I've never heard a story like yours, at least not one that took place so recently." With a look of disgust, Troy added, "I hope that company got caught and was put out of business, and I hope all their top brass went to jail."

Matter-of-factly, Michael replied, "The mill's closed. Been closed mor'n fifteen years. But nobody's ever answered for what they did. And the company that owned it, they're still in business. That's why their lawyers oughta be real careful about the bones they try and rattle."

Suddenly, Troy figured out the reason why Michael had told him the disturbing details about the nightmarish job from his past. Even so, it was a shock, the kind that felt as if he had been kicked in the gut by a mule. The breath was gone from his body, and he had a difficult time speaking. "You mean to tell me the company that owned that textile mill, the one that cheated you on your pay, exposed you to toxic chemicals and buried illegal toxic waste was Monsanto?"

Michael solemnly nodded in the affirmative, "Yep."

CHAPTER 34

The battle with Monsanto was taking a formidable toll on every aspect of Michael's life, and his bank account was certainly no exception. To try and save some money, he was serving as a de facto legal clerk for Don Word, and it was quite an eye-opener for a man who had spent most of his life tilling the soil. It was the equivalent of an education in both the legal process and the voluminous research required for a case like his. Finding out how the federal court system works—and doesn't—was also part of his education.

In federal court each civil case is randomly assigned to a federal judge. However, in the vast majority of cases the evidentiary process—motions, depositions, etc.—is handled by a magistrate judge. Magistrates are full-fledged judges, albeit a few rungs down the ladder from a federal judge. Nevertheless, the magistrate can rule on motions, and even hear the case out to the very end; they can even render a summary judgment.

Michael had done some homework and been told by an acquaintance that Judge Harwell Davis, the magistrate handling his case, had a reputation for being pro-business. To Michael's way of thinking that was a very good thing. After all, wasn't Michael a businessman? He owned and ran a profitable farm. And right up until Monsanto scared off his customers, he had a successful seed business. He had employed people, paid taxes, was an integral part of his community. Certainly that counted for something?

Apparently not. At least not for those who thought of themselves as 'pro-business.' To a man like Michael who had actually built a business from scratch with his own hands this was logic turned upside down. How could it be that a business built on blood, sweat, and tears was the antithesis of the catchphrase? If Michael's businesses lost money, he didn't get a paycheck. He had to make do, dip into his savings, or take out a loan—assuming his situation was such that he could get one. On the other hand, if Monsanto lost $100 million, or even $500 million, it was a fairly safe bet that its top executives would not only continue to get their gargantuan salaries, in all likelihood they would probably still get big fat bonuses, too. If 'pro-business' meant siding with a bunch of guys without an ounce of skin in the game over a hardworking business owner and farmer like Michael who had all ten fingers and toes deep into the pot, then the term itself was a cruel, sick and twisted joke.

But it was no joke—sick or otherwise—when, out of left field, Monsanto filed a motion for summary judgment against Michael. In essence, the conglomerate was asking Davis to rule against Michael, and in its favor, without allowing a jury to hear so much as a single word about what it had done to Michael and his family, or other farmers. Michael was incensed: it seemed to him that it was a thinly veiled attempt to portray Monsanto as a victim, as if a farmer in rural Alabama could victimize a multi-billion dollar conglomerate. For a company that once made Agent Orange—and was still battling people devastated by the toxin—to play the victim card was beyond unconscionable to Michael. Monsanto's impudence was outdone only by its utter and complete amnesia when it came to its own outlandish and brazen sins. Yet Michael realized that the most frightening aspect was that the judge could actually rule in Monsanto's favor.

As the ruling got closer, with motions volleyed back and forth between lawyers for both sides, Michael asked Don a series of questions he had already asked more than once, yet felt needed repeating. This time he asked them with bile rising in his throat, the kind borne of righteous indignation. "Don't this judge know Monsanto's history? Don't he know this is the same bunch of heathens that dumped tons and tons of PCBs into

Anniston's soil and water for forty years? Does he have any idea how many people—good, decent, innocent people—have died of cancer 'cause of that poison? Does he know how many babies were born with birth defects? Has he ever heard of Agent Orange? Does he know how many lives have been destroyed by this company?"

Instead of answering Michael, Don let out a long and heavy sigh, then slowly turned and stared off into the distance. He had no answers. But it stood to reason: if the judge wasn't aware of Monsanto's egregious sins in Anniston he was probably the only person in the entire state working in the legal profession who didn't know something about them. Nevertheless, although it seemed absurdly unfair under the circumstances to Michael, Monsanto was not on trial for its past sins. Even worse, it seemed there was a possibility that the crimes it had committed against Michael and his family might get washed away during the legal proceedings as if the conglomerate was coated with Teflon.

* * *

If Michael had thought he was operating on almost no sleep before, he found things could actually get worse. With a ruling on the summary judgment coming any day now, most nights he didn't sleep at all. And what was keeping him up? He kept wondering how in the world Monsanto's 'expert' had come up with that figure of $2.4 million dollars as the amount he had damaged the conglomerate. Was he the only person who saw a direct and highly disturbing parallel between that figure and the value of everything he owned in the world? It seemed far too convenient for him that the 'damages' Monsanto had 'suffered' because he planted some GM seeds for about four years and sold some for a couple of years was exactly the same as his total assets.

On paper it looked like Michael was quite well-to-do, even wealthy to a number of people. But his main asset was land, farm land—not beach front property. And those who own farm land in rural Alabama lament it's not known for generating much income, it appreciates at an agonizingly slow rate—some even goes down in value, and finding a buyer for it can take years. Generally speaking, it's a hard sell even in the best of times.

But even if Michael found a buyer for his land, along with everything else he owned—including the old and worn out boots on his feet, he couldn't come close to paying the mind boggling $7.2 million dollars (triple the $2.4 million) Monsanto was seeking in 'damages.'

Michael couldn't help but wonder why Monsanto had not been required to pay triple the value of its assets to the people in Anniston, if not more? After all, it dumped PCBs into that town's ground and water for almost four decades . . . whereas he only tried their seeds for about four years. And, of course, in his deposition he readily told Monsanto's lawyers that he had tried the GM seeds and even sold some, yet his experience had been that they were substandard to the seeds he had used for years; he wasn't about to lie under oath. Monsanto, on the other hand, had deliberately covered up the truth about Anniston for decades, and went to great lengths to do so. Nevertheless, Michael told the truth and was facing catastrophic financial ruin for having used some GM seeds for a few years and Monsanto hid the truth and got off with little more than a dent in its bank account after poisoning a community of some 20,000 people for almost 40 years.[8]

The settlement in Anniston worked out to a paltry $7,800 per victim of the toxic chemical that Monsanto knowingly and secretly dumped into their water for decades. Vietnam veterans who were exposed to Agent Orange

---

[8] The U.S. Environmental Protection Agency issued a report on January 31, 2013, which states, "PCBs have been demonstrated to cause a variety of adverse health effects." It also states, "Studies in animals provide conclusive evidence that PCBs cause cancer. Studies in humans raise further concerns regarding the potential carcinogenicity of PCBs. Taken together, the data strongly suggest that PCBs are probable human carcinogens."

and suffered irreversible debilitating health problems faired even worse, receiving a measly $5,700 each, while those who died only got $1,800, not even enough for a proper burial. Nevertheless, Monsanto felt it had been egregiously wronged by Michael to the point that it was entitled to $7.2 million dollars because he had used some of its seeds for a few years.

A man such as Michael could not possibly comprehend the thought processes, logic, motivation, ethics, or values of anyone—corporate executive or lawyer—who placed patent misuse so astronomically far above the health, well-being and lives of humans. That was, of course, a very good thing . . . for Michael.

* * *

Don didn't have to tell Michael the outcome of the ruling regarding Monsanto's request for summary judgment. Don's face said it all. As hard as it was for Michael to fathom, the judge had somehow seen fit to hold for Monsanto. Almost right down the line, Judge Davis had sided with the conglomerate against Michael. However, he could not do the same with Wayne because Monsanto had not offered any evidence or witnesses against him. Even with Monsanto's vast resources it failed to produce a single shred of evidence against Wayne. That meant the case against Wayne was bogus, which Michael had asserted from day one. In spite of this, the conglomerate still did not drop Wayne from the suit. Although it thoroughly upset Michael, it didn't surprise him. After all, this was the same company that refused to acknowledge any responsibility for the farmers in India who, wracked with despair because of GM crops, had committed suicide by the thousands.

There was no attempt by Don to sugarcoat things. Instead, he laid out the basic options for Michael. He could throw in the towel and try to negotiate a settlement with Monsanto, or they could file a motion—a reply—in an attempt to have the judge reconsider his ruling. But the odds of Judge Davis, or any judge, reversing himself at this point on a summary judgment were extremely long at best.

There was, however, a slight glimmer of a hope. Since the summary judgment came from a magistrate, if Don filed a reply contesting Davis' ruling then there would definitely be a de novo review by a federal judge. In legal circles the expression de novo, from the Latin, generally means that a matter will be heard "a new" or "from the beginning," as if it is being heard for the first time.

Of course, there was a real possibility that a federal judge might very well agree with Davis's ruling. But at the very least a fresh set of eyes would take a look at the case, and Michael could certainly hope a federal judge would see things much differently. If not, he would be at Monsanto's mercy. And if history was any indicator, Michael was convinced that the conglomerate had none - - - at least not for the people in Anniston or India, and not for those who had been exposed to Agent Orange.

CHAPTER 35

Driving in his truck, Michael was headed home on a dark, starless night when the ringing of his cell phone interrupted his thoughts, which were drifting in all directions. It was Troy, and the first words out of his mouth made Michael's blood run cold, "There's trouble out at your daddy's house, big trouble!"

Panicked, Michael all but wailed, "Is he OK?" He wanted to slam the phone down and drive straight to his father's house, but he knew it would be better to get the whole story first. "Please tell me he's OK? Please!"

"He is right now. But I don't know how long he'll be OK."

Frantic, Michael could barely breathe. "Oh my Lord! What's wrong?" He knew Monsanto's spies had to be involved. "What have they done?"

Everything gushed out of Troy like a broken dam. "They got an unmarked helicopter sitting on top of his house. I'm telling you, it's hovering like a vulture; can't be mor'n a hundred feet above his roof. And it's got a giant spotlight blasting his house like there's an escaped convict from death row hiding out there. If that copter was to misfire or a strong wind was to hit it, well, it could crash right into his house, probably right where he's taking cover from it."

"Oh no! No!" Michael could picture his elderly father, all alone, trapped inside his own home. He had to be terror-stricken. Who wouldn't be? The frail old man probably had no idea what was hovering above his home and making enough noise and wind to shake the rafters. He probably thought it was a tornado about to touch down and turn his house into rubble, a very real fear for anyone living on the mountain.

It was an excruciatingly horrible thought for Michael; at this very moment his father was being harassed and victimized, and there was nothing he could do about it. The thought was tearing him up inside. How in the world did these monsters have the audacity to treat an elderly man, one who had been a pillar of the community for decades, like a common criminal? "There's criminals involved here," Michael fumed to himself. "But they're above the house, not in it!"

More or less screaming, Michael shot back, "I'm on my way. Be there in fifteen minutes at the most." With that Michael hung up and, while blasting down the road, he dialed a number the sheriff had given him. It was his personal cell phone. As soon as Michael heard the sheriff's voice everything came spilling out.

Michael didn't beat around the bush. "I don't know if you got anyway to contact those monsters or not. But I do know they monitor the police bands. If you can contact 'em, just get the message to 'em that the helicopter they got sitting on top of my daddy's house better be gone before I get there. They ain't gonna play games with my daddy's life! I'll take care of this mess tonight!" The rage and intensity in Michael's voice was unmistakable. It was the voice of a man who'd been pushed too far one time too many.

The sheriff quickly advised Michael not to do anything foolish, not to take the law in his own hands. He reminded Michael that he'd done an admirable job of following the law. Michael, of course, noted that his enemy had seen fit to break it at seemingly every turn. It seemed the sheriff didn't want Michael to fall into one of their traps now. But before he could finish, Michael hung up. He had to concentrate on getting to his father's house as quickly as humanly possible without having an accident.

As he burned up the asphalt, a memory jarred Michael. It was in the form of Wiley Kemp's voice. Michael could hear the old aviator's cryptic words once again, 'If someone were to shoot the tail rotor of a chopper in the right place . . . well . . . theoretically, that can throw it into a spin it can't come out of.'

Without taking his eyes off the road, Michael reached back with his right hand to make sure he had a rifle in his gun rack. He did. It was a 7mm magnum with a scope, a rifle that not only had the power to stop a charging grizzly, but in the right hands it could accomplish that formidable task from more than five hundred feet. From three times that distance Michael could blast a door knob off a door, and it would be a clean shot.

Because of Troy's location near Wayne's house, he pretty much pinpointed the approximate time that the helicopter abruptly turned off its spotlight, quickly made a vertical maneuver, and then took off as if it was fleeing the scene of a heinous crime. It was, more or less, soon after Michael had spoken with the Sheriff.

To Michael that meant one of Monsanto's thugs had either been monitoring the police band radio, or had listened in on Michael and the Sheriff's private call. It was beyond unnerving to think that Monsanto's spies might have tapped into Michael's phone, or, worse, the Sheriff's private line. But Michael could only speculate on those points, nothing more, because he had no solid proof whatsoever that they'd tapped anyone's phone. One thing he did know for sure: the Sheriff was a good and decent man, and was not in cahoots with Monsanto's spies.

In the end it really didn't matter how the pilot got his information, the fact is that he had gotten the message loud and clear. And the pilot clearly understood that if Michael got there and he was still harassing his elderly father it might very well be his last mission for Monsanto, or anyone.

That night Michael stayed at Wayne's house, and he stayed there the next and the next. He was prepared for the worst, for the chopper to come back late one night with reinforcements. But he hoped for the best. And each night Michael said a fervent prayer that he'd never again be forced into a situation where he even had to contemplate taking the law into his own hands. Yet even as he prayed for peace, he could not help but wonder, 'What kind of sick, twisted and depraved barbarians try to terrorize a frail, helpless, 81 year-old widower? . . . and what kind of perverted fiends would pay them to do it?'

CHAPTER 36

There were two ways Michael looked at the airborne assault on his father. It was simply Monsanto's spies none too subtle message that they would use whatever means necessary and weren't particularly fearful of repercussions. Or it could be construed that it was their attempt to flush Michael out and make him do something he'd regret, i.e., fire a rifle at their chopper. They could then use Michael's gut reaction—provoked solely by their scurrilous misdeeds—to turn the tables against him. A slick lawyer with no scruples could very well attempt to make it appear as if Michael was the bad guy. It was an age-old strategy employed by bullies, dictators and tyrants; push someone over the edge, and then try and blame them for falling.

Michael decided scenario number two was about as close to the truth as any other hypothesis he might come up with. With that in mind, he wondered just how far the spies would go to make him cry uncle, or push him into making a major tactical blunder. It was like playing chess against a computer. It wasn't thinking about the current move; it was strategizing for two or three moves down the road. That meant Michael had to be on number four merely to stay in the game.

Staring out his office window, Michael's mind drifted. He thought about the people in Anniston who'd been hit hardest by the tons of PCBs Monsanto had dumped there. They were, for the most part, blacks and poor whites, primarily people with little or no formal education. Back in 1935 when Monsanto bought the plant from the Theodore Swann Company, it wasn't hard to imagine that its executives were far more concerned about turning a profit than they were with safeguarding the people who worked there.

With the country mired deep in the Great Depression, steady jobs were extremely difficult to find, especially in the rural South. If someone in Anniston passed on a job with Monsanto, there were countless others who would jump at the chance for gainful employment, even if it meant handling toxic chemicals on a daily basis and doing so without any protective gear. And Michael had provided sworn testimony during his deposition that decades after the Great Depression ended Monsanto still had some employees handling toxic chemicals without protective gear.

Given the times, it was reasonable to believe that back in the 1930s little was known about the toxicity of the chemicals, at least among the general public. But Monsanto's very own internal documents eventually revealed that as early as 1937, only two years after taking control of the plant, the conglomerate's scientists were raising some very large red flags. They were secretly discussing information that showed some of the workers were suffering from liver damage because of exposure to chemicals in the plant. Nevertheless, Monsanto's executives kept this fact, and others like it, hush-hush. It was but one of their many dirty secrets about the plant in Anniston.

Those incriminating documents didn't come to light until almost sixty-five years after the fact, and only after Monsanto was sued and forced to release them. Michael thought about all the decent, honest, hardworking people in Anniston who'd had to swear that their lives and health had been ruined because of exposure to toxic chemicals from the plant just to get their day in court. Many of them had cancer or other serious chronic health issues and a number of their children were born with birth defects, all of which they attributed to PCB exposure. And then he thought about all the people in Anniston who never got their day in court, the ones who were dead and buried long before the conglomerate had to face a judge, much less a jury.

The truth about Anniston—intentionally hidden by Monsanto for decades—brought to mind a controversial drug the conglomerate had produced, recombinant bovine somatotropin, known as rBST, a.k.a, rBGH.[9] A number of countries have banned it, including Australia, Belgium, Canada, Denmark, Finland, France, Germany, Ireland, Israel, Italy, Japan, Luxembourg, Malta, Netherlands, New Zealand, Norway, Portugal, Spain, Sweden, Switzerland and the United Kingdom.

When injected into cattle, rBGH purportedly increases milk production without tainting the milk itself. It does increase milk production, but at what price? . . . both for the humans and animals involved? Although Michael wasn't a dairy farmer, he didn't think the drugs were safe. And he certainly wasn't alone. Under fire by concerned citizens from all walks of life in the U.S., from scientists to consumer groups to soccer moms, it seemed that a significant number of people who had done their homework wanted their dairy products free of rBGH. At the very least they wanted labels to let them know if a dairy product contained rBGH or not.

Monsanto vehemently fought consumers over their right to know whether a product contained rBGH. But the conglomerate didn't stop there. It adamantly opposed the rights of companies from voluntarily informing consumers on their own labels, and at their own expense, that their products were "free of rBGH."

Although many people felt the FDA dragged its heels, it eventually weighed in on the matter as to whether or not consumers had a right to know if milk contained rBGH. Margaret Miller, employed by the FDA's Office of New Animal Drug Evaluation, played a substantial role in the FDA's edict—issued in 1994—that companies did not have to let customers know their milk contained rBGH. Even more disappointing,

---

[9] Recombinant bovine growth hormone, known as rBGH, is a more familiar name for artificial growth hormones. Many people consider the names rBST and rBGH interchangeable when discussing this matter.

the companies that simply wanted to let diligent consumers know their products were 'free of rBGH' could not do so unless they were willing to stipulate on their label that there was no significant difference between natural milk and milk laced with rBGH . . . *even if they believed otherwise.* A lot of people were genuinely disappointed and totally perplexed by the FDA's egregiously one-sided stance, especially given that it effectively silenced companies who went to great lengths and expense to insure that their products were free of rBGH. Disappointment, however, turned into full-blown outrage for those who discovered that, prior to joining the FDA, Miller not only worked for Monsanto, but was also a supervisor for a laboratory at the conglomerate and *her job was to provide the support needed to get approval for recombinant products, including bovine somatotropin, rBST, a.k.a, rBGH.* [10]

Michael even heard that when a local TV station in Florida planned to air a report about rBGH, one that would only air in a small portion of the state, it felt the wrath of Monsanto. The conglomerate fired off a stern letter to the station's network in New York in an effort to suppress the story.

The letter, penned by one of Monsanto's high octane lawyers, insinuated that the reporters might not be competent to deal with the complicated scientific matters associated with rBST, a.k.a, rBGH. And it raised concerns that the "*good name and reputation*" of Monsanto could be damaged. In the final paragraph the lawyer surmised, "Now is the time to get a level playing field here." Michael wondered if the conglomerate withheld crucial information from the people in Anniston about PCBs

---

[10] On September 30, 2010, in a victory for consumers, the U.S. Federal Court of Appeals for the Sixth Circuit struck down a stifling ban that denied companies in the State of Ohio that produced hormone free milk the right to label it as such. Additionally, the court challenged the controversial 17-year-old ruling by the FDA in which the agency claimed there was no significant difference between milk laced with rBGH and those that are free of drugs. The court went so far as to site three specific reasons why milk free of rBGH is safer for human consumption.
  Please note: In October of 2008, Monsanto sold the part of its company that made rBGH (marketed under the name Posilac) to Eli Lilly and Company for $300 million and other considerations.

because they, too, weren't sophisticated enough to understand the conglomerate had dumped poisonous chemicals into their water supply for almost four decades? And he felt certain Loraine Blanchard could come up with a few choice words for anyone so far out-of-touch with reality as to imply Monsanto actually desired a level playing field. Yet it was the attorney's assertion that Monsanto possessed a *"good name and reputation"* that told Michael it was doubtful he ever had a meaningful conversation with any of the more than 3 million Americans who had served in Vietnam, or their family members . . . to say nothing of the multitudes of healthcare professionals who've treated—and are still treating—victims of Agent Orange.

Arthur Galston, a preeminent botanist and bioethicist, also loomed large in Monsanto's past, as well as its present and future. A friend told Michael that during the 1940's Galston was trying to make a certain crop flower and fruit ahead of schedule so that it could be grown in a wider variety of locations, particularly ones with shorter growing seasons. He found that by using small amounts of the compound triiodobenzoic acid on the plants he could achieve his goal to some degree. However, too much of the acid resulted in catastrophe. Leaves fell off the plants and they died; just the opposite of what Galston had hoped to achieve. Nevertheless, he had stumbled onto a highly potent and relentless defoliant. Because of his findings—ones that caused him great concern, Galston's primary fear was the side effects the compound could have on humans and plants if it was ever unleashed into the environment. But not everyone shared his ethics and genuine desire to protect humanity and the planet from harm. His research was used by others to spawn one of the most infamous chemicals ever produced in history, i.e., Agent Orange. That's what prompted him in later years to say, "You know, nothing that you do in science is guaranteed to result in benefits for mankind. Any discovery,

I believe, is morally neutral and it can be turned either to constructive ends or destructive ends."

Galston, a professor at Yale University for many years, worked tirelessly during the 60's and early 70's to eliminate Agent Orange altogether, lobbying scientists, politicians and government officials to achieve that end. In 1971 his efforts, along with the work of many others, finally paid off when it was officially banned from use in the United States and the Vietnam War. Nevertheless, as a legitimate, ethical and conscientious scientist he knew the dark and demented genie was already out of the bottle, and the damage done by the dioxin was already incalculable, which he described as, "... *one of the most poisonous substances ever created.*"

Michael found it bone chillingly ironic that when Galston stumbled onto what would one day become the apocalyptic nightmare known as Agent Orange he was actually trying to improve one specific crop . . . soybeans, the same crop—albeit genetically modified—Monsanto was now using as the basis for its suit against Michael and Wayne White.

Michael was haunted by Monsanto's past history of suppressing information, and battling those who disagreed with it, yet it kept him focused so that he could see dot after dot being connected in his war with the conglomerate—a war he certainly didn't ask for. After all, he believed a logical person would surmise that this was something far larger than a farmer in rural Alabama locked in a battle of wills with a gigantic corporation over merely the alleged misuse of a patent. Michael felt that even the most jaded observer would acknowledge that the overzealous manner in which Monsanto had dogged and pursued him over the years was far beyond 'unreasonable' for a mere civil suit.

CHAPTER 37

It seemed as if good news was a thing of the past for Michael. He hadn't had any in so long he couldn't remember what it sounded like. So, when Don Word phoned Michael and began their conversation with "Congratulations!" Michael was taken aback. Whatever his lawyer was about to tell him had to be better than what he had been accustomed to hearing for a number of years.

Without beating around the bush, Don told Michael that the federal judge officially assigned to his case was Lynwood Smith. He would perform the all-important de novo review . . . the only thing that stood between Michael and Monsanto's demands for a judgment equal to triple his entire assets, $7.2 million dollars.

Don didn't go into any great detail about Judge Smith, other than to assure Michael that he was a fair, honest, well respected, and impartial judge. Normally, that would've been enough for Michael. But the years had taken their toll on his faith in people and the justice system. Not long after Michael and Don ended their call, Michael made some discreet inquiries about Judge Smith. The last thing he wanted was for Smith to know he was asking around about him.

Of all the things Michael found out about U.S. District Judge Lynwood Smith, the most interesting was that he had been the presiding judge for several of the charges against Eric Rudolph, the infamous Olympic Park Bomber.

Rudolph was the sociopath behind the bombing at the 1996 Olympic Games in Atlanta, as well as several other bombings, which collectively caused the deaths of three people and injured up to 150 others. But it was the bomb Rudolph set at the Olympics that transformed him from a mere nutcase—albeit a very dangerous one—to a bona fide high-profile terrorist, the sort of demented miscreant who made headlines around the globe.

A violent extremist, Rudolph was on the FBI's Top Ten Most Wanted list from 1998 until his capture in 2003. Considered to be a terrorist by the U.S. government, Rudolph survived for five years in the Appalachians living off the land and, many people believe, the aid and comfort provided by like-minded individuals and extremist organizations.

Due to the violent and unpredictable nature of Rudolph and his fellow travelers, the utmost caution had to be taken leading up to his trials. Security at the courthouse rivaled that at a nuclear weapons site. Naturally, given the Olympic connection, the international media was out in force to cover the landmark case.

Michael was told that of all the judges qualified to hear the case, Smith was probably the only one who was able to keep Rudolph and other like-minded extremists from turning the proceedings into a media circus. A no-nonsense judge, Smith was always in control. No one dared play games with him in his courtroom.

In the end, to avoid the death penalty, Rudolph pled guilty to all charges pending against him in Smith's courtroom. And on July 18, 2005, Judge Smith sentenced him to two consecutive life sentences without the possibility of parole for a bombing he committed in Alabama, thus effectively eliminating any chance that Rudolph would ever be a free man again.

After learning Judge Smith's background, Michael felt cautiously optimistic. Even so, there was still a very real possibility that he had just leapt from a burning building into a bottomless pit.

CHAPTER 38

After pulling another all-nighter working on his legal case, Michael desperately needed some rest. So he headed for a safe house. On the way he passed by what use to be his seed business. He tried to avoid driving by it—because it made him angry, but it was almost impossible since he had a cornfield nearby.

The only bright spot for Michael as he drove past his now shuttered business was the fact that a handful of his ex-customers had recently agreed to give sworn testimony as to why they stopped doing business with him. Each and everyone of them was prepared to share more or less the same story; they had been intimidated by Monsanto, either with the threat of costly litigation, or the conglomerate's goons began stalking them, or both. They all agreed that Monsanto had effectively scared them off, as well as others, and killed Michael's once thriving business.

The saddest part was, Michael had a lot of former friends and customers who simply refused to discuss the matter. They acted as if they had amnesia. They wouldn't talk with his lawyer, Don Word. They wouldn't even return Michael's calls. He had become almost a leper with a number of people he once counted as good friends and customers. Of course, Michael understood why they were afraid. They had seen what a nightmare his life had become as a result of the litigation and incessant spying. Even the county's own Chief Deputy stated without hesitation, "They made Michael's life a living hell."

Losing his seed business meant that a sizable chunk of Michael's income had been strangled off, and that made it extremely difficult for him to fund his defense. He felt it was the equivalent of having his feet whacked off with a dull axe and then having the hatchet man challenge him to a foot race where the winner takes all.

As Michael drove to the safe house, he thought about the old axiom for those stuck in quicksand, "You can't dig yourself out, not even with a gold-plated shovel. You have to be pulled out." In his case, Michael had put his faith and trust in Don to pull him out of the cesspool Monsanto had dredged. With his hands tightly gripping the rope, and Don pulling mightily, Michael felt there was a chance for escape from this quagmire. It was the only ray of hope that got him through a lot of dark and frightening days, to say nothing of the nights.

Arriving at the safe house, Michael saw that all the cars were gone. That meant everyone who lived there had already left for the day. That was fine with him because it meant he wouldn't be in anyone's way. Inside the empty house, Michael made a quick detour through the kitchen for something to drink.

The kitchen still smelled of fresh eggs and bacon. He thought of his own children, laughing, talking, and cutting up between bites of scrambled eggs and toast. They loved morning time, just as he once had. For most of his life it held the promise of a fresh start, a chance to make a difference, the feeling that most anything was possible. Now, however, it didn't spell the start of a bright anything. It was simply another life-sapping page in his never-ending legal saga, a ball and chain that kept dragging him further and further down.

As Michael poured himself a glass of water, he hoped his children had slept well. He hoped they had gotten to school on time, and hoped that one day in the not-so-distant future they could put this wretched nightmare of spies, stalkers, and unmarked aircrafts behind them. That day couldn't come soon enough.

Operating on autopilot, Michael picked up a note on the counter with his name and the word 'important' on it. Rubbing his eyes so he could focus, Michael gave the note a quick read. But he didn't finish it. He stopped reading, in part, because he thought his eyes were playing tricks on him. Yet starting over from the beginning didn't help any. The words on the message were just the same as before, and even more devastating the second time he read them: "The federal judge ruled that Don Word has a conflict of interest and has taken him off your case."

Michael staggered. He felt as if his legs were made of liquid. Afraid he might collapse, he grabbed on to the edge of the sink for support as a million thoughts ricocheted through his head. How in the world could he get another lawyer he trusted at this point? Could he even afford one if he found the right one? It was all just too much for him to think about as slumped down onto the floor, consumed by utter despair.

CHAPTER 39

It turned out that losing Don as his attorney was but one part of the most bittersweet day of Michael's entire life.

In the course of a single day, Judge Lynnwood Smith issued a number of orders, decisions and opinions regarding Michael's case, including dismissing Don as his attorney. However, the most important was his de novo review of the case.

After carefully reading through the entire case—sifting through fact, fiction and hyperbole, the highly respected federal judge had some less than complimentary words for the conclusions the 'pro-business' magistrate judge had delivered. At one point in the explanation for his ruling Smith stated, "The Magistrate Judge ignored this evidence." and on the very next page he added, "Moreover, the Magistrate Judge neglects another important piece of evidence." And Smith's final ruling? He rejected and reversed the summary judgment the magistrate had granted to Monsanto on virtually every count.

It was a clear and resounding victory for Michael!

But there was scant little time to celebrate. Michael not only had to find a new lawyer, but he had to have one in time for an important hearing Smith set for the case on January 25, 2006 . . . only 39 days away. Not only was it just around the corner, but the Christmas and New Year's holidays were bound to cut deeply into the time Michael had to seek out a new lawyer.

Although Michael was elated that Smith had ruled so decisively in his favor, he could hear a loud and ominous ticking in his ear. He not only had to find a good lawyer, get him up to speed, and do it in five weeks, but he also had to find one he could afford. It was a tall order. Fortunately, he knew right where to start the search.

* * *

No one, save for Don Word or Michael himself, knew Michael's case better than L. V. did. So Michael went straight to his house to discuss the matter.

The first thing Michael did was explain why Judge Smith had dismissed Don from the case. It seems Don was representing another farmer involved in a suit with Monsanto and Smith had determined that it constituted a conflict of interest. Don had dutifully informed Michael about the other case quite some time ago and Michael was fine with it, but Smith's ruling was fair and just because of some unexpected evidence that had come to light, evidence that could possibly pit Don's clients against each other.

More than a few times Michael had told L. V. that not only was Don the perfect lawyer for his case, but also that he trusted Don, and that meant a great deal to him. So, naturally, he expected a similar reaction from L. V. that he'd had himself. He was certain L. V. would share his feeling of doom, dread, and impending catastrophe. But L.V. took the opposite tack.

Leaning close to Michael and speaking from his heart, L.V. said, "Michael, a Philadelphia lawyer wouldn't be half as good as you on this case, 'cause a Philadelphia lawyer don't know a plow from a polecat. Whoever's riding herd over this thing has gotta be the kind of lawyer that either knows farming, or knows they gotta listen to you . . . instead of talking all the time, which is what most lawyers like to do."

Michael immediately came to his former lawyer's defense. "But Don listened. He listened to every word I said."

L. V. nodded in agreement, "I know that. And I've said many a time that Don's a good man and a talented lawyer. But the judge says you got to get another one." He symbolically dusted his hands, signifying the discussion about Don was closed. Then, leaning a bit closer to Michael he said, "You need a lawyer that's well into the winter of his life, someone who no longer fears what other men can do to him because he knows death is inescapable. You need someone who cares more about finding the truth than filling his wallet."

Michael nodded. If he'd had a month to think this over, he couldn't have said it better, and certainly no more succinctly than L. V. had. Of course, it was one thing to describe a dream lawyer. It was another thing altogether to actually find such a person. That is, if such an individual even existed.

Although Michael figured there was no such lawyer, he saw a twinkle in L. V.'s eye. That almost always meant his friend had some valuable information to share. With a gentle nod, L. V. said, "Buck. That's the answer." His words were spoken with a comforting finality. However, upon seeing that Michael wasn't following his line of thought, L. V. added, "Watson." With a hint of a smile and a friendly wink, he pronounced, "Herman 'Buck' Watson. Best damn lawyer I know."

All but a legal virgin—that is, until Monsanto came along, Michael had never heard of Buck Watson. But it didn't matter. If L. V. said he was the best man for the job, then he most certainly was.

CHAPTER 40

With more than forty years of experience, a commanding knowledge of the law, and an uncanny ability to sway juries, Buck Watson was indeed a good lawyer. But he was also scaling back his practice a bit so he could spend more time with his family and enjoy life. Michael could certainly understand Buck's desire to smell the roses, even if he didn't have time to do so himself.

Fortunately for Michael, after hearing about his case, Buck was intrigued enough to sit down with him, and did so right away. The two men had a long talk in which they sized each other up as much as anything else. Michael came away from the meeting impressed by Buck, and most likely it was a two-way street because the old barrister decided to take on Michael's case. However, there was a catch of sorts, if it could be called that. Buck would assign the case to a partner who had worked under him for years. To be sure, Buck would be involved, but his partner would shoulder the bulk of the work.

Weighing the option of having one of Buck's understudies take his case, Michael thought about his own desire twenty-five-odd years ago to become a bona fide horse and mule trader who could hold his own with the best on Sand Mountain and beyond. Michael had achieved his goal, and then some. However, in the beginning he was anything but good. He was downright lousy. The deals he made stunk, and he always wound up kicking himself for making them. That is, until he began observing the masters, the handful of seasoned traders in his area who made a living at one of the world's oldest professions. Over time, he came to know these men quite well who could judge horseflesh better than all the rest. More than that, he discovered their secret was that they could also read people.

It was uncanny, but they could literally predict down to the dollar how high a bidder would go on any given animal. Learning from these men was the equivalent of getting a Ph.D. in human nature.

Naturally, Michael reasoned that if he couldn't get Buck for his lead lawyer, having someone who had studied under him was the next best thing. And that person was Rebekah Keith McKinney. There was even an added bonus. She wasn't merely a pupil of the old barrister, she was also his daughter.

Feeling good about his new law firm, Michael immediately brought over the voluminous files for his case so Rebekah could get started right away and get up to speed in time for the hearing on the 25th, which was now only a scant few weeks away.

After reviewing the files, Rebekah requested a special meeting with Michael. She was not the sort to string anyone along or play games. She put all her cards face up on the table. She was pregnant with twins, which Michael already knew. But now that she'd had time to truly go over Michael's entire case she realized that, given the fact she'd soon be taking an extended maternity leave, she could not in good conscience provide the kind of legal representation she knew he needed and deserved.

Michael was devastated.

Luckily for him, Rebekah was not the sort to leave anyone hanging. She handed Michael a piece of paper, "That's the number for Hal Mason; a good lawyer. I believe he can handle your case." And then with a quick wink, added. "And he's not pregnant."

Michael smiled at her joke, but he was already convinced that Rebekah was the ideal lawyer for his case. "Any chance you can help this Mason fellow? Maybe partner up with him on this thing?"

It was obvious Rebekah was flattered by Michael's confidence in her. But there was a reason why she was such a good lawyer. "Michael, you wouldn't get my best work. And I don't handle a case unless I can give it my best."

Disappointed as he was, Michael nodded with appreciation; it was nice to know there were still decent people in the world, especially in the legal profession, which he was beginning to believe was overrun by moneygrubbers with no scruples or conscience.

* * *

The long drive for Michael all the way to the offices of Ewell, Richt & Elden in Birmingham, Alabama, was tedious and time consuming. Fortunately, less than a minute or two after greeting the firm's receptionist he was ushered into the office of Hal Mason. Michael was impressed. It seemed that too many lawyers, like a lot of doctors, kept people in a perpetual state of waiting. He appreciated the fact that the firm not only valued his time, Hal had juggled some appointments so he could see him right away.

A boyish shock of thick red hair, a slim build, along with a face spattered with freckles, made Hal appear even younger than he was. Right off the bat he assured Michael in a joking manner that he was old enough to practice law. And without being overtly boastful, he quickly outlined his credentials and accomplishments. For such a young man, he was on track to have a reasonably impressive resume not too far down the pike. Still, he was certainly no Buck Watson or Rebekah. But Michael had reconciled himself to the fact that he wasn't going to have the likes of a Buck Watson in his corner.

Luckily, Michael immediately felt comfortable with Hal because he was already up to speed on the basics of his case. And he seemed genuinely interested, and not only from a legal standpoint, but as a concerned citizen. He had even gone so far as to discuss Michael's case with the firm's partners before their meeting. That impressed Michael. It said he was getting the entire firm, not just this young lawyer. But he also knew that with that goes a price. "Say you've discussed this with the firm's partners?"

Hal nodded. "I have indeed."

"And what do they say?"

"We can handle this case for you." Hal said with a convincing voice that all but sold Michael. Still, there was a nagging issue of utmost importance. And it wasn't about money.

"What's gonna be our strategy?" Michael asked. He intentionally said 'our' instead of 'your' so Hal would know he wanted to work with him. Assuming, of course, Hal's strategy was right for his case.

"The partners want to share that with you in person." Hal quickly pulled up his calendar on his computer, checked it carefully, and then looked at Michael. "Can you come back on Wednesday? Say around 2 p.m.?"

Michael didn't need to check his calendar. Time was of the essence. If the partners of this firm could make the time, he would do the same, nodding, "Two o'clock it is."

"Do you have any documents or paperwork or evidence that I can share with the partners? Anything that will help us with your case?"

"Sure do," Michael replied. "Got a truck load." And he meant that literally.

It required a heavy duty hand truck for Michael to move all the material into Hal's office. It would take quite awhile for Hal and the partners to review it all. So rather than take up any more of Hal's time, he figured it was best to hit the high points before they parted.

"There's a whole heck-of-a-lotta stuff here. Some of it's good, and some is downright incredible."

Hal immediately perked up. "What's the incredible part?"

"My tapes."

"Tapes? Like cassettes?"

"No. Videotapes. I got tapes of Monsanto breaking more laws than you got law books in this here office." It was an extreme exaggeration, to be sure, but it was the simplest way in which to make his point.

The eyebrows on Hal's face went straight up. "You're telling me you've got a Fortune 500 company on videotape breaking laws?"

Michael quickly clarified his statement so there would be no misunderstandings. "I got their spies on tape. Got 'em red-handed. Can't say if they're on Monsanto's payroll or not. But I sure got 'em." He cleared his throat, "And I ain't gotta tell you how important these videotapes are to my case. So I don't want you to copy any of this, not my files, not my papers, but especially not my tapes, that is, not till we've talked strategy and money."

Hal stuck out his hand. "You have my word on it, Michael."

* * *

Michael took the scenic route home, a detour he felt was worth taking. Riding along the perimeter of Lake Guntersville, a vast and scenic body of water, he cleared his head of everything about the case, or as much as he could. It was close to impossible to completely put it out of his mind. But the calm waters of the picturesque lake helped.

The serene water was clear as a mirror and created a reflection of everything on it, beside it, and above it. The trees overlooking the lake were reflected as if a surrealist had painted them onto the water. Even big, puffy clouds overhead had an image all their own.

As Michael took a final look at the beautiful reflection before moving on down the road, he caught a glimpse of something else that appeared in the lake, one that ruined the spectacular moment for him. It was the reflection of a small plane flying directly overhead.

Was it one of Monsanto's spies? And, if so, how long had he been following Michael? Did they know about his new law firm? The mere thought of the incessant stalking made him sick to his stomach.

CHAPTER 41

When Michael arrived at the law offices of Ewell, Richt & Elden on Wednesday the receptionist greeted him warmly and said Hal was waiting for him in the conference room, which was located on the top floor of the building. An intern appeared less than a minute later to escort Michael upstairs because the elevator required a special key to reach the conference room. When Michael stepped off the elevator he understood the reason why a key was required. It opened directly into the conference room. Much to Michael's surprise, Hal had a lot more company than he was expecting, perhaps half the firm's lawyers were there, maybe more.

Hal quickly made introductions, providing Michael with the name of each person and their position within the firm. Normally, Michael was fairly good at remembering people, but given that he was operating on almost no sleep he was glad he wouldn't be quizzed on any of the names and titles later on.

Right away an older man, Mr. Richt, took center stage. This one Michael had no trouble remembering. Wearing his loud, ever-present trademark purple tie embroidered with his family crest, and sporting a long gold chain—ostensibly for a pocket watch—draped conspicuously across a vest stretched tight against his rotund belly, he appeared to rely on too many affectations for Michael's tastes. There was a pompous air about him, and Michael quickly learned that he was the sort who loved to hear himself talk, probably in part because of his hourly rate and partly due to an ego as big as his bulging belly.

After listening to Mr. Richt ramble on for more than half an hour Michael finally interrupted him. The portly lawyer had done nothing more than regurgitate the case history, and hadn't even done a good job of it.

"I already know the facts in my case. I came here to find out what your firm's strategy is gonna be to win this thing."

Suddenly, the room became deathly quiet. Not sure what was wrong, Michael looked at Hal for guidance. Yet instead of reassuring Michael that all was well with a smile or nod, Hal turned away. Mr. Richt cleared his throat loudly. "Michael, I thought Hal had already told you."

"Told me what?"

"The basis of our strategy." Mr. Richt all but snapped, doing a poor job of keeping his agitation at bay. He was put out, both at Michael and Hal. Then he needled Michael like a fed-up grade school teacher confronting a student who had just blamed a stray dog for eating his homework "Are you absolutely sure he didn't tell you?"

With an important hearing right around the corner, Michael hadn't slept a wink because of the fact that he was in the dark about the firm's strategy. So he quickly shook his head. "Naw, he didn't. I'da' remembered."

"Well, I'll explain it to you. And let me know if I go too fast for you."

Normally, Michael didn't let such comments throw him. A lot of people assumed all farmers were slow and dimwitted. And he knew anyone who would have such a blanket mentality wasn't worth worrying about. But the difference on this occasion was that Michael was paying to hear Mr. Richt insult him, and the talk wasn't coming cheap.

"We see your case in two phases," Mr. Richt began. "Phase one is the immediate. I refer to their suit against you for patent infringement." Gesturing grandly as he spoke, Mr. Richt seemed to be pantomiming the information. "We surprise them by having you plead guilty and paying a settlement."

Michael wasn't sure if he had heard right, so with more than a bit of trepidation he interrupted. "You want me to plead guilty?"

Mr. Richt smiled and waved off his concern. "They'll want a settlement from you, probably a hundred-and-fifty thousand. But don't worry about that. We'll negotiate that way down. You probably won't pay more than forty, fifty tops."

"Fifty thousand dollars?" Michael couldn't believe his ears. Fifty thousand was a king's ransom, especially when he had never signed one of Monsanto's technology agreements stating he would abide by all their stifling rules and regulations. "And that's just to settle? And you know I ain't never bought so much as a single one of Monsanto's Frankenstein seeds from 'em? Right? And I ain't never signed one of their technology agreements, either."

Mr. Richt nodded that he understood, then added. "Of course, that figure doesn't include our fee." Then he continued as if Michael's interruption had been an uncalled for nuisance. "That initial guilty plea makes them complacent. They figure, 'Oh well, White knows he can't beat us and he's thrown in the towel'." Mr. Richt winked and then snapped, "And that's when we shift to phase two."

Michael wasn't sure he wanted to hear any more. He glanced over at Hal to gauge his reaction, but Hal was positioned so that he and Michael couldn't make eye contact.

"In phase two," Mr. Richt continued, gesturing at Michael. "We'll have you go to one of your farmer friends and buy some of Monsanto's seeds. Now these seeds will have to be straight out of your buddy's bin. No bags, no tags. You'll plant them and treat them like any other crop," he said, pausing to give Michael a wink, "that is, till it comes harvest time. And that's when we'll hit Monsanto like they've never been hit."

Michael cleared his throat. "This ain't making a whole lotta sense to me."

Mr. Richt held up his hand, "Oh, it will. Just let me finish." Then he dove back in. "Once you harvest that crop we'll let Monsanto know that you've grown their GM crops, but you bought them on the open market, not from one of their licensed reps."

"What difference does it make who I buy 'em from?" Michael blurted out.

It was obvious that Mr. Richt was becoming tired of Michael's interruptions. "It'll show they have no control over their own product. They have no idea who's selling it. The point is: they either can't police their own patent, or won't."

One of the other partners piped up, "The key to your case is proving they have no control over their own product. Simply put, if a billion-dollar corporation with its vast resources can't keep tabs on its product, they certainly can't expect a simple farmer like you to do it." The head of every single lawyer in the room bobbed simultaneously as if they were all being pulled by the same string.

Sleep deprivation had taken a toll on Michael. He realized he simply wasn't in the right frame of mind to digest this strategy, or any strategy. Glancing around, he looked again for Hal. But he was still in such a position that Michael couldn't get his attention, not without calling his name.

"Michael, what we need to get the ball rolling is a retainer from you." Mr. Richt was back in charge and loving it.

Without thinking, Michael nodded. "Sure."

"A hundred thousand is sufficient to get things going."

"A hundred thousand?" That woke Michael up. "As in a hundred thousand dollars? And that's just to get things going?"

Mr. Richt nodded and dismissed the amount with a wave of his hand, as if handing a hundred thousand bucks in cash over to a law firm was no big deal. He waited a moment for Michael to respond, but when he didn't, Mr. Richt finally asked, "Is Friday good for you?"

Michael was still trying to digest the enormous amount of money Mr.

Richt had thrown at him. "Friday? For what?"

Mr. Richt's impatience was palpable. "To give us the retainer." He then interrupted himself to check his pocket watch, which Michael found rude, if not insulting. Then, to compound things, Richt all but snapped, "We must have it before we can work on your case."

"The entire hundred thousand dollars?" Michael asked innocently.

Mr. Richt reacted as if he was spoon feeding an adult, and wasn't the least bit happy about the onerous task. "Yes, the entire hundred thousand. Is Friday good for you? Same time as today?"

There was a very long period of silence, then Michael finally spoke. "I'll be here Friday at 2 p.m., just like today."

With that Mr. Richt's demeanor changed considerably. He flashed Michael a big smile and nodded. "See you then."

CHAPTER 42

Following his meeting at the offices of Ewell, Richt & Elden, Michael holed up at a friend's cabin nestled deep in the woods. It was a safe house he used from time to time.

Given all he had on his mind, especially the unsettling meeting with his lawyers, Michael didn't get more than an hour or two of sleep. Still, the next morning found him up early checking his crop of soybeans. It was his make-or-break crop. The failure and success of his farm rode on it. Naturally, the bulk of his time was spent working with it, but even Michael couldn't begin to guess how much time went into the crop. It was best not to know how many hours he worked in a month, or even a week. If he knew he would be tempted to divide his pay by those hours, and that could be extremely depressing, not only for Michael, but virtually any farmer. Some didn't even make close to minimum wage.

Scraping by on minimum wage would be bad enough for someone bussing tables while waiting on something better to come along, but it was another thing all together to work for a pittance while simultaneously taking on a level of financial risk most people can't even fathom. Yet it wasn't unheard of around Sand Mountain for a really well established farmer to have a million dollars in loans, perhaps even more. At any given moment a farmer might have a six-figure crop loan that had to be paid off quickly, usually within seven to nine months from inception, and on top of that he would probably have a few other business loans on the books. And that didn't even count the mortgage on his home, the loans for the cars and trucks in the driveway or the kids' braces.

With a small fortune riding on a crop of soybeans, something as simple as a heavy rain—or lack of it—could spell financial disaster for even the best of farmers. Michael couldn't help wondering, 'When was the last time a corporate executive had to beg his banker for an extension on a loan 'cause it rained too much last night?' The only time big shots ever worried about whether it rained or not was if it interfered with their golf game.

The enormous pressure of juggling a million dollars in short-term loans to keep a farm operational while working a hundred plus hours a week was enough to quickly separate those who merely want to farm from those who love to farm. No one farms—not for long, anyway—unless it's their passion. Michael likened it to an artist who must paint; one either follows their heart or dies a slow and agonizing death. As Michael stared out at his field, momentarily wondering if he should harvest a bit late because a mild fall was predicted, he realized he was doing it once again—he was thinking ahead, planning for the future. It was something he always did, because he had no choice. Rarely could he focus on, let alone relish in, the present because to him it was already past. That was the curse of his passion for farming. Yet it was that very passion that had driven him for years to get up hours before daylight every day, seven days a week. It was what made him take high-stake financial risks, and it was what made him feel alive—a passion that completed his existence.

Michael believed that when a person has passion, he or she not only feels it down deep in their marrow, they recognize it in others. And try as he might, he could not find it in his lawyers. They did not love what they did, at least not his case. It seemed to Michael they were treating it like a multiple choice test, and their strategy was derived by the old 'pick an answer and see if it works - - - or not' method.

Their top lawyers billed their time at around $400 per hour and they were guessing? Had they lost a single night's sleep over his case? Were they '*betting the farm*' on the outcome of this case the way Michael quite literally was?

Michael felt bile rise in his throat. The lawyers wanted him to pony up a hundred grand just to get the ball rolling, yet how truly vested in it were they? Did they honestly care about the outcome—how it could affect Michael's life, his family and the lives of others? Could they even understand what he was putting on the line?

Another thing that was really lodged deep in Michael's craw was 'phase two' of Mr. Richt's plan. Specifically, having Michael buy Monsanto's GM seeds from a fellow 'farmer friend,' plant them, and then harvest them to demonstrate the conglomerate had no control over its patent. Michael knew exactly what Monsanto had done to the customers of his seed business, i.e., scared them into ex-customers. He could only imagine what Monsanto might do to a 'farmer friend' who was helping him. He suspected that his 'farmer friend' would be subjected to the same unmitigated hell the conglomerate's spies had put him and his family through. Michael wouldn't wish that on his worst enemy—not even Monsanto's own executives, certainly not a friend.

'Phase two' showed that Richt not only failed to calculate the backlash of his idea, but also that he hadn't even bothered to study the case well enough to know about the sordid tactics Monsanto's spies had used on him. That infuriated Michael to no end.

The mere notion that any law firm would advise Michael to plead guilty to Monsanto's suit against him was enough to make him see red. What made it truly insulting was that the firm knew full well he had caught the conglomerate's spies red-handed on videotape, and that some of the thugs had violated enough laws in Michael's estimation to qualify for habitual offender status. Yet it seemed his own lawyers thought of him as the village idiot, a man who didn't have enough sense to get out of the rain.

Michael had made his living from the rain, and he knew when he was about to get rained on. And he had no intentions of getting soaked by a bunch of lawyers with a half-baked strategy.

* * *

In less than twenty-four hours Michael was scheduled to show up at Ewell, Richt & Elden with a check for a hundred thousand dollars so they could get started on his case. He had every intention of making the meeting, but no intention whatsoever of giving the firm even one penny of his hard-earned money. Unbeknownst to the attorneys at Ewell, Richt & Elden, they were no longer his lawyers.

The tricky part of the divorce would be getting all of his files back, every last document, picture, videotape, even the scraps of paper with cryptic notes he'd entrusted with the firm.

Of course, his greatest concern was that someone might have already copied his videotapes. Who's to say that some cash-strapped employee with no scruples at the firm didn't realize the tapes alone would be worth a fortune to Monsanto? If they landed in the wrong hands then Michael's case could be severely compromised, if not completely devastated.

CHAPTER 43

After circling the block several times to be sure no one was following him, Michael found a parking space not far from the entrance of Ewell, Richt & Elden. He slumped down in his seat, adjusted his rearview mirror just so, and took a gander at the building that housed the law firm.

Checking to make sure no one was coming in or out of the building, Michael exited his pickup, grabbed a large hand truck out of the bed, and quickly made his way toward the front door. Stopping not far from the entrance, he peeked through a side window where he could see the receptionist, yet she would have a hard time seeing him. She was busy answering calls, which seemed to come fairly often. He not only needed to walk right past her without having to explain why he had a hand truck, he had to somehow get inside the elevator, which wouldn't open unless it was summoned by the receptionist.

After watching the receptionist for only a few minutes, Michael caught a break when a deliveryman arrived. Pacing around near the entrance, Michael glanced at his watch, as if he were waiting for someone and was a bit impatient. The deliveryman, likely on a tight schedule, didn't give Michael a second look as he entered the building. And he didn't notice when Michael followed him inside, almost on his heels.

The receptionist put on a big flirty grin when she saw the deliveryman, and the two of them instantly slipped into some cozy small talk. It gave Michael the perfect cover. Very casually, he walked toward the elevator with the hand truck gliding behind him.

As luck would have it, with Michael seemingly on a collision course with the elevator's door, they opened and a couple of people coming down exited. He stealthily managed to slip inside without the flirting receptionist and deliveryman raising an eyebrow.

Ideally, Michael wanted to go straight to the conference room on the top floor. But there was no button for that floor; a key was required to get there. So he pushed the button for the floor where Hal's office was located.

When the doors opened on the third floor, Michael exited the elevator and hurried around the corner, pulling the hand truck along behind him until he found the utility room door he'd seen on his initial visit. Wedged between the men's and women's room, Michael tried the knob. He caught another break; it was unlocked. He put the hand truck inside for safekeeping, and then moments later with an air of nonchalance made his way into Hal's office where he was greeted with a hearty hello and a firm handshake. They traded small talk for a minute or two before Hal announced, "The partners are waiting for us in the conference room. Guess we better get going." Then, as if it were an afterthought, he asked, "You've got the retainer check, right?"

Michael tapped the left pocket of his shirt. "Right here." He had actually gone to the trouble of writing out a check for one-hundred thousand dollars, even though he had absolutely no intention of giving it to anyone at Ewell, Richt & Elden.

"Excellent," Hal responded, shooting Michael a boyish smile.

Without any further ado, Hal led Michael to the elevator. As soon as the two men got inside, Hal inserted his key into the control panel and turned it in order to access the top floor. When the doors began to close, Michael reached out and grabbed the edge, instantly stopping the doors from closing. As they slowly reopened Michael turned to Hal. "Gimme just a second. I'll be right back."

"Michael, if you've got to use the restroom you . . . " Hal trailed off because Michael had already exited the elevator, rounded the corner, and was gone before he could finish. With no other options, Hal held the elevator door open and awaited Michael's return.

One of the first things students learn at law school is to never ask a question in court unless they know the answer. It not only saves embarrassment, but quite a few cases, to boot. Perhaps Hal had taken the advice to heart. That would explain why he didn't say a word when Michael reentered the elevator with the hand truck in tow. Even so, he definitely had a reaction: his eyes bulged and his face went pale. And there was no small talk for the duration of the ride, only stony silence and the muted whir of the elevator's moving parts.

When the elevator's doors opened into the conference room the three dozen or so people gathered there were all chatting and joking and didn't even seem to notice Michael or Hal.

Hal hesitated, not moving from his position in the elevator. Michael, however, quickly stepped into the conference room, pulling the hand truck behind him. At first, no one raised an eyebrow. But then Mr. Richt himself saw Michael and, more importantly, his hand truck. Richt's immense displeasure could be seen and felt instantly. As if taking their cue, everyone else in the room fell silent and replicated Richt's icy gaze.

Mr. Richt cleared his throat before addressing Michael. "Did you bring us some more files?"

Michael shook his head. "No. I came for the files I already brung you." By this time Hal had finally gotten off the elevator and let the doors close behind him. He watched in cold, uncomfortable silence as the client he had brought in faced off with the firm's senior partner.

Gesturing toward his hand truck, Michael announced, "I want all my files, and I want 'em now. And that includes any copies you might have made."

"Why would you want to do this, Michael?" Mr. Richt asked, as if he were placating an unruly child so as to avoid a nasty scene in public.

"I ain't about to plead guilty."

With a casual shrug, Mr. Richt responded, "Then you won't have to."

Things that had been building up in Michael since their last meeting began to pour out in a torrent of words. "I can't believe you folks wanted me to plead guilty and then set up one of my friends and probably get him stuck neck-deep in this mess. Heck, I barely graduated high school and I could've come up with a whole lot better strategy than y'all." All but shouting, Michael continued, "And you wanted a hundred thousand dollars of my money, earned with my blood, sweat, and tears, for this crap you call a strategy? I wouldn't give you two dimes for it."

The room was so quiet you could have heard a cotton ball bounce on its Persian rug. Mr. Richt was put on the spot in a way that was surely unfamiliar for him. In all likelihood, rarely did anyone speak this candidly with him, certainly not inside his own offices. He cleared his throat, tugged at his gaudy, trademark purple tie, then finally spoke, choosing his words with extreme care. "Michael, you're right. The strategy we came up with might not have been our best effort. I'll concede that." Gesturing around at all the lawyers in the room, he continued. "But I assure you that, collectively, we can come up with one that is right for you. One that we hope will bring you a favorable outcome." For a moment, all was quiet, and it appeared that Michael was actually considering Richt's Hail Mary of a proposal. But then the old man, the sort who couldn't resist hearing himself speak, made an odd request, especially considering that time was running out with an important hearing looming right around the bend. "All I ask is that you leave your files here one more day so we can sort this out."

It was the worst possible thing for him to have said. Michael's radar went on ultra high alert. If Richt had asked him to leave the files for two or even three days so they could review some of the more important evidence it would have sounded like a reasonable request. But one single day? That wasn't nearly enough time to go over the case—not even the high points, but it was just enough time for their office staff to make a copy of every single document, note, picture, and videotape.

Michael quickly shook his head. "Nope. I want my files now."

"I don't even know for sure where they are," Mr. Richt said, glancing around the room as if he were hoping someone else would chime in and inform Michael that his files had been moved across town to an obscure warehouse for safekeeping and couldn't be accessed until Monday. But no one said a word.

By sheer chance, Michael spied his files in a large stack over in the corner of the room. They were partially hidden by a chair and end table. Most likely, they had been brought up to the conference room so they could be referred to as they discussed his case. Michael pointed at the corner. "That looks like them right there."

Mr. Richt might have been a puppet master with juries, but the mock look of surprise on his face wouldn't have fooled a five-year-old. "Why, I'll be John Brown'd." Looking around the faces in the room, he asked a question he already knew the answer to. "Are those the files he's asking about?" When no one responded he looked over Michael's shoulder. "Hal, are these the files for Michael's case?"

There was no answer. Michael turned around to see why Hal was stalling, and realized that Hal had left the room; he was nowhere to be found.

Michael felt a catch in his throat. He suddenly felt lightheaded and his palms were getting sweaty. Why had Hal disappeared from the room? Turning to face Richt, Michael snapped. "Where's Hal?"

Feigning ignorance, Mr. Richt refined his acting job. "Why he must have left." Michael realized that Mr. Richt was being extremely careful and cautious with his words. It was as if he was reading from a finely tuned script, and Michael was the only person in the room without a copy. Pointing at his files, Michael specifically addressed Mr. Richt. "Hal or no Hal, I want my files. And I want 'em now."

Pretending that he hadn't heard a word Michael said, Richt made an over-the-top gesture—like a ringmaster at the circus—and a number of the lawyers obediently shuffled off to one side. They left behind a path down the middle of the room leading straight to a young woman who, until that point, Michael had not seen.

Probably in her late twenties, certainly no more than early thirties, she had raven hair, deep set eyes and had an international flair about her. But what really caught the eye was her overt sensuality. It would have made her stand out in any crowd, but especially so in a room filled with nondescript lawyers in dark hued cookie cutter suits who all but blended into the woodwork.

Mr. Richt winked at his potential client and then asked, "Michael, have you met Ms. Simon?" Before Richt was even finished with his question the young woman was walking toward Michael, her hips moving more like she was on a catwalk than in a conference room. Just as it appeared she intended to sidle up very close beside Michael, he told her in no uncertain terms, and said it loud enough for everyone to hear, "Miss, I came here for my files, not to get acquainted with you."

Even as he maneuvered away from Ms. Simon, Michael wasn't sure what to make of the situation. Was she there to proposition him? Did this firm actually think they could lasso him with the wiles of a woman? If that was the case, they had picked the worst possible ploy. The mere notion of this kind of behavior went diametrically against his morals and religion. And if it had indeed been their intent, then it told him the firm's brain trust thought of him as nothing more than a slack-jawed bumpkin who had just tumbled head first off a turnip truck that was passing through downtown.

Reaching into his pocket, Michael whipped out a card and held it right in front of Richt so the arrogant old lawyer could get a good look. On it was the name and number of an official tasked with investigating misconduct for the Alabama State Bar. "See this card?" Michael asked. He pointed at the name on it. "Recognize this fellow?"

Mr. Richt simply stared without saying a word. Finally, after what seemed like five minutes had passed, he replied in a huffy tone. "Yeah, I know who it is."

"I've talked to him, and more than once, and he said if I have any trouble getting my files back—any trouble whatsoever, I'm to call him." Pointing at his files, Michael snapped, "Now either I get my files, and I get 'em right now, or I'm gonna call this fellow." Staring directly at Richt, he added in a low and solemn voice, "He said a lawyer can get in trouble for refusing to hand over a man's files . . . big trouble."

Mr. Richt sneered at Michael as if he wasn't worthy to stand next to him on the same vaunted Persian rug, then turned and spoke to his minions en masse. "Mr. White can have his files. Just make sure that's all he gets." But his outsized ego wouldn't let him stop there. He simply couldn't walk away without getting in one last jab, one that was clearly below the belt. Turning toward Michael he spoke in a most condescending manner. "I hope you know this, son. But just in case you don't." The old lawyer's tone shifted from obnoxious to downright snide as he proclaimed. "You ain't even a fly on Monsanto's ass." With that, he turned on his heel and stalked off like an angry child.

* * *

No one at the firm, not even Hal—who magically reappeared after the showdown, so much as lent Michael a hand with his heavy and bulky files.

It was obvious that Richt operated in a dictatorial fashion, and helping Michael would've been tantamount to consorting with the enemy. Even after Michael loaded all his files, tapes, papers, and notes onto his oversized hand truck he had felt the need to exit the room like a marshal slowly backing out of a saloon in the Old West, the kind filled with rustlers and robbers.

Hal escorted Michael down in the elevator, but only because it wouldn't operate without a key. They didn't say a word going down. Only when Michael was about to leave did Hal mumble, "Sorry it worked out like this."

Michael wasn't sure what Hal meant. Nevertheless, he wanted to believe Hal was a good, honest and decent man working at a bad firm. Although he didn't have any proof whatsoever, Michael had a gut feeling that if he had left his files and tapes one more night someone with no scruples looking for a quick payday could have copied them. And, if so, there was a chance those copies might have made their way to Monsanto . . . or its spies, one being the same as the other in his mind.

* * *

After loading the files in his truck, Michael carefully opened the box labeled "videos." This was the heart of his case, the hard evidence that Monsanto's goons had committed crime after crime and had no regard for his rights or his family's.

Michael had been extremely clear when he brought the tapes to Ewell, Richt & Elden. Under no circumstances were they to copy them, and he said it more than once. Unbeknownst to anyone at Ewell, Richt & Elden, Michael had secretly rigged the tapes so that if anyone copied them he would know. Now was the moment of truth.

Removing the first tape from the box, Michael saw that it had not been copied. The same was true for the second, third, fourth, and fifth. He let out a sigh of relief, though total relief was still not assured. It wouldn't be until he had gone through every tape that he would truly be able to relax, knowing that none of them had been copied or stolen.

Back inside his truck, Michael couldn't help but picture Mr. Richt fuming and on the verge of throwing a tantrum. It served him right. Not only had he insulted Michael numerous times while pitching his firm's lame strategy, but the idea that he might have entertained the notion that they could lasso Michael using a comely female was comical.

Michael looked both ways, then made a quick U-turn in case anyone was trying to follow him. Confident that no one was, he hopped onto I-65 north, left Birmingham behind, and headed toward Huntsville to meet the lawyers who would be taking over his case. Finding them had not come a moment too soon, because the hearing Judge Smith set for his case on the 25th was now only a few days away.

CHAPTER 44

Huntsville had a laid-back quality and could even be considered quaint by some standards. Yet it was also the place where the legendary Saturn V (five) rocket had been designed and engineered. One of the largest and most powerful launch vehicles ever conceived of in history and brought to fruition, it powered the fabled *Apollo 11* mission that took astronauts Neil Armstrong, Buzz Aldrin, and Michael Collins to the moon; the first time mankind set foot on another celestial body. And it accomplished this phenomenal feat at a time when the mere notion of space travel—manned or otherwise—was still considered borderline science fiction. So "Rocket City" wasn't merely the moniker some PR hacks cooked up. The town had earned its stripes at a time when most of Silicon Valley's best and brightest were still wearing diapers or were merely a glimmer in their parents' eyes.

Naturally, more than a few of the world's top scientists, inventors, thinkers, and tinkerers had been drawn to the city. That fueled the formation of a plethora of companies that were on the cutting edge of technology. Of course, that in turn led to an influx of bright patent attorneys. So even though Huntsville's population was less than 200,000 at the beginning of the twenty-first century, it probably had more attorneys with experience in intellectual property law than many cities five or six times its size. Good lawyers graze where the grass is greenest, and in the case of intellectual property, Huntsville was a lush, dark green oasis.

Inside the entrance of Lanier, Ford, Shaver & Payne there was a polished marble floor and the furniture was tasteful. It was understated elegance, the kind that whispered success instead of doing so with a crass shout. Even so, it wasn't a great deal different from countless other accomplished firms in cities all across the country. The difference, however, was that it was as quiet as a library. It was the first thing Michael noticed when he entered, and he immediately approved. It told him that no one here had to pretend they were busy. More importantly, they weren't in a rush because they were organized and knew what they were doing. The silence had a studious air about it, one of confidence, not cockiness.

Everything Michael had heard about the firm was impressive. But reputation aside, it was imperative for him to have lawyers who would recognize his case was a matter of justice, and there was much more than a big fat retainer and the possibility of a large settlement at stake. They had to understand that the safety and well-being of America's food supply might very well hang in the balance. And, given the enormous amount of food the U.S. exports annually, it could impact the world's food supply, as well.

After waiting a few minutes in the lobby, just long enough to thumb through a few pages of *Newsweek*, Michael was ushered into the office of Stephen Hall, a skilled young lawyer with a shock of thick hair and a friendly smile.

With stacks of loose papers and files here, there, and everywhere, the office had an unmistakable lived-in feel. Yet unlike other attorneys, Stephen didn't apologize for the lack of neatness in his office, and for that Michael was grateful. A spotless desk without so much as a pen or paper-clip out of place might have looked great to a maid or decorator, but not Michael. His own office wasn't for show. It was functional, and anyone who saw it knew it. Michael quickly assessed the same could be said for Stephen. Here was someone who actually worked hard in his office, as well, and wasn't about to hide it or apologize for his work ethic.

But Stephen would not be alone on the case; he was teamed with another attorney at the firm, J. R. Brooks, a seasoned, no-nonsense litigator who looked as if he'd been sent from Central Casting. From his carefully coifed dark hair, leading man good looks, tailored pinstripe suit, to his burning stare, it was obvious that J. R. was all business.

After laying out the most complex aspect of his case, the part about genetically modified seeds, something that went over most everyone's head, Michael not only sensed that J. R. and Stephen understood it, but that they also were genuinely interested, and not only from a legal or scientific standpoint, but from a perspective of ethics, as well.

For eons people such as farmers, horticulturists and botanists have cross-pollinated plants to strengthen good traits while trying to hinder bad ones. But now companies were taking existing plant breeds that have been around for hundreds, even thousands of years, and claiming that their 'genetic' changes in the lab constituted a completely new breed. To be sure, Monsanto had indeed produced plants that could not occur naturally outside of a lab, which by definition meant they were not natural.

Even so, Michael felt that until they created a plant that produced a never before seen fruit, vegetable or nut they were doing nothing more than altering a few traits of an existing breed. It struck him that claiming a few alterations on an existing plant constituted an entirely 'new breed' wasn't much different from a slight of hand artist making a big to do about pulling a rabbit out of his hat, except that even a child knows the rabbit doesn't appear out of thin air.

Another thing that perplexed Michael was that on one hand Monsanto based its patents on the premise that it had created new plant breeds— ones it openly touted as having been created in a laboratory, yet companies that used them in their processed foods routinely promoted their products as "natural." It was akin to a company claiming that shoes or a jacket it made out of vinyl were constructed from "natural" materials, when it's common knowledge that leather is a natural material, whereas vinyl is the manmade alternative.

Michael felt that if Monsanto let the practice continue (allowing companies to promote food products containing GMOs as "natural") it would be more than reasonable for the patent office to invalidate Monsanto's patents for GMOs, if not serve as an invitation for a class action suit by concerned citizens. Case in point: Monsanto couldn't tell the patent office that their products were brand new entities made possible only because of man's input, and that they cannot possibly occur in nature without that input, yet on the other hand knowingly allow third parties to make contradictory claims on their product labels. After what he'd been through, Michael couldn't help but wonder why Monsanto had not sent its spies after big companies whose labels touted foods derived from GMOs as "natural" when Monsanto's very own patents made the claims invalid. After all, weren't these big food companies, in essence, doing the same thing as the farmers that Monsanto had sued? . . . i.e., putting Monsanto's patents at risk? [11]

The issue of ethics was far more than merely important to Michael, as well; it was crucial. Doing the right and honorable thing may have seemed old-fashioned, even passé, to a lot of people, but if his lawyers didn't realize that ethics mattered in this case there would never be a meeting of the minds. And without that, Michael would have nothing more than a hired gun, someone who would take potshots at his adversaries, yet never really care if what they were doing was right or wrong. Since they were essentially starting from scratch very late in the game, Michael not only had to quickly bring his new lawyers up-to-speed, but also to establish a mutual understanding and trust. That meant the first meeting with J. R. and Stephen was the kind that required blunt talk on both sides.

---

[11] The American Heritage Dictionary of The English Language defines "natural" as: *present in or produced by nature; not artificial.*

J. R. didn't believe in sugarcoating things. The bottom line was that he believed in Michael and was genuinely intrigued by his case. Yet he knew the legal system all too well. Wrong can and does triumph over right; it happens all the time. Succinctly, they were not only fighting an uphill battle, they were coming on board during the final quarter with the clock ticking louder and louder with each passing day.

At the end of their meeting, Stephen didn't talk to Michael about his fees. Instead, he asked Michael a question that up until that point no other lawyer had. "Michael, you had a good seed business, a successful farm, a nice home and a great family. You had everything a man could want. You had the proverbial American Dream. And you could've easily settled this mess early on for less than the price of a used tractor and made it all go away." He paused a moment, then asked the sixty-four-thousand dollar question. "So why'd you put yourself through this nightmare? Why'd you risk it all? Why did you put everything on the line when the odds of beating a multibillion dollar conglomerate through the lengthy appeals process are all but nil?"

It was a question Michael had been waiting to answer for a very long time. For a moment he stared off in the distance while he collected his thoughts, then he locked eyes with Stephen. "I've studied on this thing, I've prayed on it, and then I prayed on it some more. What I'm doing, it's the right thing to do. That means it's the only thing I can do. I got no choice." He had spoken directly from the heart in a way that few people even know how.

Both J. R. and Stephen nodded with approval, and J. R. said, "It'll be our pleasure to have you as a client."

CHAPTER 45

When he needed a break from work, sometimes Michael piddled in the little garden at his father's house. It may have seemed odd for a man who earned his living farming to have gardening for a hobby or stress reliever, but he enjoyed tending the small plot of dirt where he could work with his bare hands. He loved feeling the rich, dark earth between his fingers. And gardening always put him on his knees, which put him in a prayerful state of mind. Often, when he was planting seeds or pulling weeds, he was also talking with God. He could be deep in prayer, yet to the outside world he was simply weeding the garden.

During the last year or so the garden had gotten smaller. That was due to Wayne's declining health and, of course, the fact that Virginia had passed away. Her passing had taken a lot out of Wayne. It also reminded Michael that every moment spent with his aging father was all the more precious.

Back in late spring or early summer, Michael had been tending the garden one day while his father sat nearby on an old folding chair. Wayne could no longer do any work for more than a few minutes at a time, and even then he needed lots of rest after each session. Nevertheless, he enjoyed the time spent with his son, and vice versa.

Michael noted that the garden was coming along nicely, especially the string beans. He had planted them by hand, each and every one, so he took no small joy in the fact that they were not only surviving, but thriving.

Out of the corner of his eye Michael spied something that he hadn't planted. It was a single stalk of corn. It wasn't even three inches high, and some people wouldn't officially classify it as a stalk just yet, but it most definitely was corn—a single plant all but hidden between the rows of beans. Michael reached over and gently touched the small corn stalk. Give it a few more weeks and it would be a foot taller than the beans and easy to spot. With sufficient rain and sun, in a few months it might even be taller than Michael.

Some people would've yanked it up right then and there, especially since it hadn't been planted. Michael, however, left it there to grow. 'Volunteers,' the farmer's term for any plant that takes seed on its own, were not a major problem to Michael. They didn't hurt anything. Besides, he figured they were meant to be there; part of nature's plan.

He paused a moment to consider where 'volunteers' came from. After all, seeds don't just waddle into a field and plant themselves. He knew with 100 percent certainty that he hadn't planted the corn. But he also knew there were a number of ways the 'volunteer' stalk could've wound up in their garden. Most likely, a bird flying over had dropped it by accident. Probably a crow; they were partial to corn. And, of course, a bird also could have dropped it when it relieved itself while flying by. This common occurrence is how a number of plants in the wild get their start.

The seed also could have been temporarily stuck somewhere on the tiller that was used to plow up the garden and simply fell off during the process. A lot of seeds fall off tractors and other equipment working the fields. It was impossible to completely clean a farm implement of seeds, not with all the nooks and crannies they have. Sammy Joe Denton once told Michael, "The only tractor or combine (harvester) that don't have at least a bushel of seeds wedged in its parts is brand new and still at the factory."

Seeds can even get stuck on the bottom of a farmer's muddy boots. And if one accidentally dislodges while he's working in the field it can easily become a 'volunteer.'

Anyone who knew beans about farming knew 'volunteers' were a fact of life, and trying to eradicate them was like attempting to eliminate bugs.

You might get some of them. You even might get a lot of them. But completely eliminating bugs in the wild was impossible; only a complete and utter fool thought differently.

Michael gently touched the corn with his fingertips, and as he felt the tiny plant, something akin to a charge of electricity went from his fingers to his brain. It appeared to Michael that Monsanto expected zero tolerance when it came to the use and regulation of their GM seeds. Yet for all Michael knew, the tiny cornstalk in the Whites' garden might very well be genetically modified, meaning its presence was in strict violation of Monsanto's policy. Did this mean that Michael, other farmers, and all home gardeners were supposed to police the bird population? Did Monsanto really expect farmers and gardeners to follow every bird around with a plastic bag, picking up its poop, so it couldn't accidentally leave a GM seed behind?

To Michael, the demands Monsanto placed on farmers were the height of hypocrisy and arrogance. After all, the conglomerate was essentially insisting that farmers help control, manage, police and protect its patents. Not only was it unreasonable, it was impractical, terribly frustrating and seemingly impossible, to boot.

Michael had tried to put all this into words so that his new lawyers would understand the plight of farmers. He truly hoped that they understood that farming is not an exact science, and forcing rigid and unbendable rules onto agriculture is the equivalent of using them for a game of horseshoes where close still counts; it won't work and, worse, it means everyone loses . . . except Monsanto.

CHAPTER 46

Normally there's a honeymoon with any relationship, even that of attorney and client. But the lawyers at Lanier, Ford, Shaver & Payne and Michael didn't have that luxury. By the time the parties agreed upon the terms of their relationship they were staring down the barrel of a cannon. Judge Smith was moving the case into high gear and Stephen Hall and J. R. Brooks had to ramp up quickly simply to stay on top of things. Getting prepared for any case, even a minor one, can require a lot of work. But preparing for a case involving alleged patent infringement can mean an enormous amount of work and meetings. Michael and his lawyers would somehow have to squeeze months, even years, of preparation into days.

Getting only a bare minimum of sleep, Michael, J. R., and Stephen burned the candle at both ends. Both J. R. and Stephen were extremely talented lawyers. However, neither was even a novice farmer, though as a child J. R. had picked cotton by hand on his grandfather's farm. The grueling, backbreaking manual labor had instilled in him the kind of work ethic that few people have, as well as a genuine appreciation and respect for farmers that even fewer can fathom. Nevertheless, just as the two attorneys had to spoon-feed Michael the law, so Michael had to teach them the basics about modern farming. Each got a crash course in the other's profession.

* * *

Whenever the phone rang around midnight, there was rarely good news on the other end. For that very reason Michael didn't want to answer his. He was way behind on his work because of the lawsuit. In fact, he was up at this late hour doing his best to play catch-up on the ledger for his farm. Besides, he wasn't sure if he could handle anymore bad news at the moment. On the other hand, it could be his lawyers. Things were getting down to the wire, and they might need a document or some obscure tidbit of information that only he could give them. He finally picked up the phone after the fourth ring.

The voice on the other end was frantic. Panic and confusion caused the caller's words to come out in a fractured jumble as if they had been blasted through a blender. Reflexively, Michael stood-up and pushed aside his paperwork. He focused on keeping his own composure so he could calm down the caller.

"Just calm down. Just calm down, now," Michael said in a very gentle yet firm tone. "'Cause I can't understand you." He had no idea who the caller was, but he kept that to himself so as not to make matters worse than they already were.

The caller took a deep, halting breath. "Son, this is your daddy and I need help!" Michael was racing out the door before Wayne could even tell him why he needed help.

As a long time member of the Jackson County Rescue Squad, Michael knew that in an emergency the most important thing was for the rescuers to get to the scene of the accident or crime safely. But on hearing his father's distress, Michael's logic had been thrown out the window and replaced by raw and powerful emotions. With his foot flat on the gas pedal, he raced down the old country road that led to his father's house with reckless abandon. All he could think of as he drove was that he had never heard his father sound like he just had over the phone. Throughout Michael's life Wayne had been a rock, the foundation on which his family was built. What could have happened that had gotten him so upset? Michael couldn't even let his mind go in that direction. It was too painful and horrific to even imagine.

When Michael arrived at his father's house it looked as if a strange party was going on. Every light in the house was on and burning brightly. But it was deathly quiet. More unsettling was the fact that every exterior door was standing wide open.

Beset by many of the infirmities inherent with old age, Wayne's circulation was not nearly as good as it once was, so he had become quite susceptible to chills and feeling cold. Even on mildly cool nights he cranked up the heat, and this night was anything but mild. Probably no more than 15 - 20 degrees, it was bitterly cold by anyone's standards on Sand Mountain. Factor in strong, gusty winds and the temperature felt closer to single digits. It certainly wasn't the kind of night that anyone, especially someone who was old, frail, and easily chilled, would leave all his doors wide open.

Realizing the situation was dire, Michael reached into his glove box and retrieved a 9mm pistol, then loaded it with a full clip. As soon as he stepped out of the truck, he switched the safety off.

Holding the pistol in a ready-to-fire position, he headed for the carport entrance, expertly pointing the gun's barrel to check every dark spot and shadow along the way.

Once he got to the door Michael stopped and took cover beside a brick wall, then shouted, "Daddy, you OK?"

There was no response.

Michael took a deep breath and tried to determine his next step. He could burst into the house, weapon ready to fire in an instant. But after the air assault on Wayne's house by the helicopter, Michael had made sure there was plenty of ammo for Wayne's old .38 special. In his younger years Wayne had been a crack shot, but his aim wasn't what it once was. What if he mistook Michael for one of Monsanto's spies? The natural train of thought led Michael to consider the most frightening horrific scenario of all.

What if Monsanto's spies were in the house and holding Wayne at gunpoint? If Michael came bursting in they could shoot Michael with Wayne's gun, and then once Michael was dead they could use his 9mm to shoot Wayne. It would be the perfect way to get rid of both father and son and make it look like a tragic accident. After all, given the bogus suit Monsanto had filed against Wayne, they probably wanted him out of the picture as much as they wanted to see Michael gone.

It was a horrible thought, one that gave Michael fits, yet he still had to do something. He couldn't simply wait around till daylight. Knowing Wayne's hearing was impaired, he screamed at the top of lungs, "Daddy! Are you OK?"

For a long moment there was nothing. Then finally Michael heard a weak and frightened voice reply, "I'm cold, but I ain't hurt." That was all Michael needed to rush into the house. For safety, he kept his 9mm at the ready.

Entering the den and kitchen area Michael quickly looked for Wayne, but he was nowhere to be seen. Right away Michael realized it was so cold inside the house he could see his own breath. That was not good.

Using the utmost caution, Michael slowly walked down the hallway until he got to Wayne's room. Once there, he slowly poked his head in the doorway just far enough to see inside the room. But, again, Wayne was nowhere to be found.

Michael cocked his head and listened carefully. He thought he heard something, though he wasn't sure what it was. Following his ears, he moved slowly down the hall until he reached the room where his mother had passed away. Although he had been in the house dozens of times since his mother's death, he hadn't been able to enter that room. He had simply avoided going anywhere near it. But now he had no choice.

Cautiously, Michael put his head inside the room only long enough to get a quick look. And that's when he found his father seated on a chair beside the bed where Virginia had lived out the last months of her life, the same chair where he sat each and every day by her side, holding her hand. Wayne's eyes were clouded with tears, and his breathing was labored. He spoke without turning or looking at Michael. "Someone broke in the house tonight, son. I was sacred to death. I could barely think. But the first thing I thought of was that I didn't want 'em to hurt your mother. So I came running in here and . . ." His voice trailed off. He stared out the window even though there was nothing visible outside in the dark night.

As gently as possible, Michael reminded his father, "Daddy, Momma's gone."

A deep, unsteady sigh slipped out of Wayne, and he slowly nodded. "I know that, but I got so confused that, well . . . I guess I forgot for a minute there."

Keeping his voice as soft and controlled as possible, Michael asked, "Did you see the people that broke in?"

Wayne sadly shook his head. "I heard some noise, then I sat up and realized there was light in the house, lots of it. And it was cold; freezing cold. That's when I thought about your momma. I didn't want her to get the flu. Remember, the doctor told us if she got it in her condition it would . . ." Again, his voice simply trailed off.

As much as Michael wanted to find out all he could about the break-in and the robbers, he knew it was futile to question Wayne. Given that he couldn't provide any concrete answers, the feeling of helplessness would only upset his elderly father even more than he already was.

In his head, Michael wrestled with the notion of calling the law so they could get the crime on record. He knew it had most likely been a professional job, which meant the odds of catching the culprits were about zero. Even so, it was a no-brainer who was behind it. Who else would orchestrate the break-in of this particular octogenarian's house after midnight and, it appeared, not take anything? But what really nixed getting the law involved for Michael was the fact that he knew Monsanto's spies monitored the police band radios. They would hear Michael's report and, no doubt, find out how badly it had upset Wayne. Plus they would also know they had hit a highly sensitive nerve with Michael. He now realized that he had made an egregious tactical error when he let Monsanto's spies know how furious he was the night they pulled their air raid on his father's house. He would not give these sleazy, lowdown stalkers that satisfaction again.

Playing the role of diplomat, Michael told Wayne, "Whoever broke in here is long gone now. So you can go back to bed."

"But what if they come back?"

"If they do, I'll be sitting in the den waiting for 'em with my 9mm. They come back in here tonight and I guarantee you it'll be the last thing they'll ever do on earth." Wayne nodded with understanding. It gave him the peace of mind he needed to get some rest after his horrific ordeal.

Michael walked over and helped Wayne to his feet. His father was thin, frail and felt as if he didn't weigh more than a hundred pounds, next to nothing for a man who was over six feet. As Michael gently guided Wayne back to his bedroom, the elderly widower asked, "Why'd they do this to me, son? I ain't got none of their seeds, and I sure never planted any of 'em."

Michael wanted nothing more than to unload his anger and frustration, but he bit his tongue. It occurred to him that while Monsanto's spies were inside Wayne's house they might have bugged it. So he chose his words carefully, in case they were listening. "Daddy, I can't tell you why they'd break into your house. You'd think a multibillion dollar company would have more important things to do."

Looking at Michael, Wayne all but moaned, "I'm long past eighty. Ain't got no money to speak of; no valuables. This just don't make a lick of sense. There ain't been anything in this house worth stealing since you moved all your stuff out."

Suddenly, Michael knew exactly why Monsanto's spies had broken into Wayne's house. For a long time Michael had kept not only a lot of important documents at his father's house for safekeeping, but he had also kept a copy of his videotapes there as well. Now it all made sense.

Michael was convinced that Monsanto's henchmen narrowly missed out on the chance to get his tapes from someone at Ewell, Richt & Elden, so they were probably more desperate than ever to get their hands on them. If they didn't, they would have to fess up to practically everything they had done, or have Michael and his lawyer use the tapes against them for rebuttal. The spies had, more than likely, caught wind of the tapes' one-time location, or perhaps they simply acted on a hunch that Michael was keeping them at Wayne's; they had certainly taken enough pictures to know he was in and out of the house often, and that he usually carried a handful of items with him when entering. Either way, at this point they were probably past desperate. They were obviously ready to do anything necessary to grab the tapes.

This time, however, Monsanto's spies had guessed wrong. Michael had removed the tapes from Wayne's house shortly after the helicopter incident, and they were now safely hidden away at another location.

Michael helped Wayne get back in bed, then speaking as softly as possible, yet loud enough so Wayne could hear, he said, "I'll be in the den if you need me. All you gotta do is call, and I'll be right here."

Wayne nodded, then wiped a tear from his red, swollen eyes and said, "Son, for the first time I'm glad your mother is gone, 'cause this would've been too much on her. She didn't deserve this kind of treatment."

Now it was Michael's turn to fight back tears. Wayne had never done anything in his life to deserve this kind of abominable treatment, either. It made Michael so angry, upset, and frustrated that he couldn't even speak. So he simply nodded at Wayne, left the room, turned out the light, and hoped his father could get some sleep.

Before taking a seat on the couch, Michael make a quick inventory of the house to double-check that nothing had been taken and also close all the doors and windows. Turns out, no windows were open, but every door in the house had been unlocked and left standing wide open. Finally, assured that the house was secure, and nothing was missing, Michael sat down on the couch to serve as watchdog until dawn, and that's when he spied the absolute last thing he ever expected to see.

Sitting front and center on Wayne's coffee table was a notebook. But it wasn't just any old notebook. It was one Michael had used for quite some time to keep a record of crucial notes. Whenever he saw one of Monsanto's spies following him he would jot down the tag and the make of the vehicle. Of course, the tags were all bogus, but at least it gave him a record of sorts. However, the notebook was completely worthless without the accompanying videotapes; there weren't any notations as to what Michael had or didn't have on tape.

But the really unnerving part of this equation was that the notebook had gone missing about a year earlier. On top of that, it had been stashed in a secret hiding place at Michael's house. That could mean only one thing: Monsanto's spies had broken into his home, taken it, and then used it as a calling card when they broke into Wayne's. It also meant they knew where one of Michael's secret hiding places was. Luckily, there were no tapes in that location. Even so, it seems this was their perverse way of letting him know where they had been.

Michael picked up his notebook to see if they had ripped out any pages. Most likely, they had copied it. As his eyes scanned the first page they stopped about three-quarters of the way down. His blood went cold, colder than the darkest night of a Siberian winter.

Several words had been imprinted (not printed) onto the paper. Though crudely or hastily written, and seemingly in random order, the words were unmistakable. It looked as if it had been done with a sharp object using a lot of pressure. Perhaps they used a letter opener to write them? Or a dull knife? Yet how they wrote them was far less important than what they wrote; *David, kill, will, Michael.* Flipping them around in his head like a word jumble, Michael realized they could be used to make a sentence; 'David will kill Michael.'

Michael took it as yet another disturbing and intimidating message from his tormentors. It would be a long night on the couch, even with a 9mm in his right hand.

* * *

After a very tense and uncomfortable five hours spent on the couch waiting, watching, and listening for Monsanto's henchmen to return, Michael was grateful to see the first rays of sunlight. Figuring the danger had passed, at least for one night, Michael tiptoed out of the house and put his notebook in his truck for safekeeping so Wayne wouldn't see it. Then he took a walking tour of the grounds. He wanted to see if the perpetrators had made any tracks or left behind any telltale signs during their break-in.

There was a set of footprints that led to and from the barn. They appeared to be fairly fresh, but given that the ground was frozen it was hard to tell if they had been made in the last few hours, or a day or two ago. To be on the safe side, Michael tracked them all the way to the barn, behind it, and into the woods about thirty yards before deciding they had been made several days ago. But for the life of him he couldn't figure out who had made them. They appeared to have been made by someone wearing athletic shoes, footwear neither he nor his father ever wore. Michael racked his brain trying to think of someone, anyone, who might have been around the house or barn in the last few days who had worn athletic shoes, but his thoughts were interrupted by a loud banging sound. It was coming from inside the house.

Turning toward the house, but unable to see inside, Michael panicked. While he was out back chasing down old footprints had the goons who had broken in last night come back? Realizing seconds were crucial, Michael yanked the 9mm out of his waistband and raced toward the house as fast as he could run to try and rescue his father.

When he got inside the house, out of breath and shaking with adrenaline, but with his 9mm at the ready, Michael got a big surprise. Instead of an intruder he found his elderly father hard at work; he was methodically hammering doors and windows shut.

Michael was so genuinely relieved that he didn't ask Wayne a single question. Instead, he grabbed a spare hammer and helped his father. As the two men settled into the task at hand, Wayne quipped, "Don't forget to leave one door free, or won't neither one of us be leaving here anytime soon."

Michael couldn't help but smile. Both he and his father desperately needed some comic relief. Sadly, it was woefully short-lived because there just wasn't any lasting humor in the fact that a frail, elderly widower who had traveled halfway across the world as a young man to fight Hitler and his Nazi war machine now had to nail his windows and doors shut in order to feel safe in his own home. It was an American tragedy of epic proportions.

CHAPTER 47

Like so many baby boomers who came of age at a time when *Perry Mason* was one of the most popular shows on television, Michael was brought up on a steady diet of carefully scripted legal dramas in which justice not only triumphed with unfailing regularity, but in the end the guilty—racked with remorse—always confessed and collapsed into a puddle of tears on the witness stand. However, J.R. and Stephen had warned Michael that wasn't the way it happened in real life in the courtroom. It was never so neat, clean, and structured, or fair.

A good case in point was the fact that they had barely had time to cram for the upcoming hearing while, according to Michael's calculations, Ernie Arden and Monsanto's team of lawyers had more than three years to prepare.

Without a doubt, on the day of the hearing Michael and his team were at a distinct disadvantage, both from a standpoint of preparation and finances. For Michael, it was merely a reflection of the entire nightmare. The system simply did not make any allowances or provisions for the average Joe who was sued by a multibillion-dollar conglomerate. From the start it seemed nothing about the case had been fair, but toss in the spying, stalking, unmarked aircrafts, break-ins, Raymer's dire warning and the scales of justice were so completely out of balance that the word 'justice' was a misnomer.

Inside the courthouse, Arden popped out of the elevator with a bounce in his step. He was most likely buoyed by the fact that Michael was starting from scratch with new attorneys. But immediately after exiting the elevator the nattily attired lawyer in his tailored suit got a most unexpected surprise. Arden found himself face-to-face with both Michael and Wayne White. Michael he was expecting, but not his father. His demeanor shifted dramatically. Although he had never seen Wayne in the flesh, it was reasonable to assume that he had seen at least a few of the many clandestine photos Monsanto's spies had taken of the elderly widower.

With nowhere to hide, Arden couldn't avoid looking directly at Wayne, who held the unenviable title of the "oldest man ever sued for saving seeds." The mere sight of the weary retiree was a sad commentary on "Monsanto's ethics," a term Michael would classify as an oxymoron. The old man was clinging onto the arm of his son for support. Bent over and all but crippled by a recent hip injury, it was all he could do to stand. Without his son's assistance he couldn't even walk.

For a brief moment Arden appeared to be embarrassed. Perhaps it was an indication of how he really felt about his client's suit against the frail old man, which was a bogus suit at that. But if it was a moment of conscience it was woefully short-lived. Without saying a word or even offering to shake hands, Arden quickly ducked into the courtroom and put an end to this awkward and close encounter.

As the hearing got underway, Michael recognized that he clearly had a chip on his own shoulder. Who wouldn't? He couldn't stop thinking about the way his family had been treated. But since the last thing he wanted was for his enemy to know when they pushed his buttons, he made a concerted effort to keep his emotions in check. He didn't want to telegraph any information to the opposition that might hurt him. Yet all it took was a single word for one face in the courtroom to turn beet red. But it wasn't Michael's face. It was Arden's. And the word that turned it scarlet was "Tupelo."

Judge Smith asked Arden to explain exactly why Michael had made a mad and hasty dash to Mississippi in the wee hours of the morning. Hearing this, Michael sat bolt upright and gripped the edge of the table where he, Wayne and their lawyers were seated.

Before letting Arden answer, the judge reminded him that each and every practicing attorney is a sworn officer of the court and it's their solemn duty to report any and all crimes to the court. Failure to do so can lead to serious consequences; an attorney can be censured, even disbarred. In some cases, withholding such information can even make them an accessory to the crime, albeit after the fact.

It was Michael's opinion that Smith was in no mood to be trifled with, and had no intentions of letting attorneys in his court use word games to sanitize unflattering facts about the actions of their clients, people hired by them, or even people loosely associated with them.

The way Michael saw it, Arden faced a quandary. In all likelihood he thoroughly enjoyed having moneyed clients like Monsanto who could easily afford his services. But was he willing to walk the plank for the conglomerate?

Michael glanced over at Arden. Sweat covered his brow and his demeanor was that of a wayward fawn who had wandered onto an interstate and been blinded by high beams approaching at an alarming rate of speed.

Suddenly, Wayne scribbled something on a piece of paper and then pushed it over for Michael to read. Almost deaf, his father couldn't hear a word of the proceedings, yet he was still sharp enough to notice something that Michael had missed entirely, which was spelled out in his note: WHY IS ARDEN'S PANTS LEGS SHAKING?

Looking directly at Arden, Michael saw that if you looked closely, very closely, there was a subtle yet definite tremor in the cuff of his pants. Biting his tongue, Michael wrote a note of his own, then pushed it over to Wayne. Wayne read Michael's note: THINGS AIN'T GOING GOOD FOR HIM. Wayne nodded with understanding, and then just a hint of a smile creased his lips. After all the old man had been through, if anyone deserved a smile at Arden and Monsanto's expense it was most certainly Wayne White.

Sweat or no sweat, shakes or no shakes, there was little doubt that Arden was more than merely a competent lawyer; he was quite talented. But talented or not, he was facing one of the toughest jobs a lawyer could ever have. He had to perform damage control in open court, and not simply for some petty infraction. It was like walking a tightrope from a dizzying height without a net.

Choosing his words very carefully, Arden implied that a regrettable incident had taken place. But Michael wasn't in the market for the old soft-shoe routine, yet that must have been what Monsanto was paying Arden the big bucks for. Otherwise, he wouldn't have danced around so much trying to admit something horrific had happened, yet all the while attempting to explain it away as merely regrettable.

Perry Mason didn't make an appearance that day. But the scriptwriters for his old TV show would've been proud of the way things played out. By the end of the hearing Ernie Arden, a lawyer for Monsanto in the case of *Monsanto vs. Michael White*, had acknowledged in federal court that Jeb Raymer—the man who had illegally stuck a sign with a Monsanto logo on Michael White's property—had done far more than merely put up an advertisement shilling for a seed company that utilized the conglomerate's technology in front of the wrong field. Raymer had issued an ominous warning to Michael White, one that Michael had construed as a death threat.

Although the actual trial was still a bit down the road, it seemed as if it was finally coming to light just how far Monsanto's henchmen—as well as an obstreperous peddler of seeds that utilized Monsanto's technology—might go in order to silence Michael. [12]

---

[12] Jeb Raymer was not a Monsanto employee. He was employed by a seed company that utilized Monsanto's patented technology for GMOs, a point which Raymer's company used in some of its advertisements, including the sign he illegally placed in Michael White's cornfield.

CHAPTER 48

There was a small handful of people in Michael's inner circle, close friends and confidantes, all of whom were waiting on pins and needles to find out how the hearing went. And one of the first he spoke with was Troy. Greeting Michael with a quick nod, Troy asked the question that had been on his mind all day long. "How'd it go today?"

"Oh, pretty good, I suppose." Michael replied matter-of-factly. He had wanted to build up a bit of suspense, but it was no use, he couldn't hide his grin; it went from ear to ear. "Actually, it went about as good as it could go."

Troy was taken aback. He had not expected such good news. "How's that?"

"For starters, the judge got Arden to admit Raymer's threat. The old boy stuttered and stumbled like a tongue-tied parrot, and was shaking in his high dollar loafers, but he finally choked it out. Of course, he called it 'an unfortunate incident'. . . not a threat."

"So Arden wouldn't admit it was a threat?" Troy asked.

Michael quickly shook his head. By this point he understood lawyer speak better than most. "Naw. He didn't call it a threat. And I'm pretty sure he never would. But I think everybody in the room knew what it was."

A big grin took hold of Troy's face. "Wow!" he exclaimed, clapping loudly. "'Bout time, yes sir, it's about time."

Reveling over the day's success, Michael gave a recap of another telling moment in the courtroom. "Arden had a local lawyer with him at the plaintiff's table. And that fellow kept inching further and further away from Arden as the hearing wore on. By the end he was sitting as far from Arden as he could get and still be in the same state."

"Guess he figured out he was on the wrong side."

Michael nodded. "Musta been something like that." Taking a moment to savor the memory, he collected his thoughts, then continued. "After Arden admitted to the 'unfortunate incident,' he got so out of whack that he told the judge he needed more time to prepare his case."

Troy was incredulous. "Arden needs more time? Hell, he's been working on this for what, two, three years? And your lawyers have barely had time to get up to speed, much less get ready. Where does this clown get off thinking he deserves more time?"

Michael fought back a chuckle. "I gotta admit, it was comical seeing him so flustered."

Troy was on the edge of his seat. "What did the judge say?"

"He told Arden he'd had plenty of time. Said Arden and Monsanto filed the suit against me and if they weren't ready for trial after all these years, well too bad." Michael thought a moment, then added, "I got a feeling Arden don't want a jury to hear about all the stalking, spying, unmarked aircrafts, and of course Raymer's threat. They don't want this thing to ever see the light of day." Then he added, "Can't say I blame 'em."

Shifting around a bit on his chair, Michael tossed in the kicker. "Here's another thing, and I know you'll love this. After hearing about all the garbage Monsanto's private detectives have pulled—the spying, using fake tags, and such—guess what the Judge called 'em?"

Troy shrugged; he didn't have the slightest clue. "You got me. What did he call 'em?"

"Sloppy privates." Michael couldn't help but laugh.

Troy couldn't believe it. "You're telling me a federal judge sitting on the bench called Monsanto's detectives sloppy privates? You ain't kidding?"

Nodding in confirmation, Michael replied, "Sloppy privates. That's exactly what he called 'em. Heard it with my own two ears. And everybody in that courtroom heard it, too."

After all that had happened the two men deserved a moment to laugh and enjoy themselves. But their moment was short-lived. Michael had to bring things back to reality. "Problem is, even with the judge knowing these private eyes were sloppy privates, I heard somebody hint that Monsanto might have 'em a get out of jail free card."

Troy scrunched his brow. "How in the world could they pull that off?"

"Monsanto probably didn't pay those detectives, not directly. They probably had somebody else do it. My guess is they probably had their lawyers do it, but I'm not even ten percent sure on that. It could've been somebody else. Heck, they could've set up some dummy corporation to pay 'em - - - same way people do to pay off crooked politicians." Michael huffed, "Anybody that can fly around in aircrafts with no tail numbers can pull off something like this and cover their tracks so that nobody'll ever know for sure who paid 'em."

"You think Monsanto created a buffer between them and their goon squad? The kind where there won't be any tracks going back to St. Louis?"

With a reluctant nod, Michael answered. "That's my guess." He let out a deep sigh. "Most likely, anything these sloppy privates did, well, Monsanto will just claim they weren't paying 'em, so they didn't have no control over 'em - - - probably say they didn't have no contact with 'em and can't be held responsible for what they did."

Troy surmised, "So any contact between Monsanto's brass and the sloppy privates was probably done through a third party to keep it secret?"

Michael nodded. "Yep. I think that's what they'll claim." He rubbed his brow, "And it looks like it could get 'em off the hook, at least for the illegal things their sloppy privates did—even the ones I got on video—'cause you can't be responsible for what a third party does." Michael couldn't help but roll his eyes as he noted the irony of all ironies, "Of course, they'll turn around and say with a straight face that if a farmer gives me some of their Frankenstein seeds then I'm accountable for anything and everything that happens to them seeds . . . even though I'm a third party at that point."

A long moment passed as Troy contemplated the obvious double-standard Michael was battling; it seemed Monsanto expected to be exempt from the very rules of law for which it wanted Michael held accountable.

Michael surmised that if the actions of the sloppy privates should in anyway put Monsanto's top executives in a bind they would probably make virtues out of "inattention to detail," "lack of internal control," "passing the buck," and blame "rogue low-level employees" to dodge any responsibility for the egregious crimes committed by the sloppy privates. The tragic irony was that Michael was in danger of losing everything because Monsanto's high octane lawyers claimed he should know the whereabouts and dispensation of every seed that had passed through his farm and seed business for years, a number that easily tallied in the millions, possibly tens of millions, even more. Michael saw it as the epitome of hypocrisy: Privileged executives who were handed multi-million dollar compensation packages and had a slew of underlings at their beck-and-call weren't accountable for anything. Meanwhile, a simple, hardworking farmer who sweated day and night just to make ends meet was accountable for everything under the sun, moon and stars.

* * *

Since Denny showed Michael the cache of photos taken by Monsanto's spies, they had not had any further contact. Nevertheless, Michael recognized the fact that Denny knew more about certain aspects of his ordeal than even some people in his inner most circle. So although he wasn't particularly surprised that Denny wanted to see him again, he was keenly interested as to 'why.'

Much like before, they didn't spend a lot of time on small talk. Denny was not the sort to take the scenic route in life. Without any ado or fanfare, he produced a Fedex envelope and held it right in front of Michael. Gesturing, he said, "I think you'll wanna take a good look at this."

Reaching out, Michael took the envelope and carefully examined it. Much to his surprise, it was addressed to Monsanto's headquarters, and the return address was local - - - it had been sent from Sand Mountain. Eyes wide and on the verge of bulging, Michael looked up from the envelope at Denny and pronounced. "This is from one of Monsanto's spies that's been stalking me. I recognize his name as well as my own. And he sent it from right here." A moment passed, then he finally added, "And I recognize the name of the executive at Monsanto he sent it to."

With a slow and deliberate nod, Denny confirmed Michael's assessment: it was a direct link between the sloppy privates and Monsanto's executive offices. Michael felt like a man who had been shipwrecked on a deserted island for years and years and had finally spotted a ship on the horizon.

Michael's mind began to spin; it was hard to keep up with where this was leading. Essentially, it meant that "*if*" the Monsanto executive whose name was on the envelope testified that he didn't know anything about their sloppy privates, then the envelope would be admissible to rebut his sworn testimony, even at the last minute of the trial. Michael was all but in shock, though a good form of it . . . for a change.

Pointing out the obvious, Denny said something that he felt had to be said, "Everything there's handwritten; every single letter, number and period. No computer involved. Nobody can claim it was a typo or mix-up or addressed to the wrong person or a fake." Then he added the kicker. "And this ain't the first one of these I've seen with my own two eyes; not even close."

No two ways about it, Michael had just been handed a smoking gun, the kind that could be used to catch some mighty big fish red-handed "*if*" they tried to lie under oath. And the flip side? If Monsanto's executives acknowledged they were *fully* aware of the actions of their hired guns they would be admitting that they condoned, if not approved, criminal activity. Michael exhaled slowly. It was one thing to prove multiple crimes had been committed by some sleazy guys operating as P.I.s, but proving the executives of a Fortune 500 company possibly knew about those crimes, or, God forbid, authorized them, or at the very least condoned them, well, that took things to a different level altogether.

It seemed that the only fly in the newly churned butter was: Would the hired goons be willing to swear they never told any of Monsanto's executives a single word about all the sleazy and illegal activities they utilized during their pursuit of Michael? If so, that could absolve Monsanto's executives of any wrongdoings.

After a long silence had passed, one in which Michael did a great deal of thinking, he handed the envelope back to Denny. "Why don't you hold onto it for safekeeping." Much like the photos, Michael felt it made more sense for Denny to retain this volatile information, thus greatly reducing any chance that Monsanto's spies would find it and destroy it.

Envisioning a tumultuous trial, the kind where he might very well need the cavalry to come riding in at the last minute and save the day by discrediting Monsanto's executives, Michael concluded. "Keep it handy. I got a feeling it's gonna be pretty important 'fore the trial's over with."

CHAPTER 49

Michael picked up his mail early in the day, but didn't go through it; didn't even look at it. He was so accustomed to bad news that sometimes he wouldn't go through it for days. But when he got to a safe house for the night, he found he was restless and needed a diversion. So he shuffled through his mail. It was only then that he realized a large envelope he had gotten was not junk mail. It was, in fact, a long overdue report he had been expecting for eight or nine months, maybe even longer.

The report contained the results of a DNA test paid for by Monsanto that was supposed to prove beyond all doubt that Michael had Monsanto's GM soybeans in his field.

A while back, Monsanto had claimed it had reason to believe that Michael was growing GM seeds without their permission. The conglomerate had even gotten a court order to take a sample from all of Michael's soybean fields. At first, Michael welcomed the test, especially given that he had tried GM seeds for a few years and his experience had been that they were inferior to the natural seeds he had used for years and years. So he knew that there were no longer any GM seeds in his fields when they demanded the test. Pretty much the only way a GM seed could've gotten there was if a bird dropped one, or a tiny handful were left over from when he tried them, or if a few had fallen off a tractor that had previously been in someone else's field sown with GM seeds.

But there was a nagging thought in the back of Michael's head, the kind that slowly morphed into a full-scale warning. It was highly unlikely that Monsanto would demand a DNA test, one that required a court order, unless it was absolutely certain the results would be in its favor.

A little investigating uncovered that Monsanto had done the same thing to other farmers and the results had been devastating—for the farmers. Once the DNA test indicated that GM traits were present in a field the farmer was a goner. The only part of the lawsuit remaining to be determined was the 'damages' the poor, struggling farmer *owed* the multi-billion dollar conglomerate.

Michael got wind that a farmer, Tommy Remshaw, claimed the conglomerate's spies had set him up by planting GM seeds in his field without his knowledge. Just as in Michael's case, Monsanto had gotten a court order to test Tommy's fields and—surprise, surprise—the test came back positive for GM traits, even though Tommy swore he never bought any GM seeds, and certainly never planted any of them in his fields. Of course, what the farmer said didn't count—not even if he was an honest, upstanding, law-abiding citizen who had never run afoul of the law. Regardless of what Michael or Tommy or anyone else personally thought of Monsanto, the conglomerate's test was based on DNA evidence and conducted by an independent third party. It was considered ironclad evidence, the kind that can serve as a slam-dunk win on an otherwise shaky case.

Like Michael, Tommy had chosen to battle Monsanto, a course that had quickly emptied his bank account—money accumulated from the sweat of his brow over a lifetime. Tommy had been convinced that if he could hang on long enough the truth would come out. Once it did Monsanto would have to cover all his legal expenses, plus compensate him for all the anguish and agony they had caused him and his family.

But all hope was lost when the DNA test came back positive, proving that—scientifically—Tommy's field contained GM seeds, or at the very least traits of them. The problem was, the DNA test did not and could not possibly explain how the GM seeds got there, especially if Tommy had not planted them.

Tommy was convinced that when Monsanto's helicopters had swooped down low over his fields they had dropped off some of the conglomerate's GM seeds. Michael believed his theory wholeheartedly. After all, he had seen the unmarked helicopters not only fly over his farm many times, but one had brazenly landed in his field while he was working. It still galled him that the arrogant chopper pilot had had the nerve to ask him, 'Whatcha' planting?' . . . after illegally landing in his field and destroying some of its all-important topsoil.

A good friend of Michael's, Kyle Reid, a farmer who lived on Sand Mountain, told Michael he saw copters hovering just a few feet above his soybean field one day, and it took off abruptly as soon as it saw him. Then not long after that he noticed large dead spots in that same field. That could mean only one thing: Monsanto's goons had—illegally—sprayed Roundup on Reid's crop to covertly test if he was growing natural soybeans, or Monsanto's GM variety. This was possible because Monsanto's GM soybeans can survive being sprayed directly with Roundup, a herbicide that's highly toxic to many types of plants and weeds—including natural soybeans. Monsanto even markets Roundup as a devastatingly effective weed killer, one that should be used in conjunction with its own GM Roundup Ready Soybeans. More than a few times, Michael had wondered what might happen to the human body over the long haul as a result of eating genetically modified fruits and vegetables that were not only impervious to a very potent plant and weed killer, but were also sprayed with that same chemical during the time the plants were 'blossoming and bearing.'

The large dead spots in Kyle's field were proof to Michael that someone had sprayed Kyle's crop with Roundup. The dead spots also served as proof that he was not growing GM soybeans. Michael and Kyle both felt this was the reason that Monsanto didn't get a court order to test Kyle's field. Although Kyle was relieved Monsanto didn't target him with costly litigation, he was still waiting to be compensated for the portion of his crop that had been illegally and maliciously destroyed.

Fortunately for Michael, Kyle was one of the brave souls who eventually came forward and signed a sworn affidavit that Monsanto's scare tactics unnerved him to the point that he stopped doing business with Michael because he feared what the conglomerate might do to him if he didn't. In his sworn statement, Kyle even made it a point to include details about the helicopter illegally spraying his crops. He even included the fact that the spraying resulted in dead spots, which was tantamount to vandalism.

With all this covert spraying of Roundup in his head, Michael figured. "How hard would it have been for the goons in the chopper to drop some seeds in Tommy's field each time they flew over?" And, of course, the same went for Michael's own fields.

Ironically, a few weeks after Jeb Raymer illegally put up the sign touting Monsanto's technology in Michael's cornfield and then issued his threat, a good friend told Michael that he saw Raymer and another man walking around in that same exact field. And it looked as if they were stealthily pulling something out of their pockets and dropping whatever it was onto the ground. Were they surreptitiously tossing GM corn seeds? Was it a setup so they could claim Michael planted them? For better or worse, Michael would never know for sure because Monsanto did not get a court order to perform a DNA test in that particular field . . . perhaps because they realized it could be directly linked to Raymer's threat?

To the average person, it would seem that Tommy must be paranoid or crazy or both to say that a Fortune 500 company was trying to set him up, especially given that he was a simple farmer who couldn't possibly do the company any real harm. But given his own firsthand experience, plus Kyle's sworn affidavit, Michael knew better.

Although Michael had come to loath Monsanto's spies and their sordid tactics, he conceded that the plot Tommy described was cunning. Without leaving the slightest trace, not a footprint or even a fingerprint, Monsanto's spies could contaminate a farmer's field by air. And the unsuspecting farmer—knowing he hadn't planted any GM seeds—would welcome the test, believing it would vindicate him, much like a wrongly convicted man on death row welcomes a DNA test to prove his innocence. Except, of course, in Tommy's scenario he believed that 'the fix was in.'

Michael felt the breath go out of his body. Not only did he believe every word of Tommy's theory, but at the time Monsanto had taken samples from Michael's fields the conglomerate's unmarked aircrafts were, simultaneously, making countless flyovers of his farm. Moreover, its spies certainly had the opportunity to drop quite a few GM seeds in his fields during the numerous times they trespassed on his property. That meant that he could be 'next.' He was convinced they were going to use the DNA test to steamroll him exactly like Tommy felt they had done to him. And there was nothing Michael could do about it.

Thinking about Tommy's plight, Michael knew he was in for a rough night. Sure enough, he didn't sleep a wink. He couldn't stop worrying about the DNA test Monsanto was running on his crop. So he prayed. Then he prayed some more. Then, sometime around daybreak, miraculously, the answer came to him.

Michael White, a simple farmer, was about to turn the tables on a mega-corporation in a way they had never had them turned before. When he was done, he suspected the company would have to rewrite its game plan.

Armed with a plan designed to trump Monsanto's DNA test, Michael assembled a team of witnesses who ranged from a veteran law officer to a certified chemical applicator specialist. And to keep things on the absolute up-and-up, *he even made it a point to personally invite Alex*

Griner, a Monsanto employee, to serve as an eyewitness for the conglomerate. Griner, a Monsanto regional sales manager whose territory included Sand Mountain, declined the invitation. It struck Michael as the ultimate paradox of his life that the very same company that had spent so much time, money and effort spying on him and his family for years would pass up an opportunity in which it could openly aim its cameras on him and be welcomed with open arms. [13]

Documenting every step of the process on video, Michael sprayed all fifteen of his prized fields of soybeans—hundreds and hundreds of acres—with giant swaths of Roundup. The swaths didn't follow any set pattern. They were random, thus eliminating any chance that the spraying was prearranged or staged. Michael even went to great lengths to ensure that the Roundup he used came out of brand new containers that had never been opened before, proving that neither he nor anyone else had tampered with Monsanto's formula for the herbicide.

If the Roundup killed his crop of natural soybeans—like he knew it would, yet Monsanto's DNA test came back positive, stating Michael's crop was grown from GM soybeans, then the conglomerate would be in extremely deep trouble. It would either have to admit that it illegally spiked portions of Michael's fields to get a positive DNA test, or it would have to publicly announce that its highly touted Roundup Ready Soybeans were a sham.

As Michael expected, the Roundup decimated his soybean fields, killing all the plants that were sprayed because they were grown from natural seeds. That information spread like pollen on a spring breeze, traveling for miles and miles around Sand Mountain. And, no doubt, it made its way

---

[13] Michael White did not choose Alex Griner at random from the thousands of people Monsanto employs. He had known Griner for many years, long before he was employed by Monsanto, and had hoped Griner would have the common decency to at least make a perfunctory showing at the test.

to the ears of Monsanto's henchmen. While he couldn't be sure of their reaction, Michael liked to think that perhaps someone else lost a few nights' worth of sleep for a change.

* * *

Michael gazed at the cover of the thick report from Monsanto's independent lab. The report should've come out a few weeks after they tested his field—a month at most, yet it had taken Monsanto eight or nine months to provide him with a copy. Michael couldn't help but grimace. He found it so typical of Monsanto. If he had held out a vital report this long—one Monsanto could use to its advantage, he suspected they might very well have tried to have him thrown in jail for withholding it.

Looking carefully at the first few pages, Michael didn't see the results of the test anywhere. So naturally he flipped to the back. Still, the results were nowhere to be found. Realizing he would probably have to read the entire report he decided he had better sit down and get comfortable. The results had to be in the report somewhere. And they were. Buried deep inside the document, about midway through, the DNA test results for Michael's fields were listed amid a plethora of inconsequential dribble. It looked as if someone had gone to great lengths to make locating the results nearly impossible.

The result was exactly what Michael knew it should be, and had to be, given his field experiment. The official result was: *Non-positive*. There were absolutely no genetically modified crops in Michael's field, and that was according to Monsanto's very own DNA test. The irony was that after all this time it didn't have the decency to use the word 'negative,' instead it used 'non-positive,' which seemed like a shifty way to muddle up the facts to Michael. But it didn't matter; non-positive or negative, he believed they were interchangeable in this case.

Although the lengthy report appeared to bolster some of the hoopla surrounding Roundup's effectiveness as a weed killer, Michael didn't find any mention of superweeds. They are weeds which, over time, become resistant to a given chemical after it's used on them over and over. They actually become stronger and harder to battle as a result, hence the term *superweeds*. When petitioning the USDA in 1993 to deregulate the use of Roundup Ready Soybeans—which must be sprayed with Roundup to live up to their alleged potential, Monsanto claimed it was highly unlikely that expanded use of Roundup would lead to resistant weeds, i.e., ones that might cause even more problems. Sadly, Monsanto was mistaken; not the first time "corporate scientists" had failed to uncover something reasonably obvious to other scientists—much in the same way that, for more than 70 years, "corporate scientists" for Big Tobacco were somehow stymied and unable to link smoking cigarettes with cancer.

Although way overdue, the report had vindicated Michael. And all it took was one word out of the enormously thick document. Never mind that he had destroyed a significant part of his prized soybean crop, which would throw his bottom line off by thousands and thousands of dollars. The decision to destroy his own crop had actually been easier than he had expected. That was probably because he realized the alternative of doing nothing would have been far worse, and could very well have cost him his entire farm. Still, it had been exorbitantly expensive, time consuming, and required an enormous amount of effort to *prove* he was in the right. Yet as galling as having to 'prove his innocence' had been, he counted himself as fortunate because he didn't know of another farmer in the country who had accomplished the same feat.

Now Monsanto would have to walk into federal court and admit in front of a judge that Michael's fields—the ones the conglomerate got a court order to test because it was certain they contained GM soybeans—didn't have a single GM seed.

Michael savored his hard-won victory, and yet at the same time his heart went out to Tommy and the Blanchards, and all the other farmers like them who hadn't been nearly so fortunate.

CHAPTER 50

In the case of *Monsanto vs. Wayne White*, Monsanto failed to produce a single shred of evidence or even one witness against Wayne. Therefore, the federal judge not only ruled in favor of Wayne, he also ruled against Monsanto "*with prejudice.*"

The oldest man on record to be sued for saving seeds won hands down. It was a legal, moral, and ethical victory for both Wayne and Michael.

Of course, all indications were that the case had been a sham from the very beginning. Michael knew it, and he felt certain Monsanto's lawyers knew it, too. Once the judge's ruling was in, Michael had no problem voicing his opinion about the conglomerate's shameful behavior. "If Monsanto's lawyers didn't know when daddy stopped farming, then filing that suit against him shows they're incompetent. And if they did know (when he stopped farming), then what they did was dishonest and disrespectful to daddy. Plus it cost the taxpayers a bunch of money." Michael felt the suit against Wayne defined Monsanto's character . . . or lack of it.

If anyone thought Michael's theory was harsh or unjust, he would gladly back it up with hard facts: Wayne stopped farming around 1971 (when he accepted a full-time job with the TVA), yet the suit accused him of illegally saving a product (seeds that utilized Monsanto's GM technology) that wasn't even sold to the public until the mid-90s—about twenty-five years after he parked his plow for good. It was beyond impossible for Wayne to have been guilty, and Michael was convinced that the lawyers who filed the suit either knew that, or failed to use due diligence before filing it.

Michael's case, however, would not go away so easily. Even though the threat Raymer made against him was now out in the open, and even though

Monsanto's own DNA test stated Michael's soybean field did not contain a single GM seed, the suit was still moving forward. In a way, Michael was glad. After all that had happened, he was looking forward to his day in court. He wanted to tell the world what Monsanto had done to him and his family and what they had in store for the food supply.

* * *

Known as the "Gateway to the West," St. Louis's population peaked around 1950. Although its metropolitan area has grown substantially since then, the city itself has seen an overall decline in population that many have tied to a decrease in manufacturing. Good jobs that once sustained a large portion of the middle class simply went away. And while a number of companies in the area either moved away or died, there was one that was still going strong as the venerable old city met the twenty-first century head on. That company was Monsanto.

Technically speaking, the conglomerate is not located in St. Louis. Its headquarters is actually in a suburb, Creve Coeur, which is French for "broken heart," something many people lament Monsanto has left them with.

Founded in 1901, one of Monsanto's first major products was saccharine, an artificial sweetener. Over the years the conglomerate has manufactured everything from aspirin to textiles.

In 2002 Monsanto re-incorporated and declared that it was now an "agricultural company." This was met with skepticism by many people in Anniston. A number of them felt the timing was more than a coincidence, especially coming so soon after the harsh court ruling handed down there against the conglomerate. Monsanto even began referring to itself in its own literature as a "relatively new company." Given that Monsanto had been operating in Creve Coeur for more than 100 years, referring to itself as a "relatively new company" seemed strangely at odds with the desire of most companies that eagerly tout their stability and longevity.

A passionate, dedicated and vocal legion of concerned citizens would undoubtedly point out that Monsanto had numerous reasons to try and distance itself from its past. After all, the conglomerate was a responsible party for more than thirty Environmental Protection Agency Superfund sites across the country—past and present, and it had faced troubling questions, health concerns, safety issues, and lawsuits related to a number of its products—past and present, such as Agent Orange, Aspartame, DDT, GMOs, PCBs, petroleum based fertilizer and rBGH. In their heart of hearts, even Monsanto's own executives, board of directors, major stock holders, attorneys and PR handlers had to know the conglomerate was saddled with a serious image problem in the U.S., as well as around the world.

Michael didn't know for sure if Monsanto re-incorporated in an attempt to escape from or salvage its woefully tarnished image or not. But he did know that—given the reprehensible things the conglomerate's spies had done to him and his family—it was way beyond escaping or salvaging at his home, and he strongly suspected his was not the only household that held that sentiment.

CHAPTER 51

With time working against them, Michael and his attorneys burned the midnight oil on more than a few occasions. They had turned their focus on three issues: a lone receipt from his seed-cleaning business that loomed large in the mix; a scheme of entrapment perpetrated by Monsanto's henchmen; and the validity of the patent Michael was being sued for violating.

Monsanto had submitted the receipt as evidence and alleged that it proved Michael, as owner of a seed business, had violated their patent by illegally cleaning some of their GM soybean seeds brought to Michael's company by a farmer.

Michael and his lawyers planned to attack the receipt on several grounds. First of all, Michael never signed one of Monsanto's technology agreements stating that he would not clean their GM seeds. Additionally, by state law, Michael was required to clean any seeds brought to him. To top it off, the receipt's origin was dubious at best. Michael was convinced it had been forged. Someone had broken into Michael's seed business after Monsanto filed suit against him, but the burglar hadn't stolen any computers, money, or anything of real value. The only thing missing was a handful of receipts, including some blank copies which could have easily been forged or doctored.

The handwritten receipt was not in Michael's handwriting nor in that belonging to any of his employees. And the date on it stated categorically that the GM seeds had been cleaned on a Sunday. Whoever created the receipt obviously hadn't bothered to check Michael's business hours. In twenty-plus years of business Michael had never opened his doors on a Sunday; it was against his religion. Lastly, the receipt indicated that the seeds had been cleaned for JJJ Farms. After a thorough search, the closest farm Michael could find to his seed business with that name was more than 350 miles away. Michael was adamant that it was way beyond improbable that a farmer would have traveled that far and burned that much fuel—passing by umpteen seed cleaners and killing any profit he ever hoped to have—all to have him do the work. It was the equivalent of, and made about as much sense as, driving all the way from Newark, New Jersey, to Montreal, Canada, to get an oil change and tune up.

Another incident that started out as a seemingly simple business transaction now loomed large. In October 2002, around the time Monsanto's spies began targeting Michael, two men—both professing to be farmers from Georgia—came by White's Seed one day. Although Michael had never met them, they struck up a lengthy conversation with him before finally purchasing a small amount of mixed (various varieties) soybeans for 'food plots'—intended to attract deer for hunters.

It wasn't uncommon for farmers and hunters to buy mixed soybeans at White's Seed for food plots, though they normally did so only once a year. But these same two men were back at Michael's again in a few weeks, and on their next visit they specifically requested Roundup Ready Soybeans. Michael certainly didn't have any for sale and told them so, and even advised them that they were more expensive than conventional soybeans and—in his opinion—not nearly as good. But apparently that wasn't enough to deter them. For the next several months they pestered Michael again and again, interrupting his work days and home life with multiple calls and visits all in an effort to "buy Roundup Ready Soybeans," which were readily available from other sources. And the primary pest, Karl Elkins, a man whose story seemed to change with each visit, brought several different 'farmers' with him on his many visits, all of them seemingly in dire need of Roundup Ready Soybeans. As much as it left a sick taste in his mouth to tell anyone to patronize Monsanto, Michael even suggested that they contact a Monsanto sales rep, but they totally ignored him. That, in and of itself, told Michael quite a lot about these 'farmers' who were *desperately* seeking Roundup Ready Soybeans; it was at this point that he got his first inkling that something was amiss here.

It got to the point where Michael had to screen his calls to avoid Karl and his gang of overbearing sidekicks. Finally, after months of trying to get Michael to sell him Roundup Ready Soybeans without any luck, Karl struck a deal with Fess Caulder (a farmer in Michael's area) for some soybeans which were purportedly of the Roundup Ready variety. Michael was glad because he figured it would get Karl off his back. But no such luck. Karl came to Michael's store and, using every scheme imaginable, tried to suck Michael into the deal. First, he told Michael he couldn't find Fess's house, and needed Michael to ride with him and show him the way. Instead, Michael gave him directions. Then Karl claimed he needed Michael's help loading the soybeans. Michael declined because he had a business to run. He then told Michael his taillights were out and he desperately needed Michael's hired-hand to help with the loading so he wouldn't get stuck driving home at night with no taillights. When Michael, a pretty fair shade-tree mechanic, generously offered to fix the lights Karl then used every excuse in his scheming mind to keep Michael away from his brake lamps. Had Karl not become such a thorn in Michael's side, the bizarre excuses he cooked up to keep Michael away from his truck would have passed for a Three Stooges comedy routine.

When it became clearly obvious that Michael wasn't going to bite on any of the hooks Karl had tossed out, the pest claiming to be a farmer then said Fess wasn't home so he wanted to leave the money—$1430 in cash—with Michael to complete his deal with Fess. After a few moments of hesitation, Michael agreed. "Fess is in pretty bad financial shape. I know he's hurting for money. So if it'll help Fess out, you can leave it here." Before the words were out of Michael's mouth Karl yanked two hundred bucks out his pocket—money that was separate from the $1430, and very conveniently tucked right inside his shirt pocket—and tossed it on Michael's desk as he proclaimed, "That's a broker's fee for all your trouble."

Shaking his head, Michael immediately set Karl straight. "Nope. I ain't taking no money 'cause I ain't got nothing to do with your deal. So put that two-hundred back in your pocket." Michael didn't say it, but it struck him as far more than peculiar that Karl would offer to pay him such a hefty fee—almost 15 percent—for doing nothing, especially given that a few months earlier Karl told him he was in dire financial straits and about to lose his farm. Like so many things Karl had told Michael, nothing ever added up. Michael deduced that he was either an idiot, compulsive liar, worked for Monsanto - - - or all three.

Karl, who had worked overtime trying to buddy up with Michael for months—and all to no avail, suddenly became visibly upset when Michael refused the 'broker's fee' he offered. It took him several minutes to regain his composure, yet when he did he completely switched his strategy. "Michael, fourteen hundred and thirty bucks is a lot of cash. I'll need a receipt from you for the money."

Once again, shaking his head, Michael came back with a flat and emphatic. "Nope." Then he gestured toward the money. "I ain't gonna give you a receipt. I ain't part of your deal. You just keep all the money and give it to Fess yourself."

Yet again, Karl changed gears. "OK. You just hold the money and give it to Fess. I don't really need a receipt."

At this point Karl had completely burned up about two hours of Michael's time. Not surprisingly, Michael was willing to do just about anything to get rid of this incessant pest. So he wrote Fess's name on a slip of paper, put that on top of the money and then put a rubber band around it and dropped it into his desk drawer. "I'll give it to him next time I see him. Now I gotta get back to work." Michael stood up, exited his own office to escape from Karl, and made a mental note to avoid the pesky Georgian at all costs in the future.

A few days later Michael saw Fess and gave him the money, and figured that was the end of it. That is, until a legal document popped up almost two years later, one in which Monsanto made the claim that Michael had 'brokered' a deal between its undercover agent, Karl Elkins, and Fess Caulder for approximately $1430 worth of Roundup Ready Soybeans.

Michael was beyond dumbfounded. Karl had bugged him for months and months, and taken up countless hours of his time, yet he had refused to take even a dime from the deal Karl made with Fess. Nevertheless, the conglomerate had the audacity to claim Michael 'brokered' the transaction. Michael recalled in his deposition stating, "They (Karl and his co-conspirators) didn't leave my place with one Roundup Ready bean unless it was stuck to the bottom of their shoe." It was in reference to the cold hard facts that after hounding Michael for months the only Roundup Ready Soybeans the spies got came from another farm—not Michael's. Also, not only did Michael not profit from the deal, he lost time and money because the pesky, obnoxious and scheming spies badgered him again and again when he was trying to run his farm and seed business.

Using a dictionary, Michael looked up the word 'broker.' It was defined more or less as 'an agent who buys or sells goods or services for another person on a commission basis.' Michael wondered if Monsanto's army of lawyers had even bothered to look the word up before making their Swiss cheesesque claim. It was obvious to Michael that he hadn't brokered anything, and that Karl's ill fated attempt to reel him in was little more than a thinly veiled scheme of entrapment. Of course, he presumed these were the same lawyers who filed the bogus law suit against his father that got tossed out of court. That spoke volumes to Michael.

But putting both the highly questionable receipt and scheme of entrapment aside, the issue on the front burner for Michael's team was the validity of Monsanto's patent 605.

After careful study, Michael, J. R., and Stephen felt they had constructed a compelling argument that Monsanto's patent 605 was invalid, a patent the conglomerate had likely made many, many millions of dollars on, and stood to profit even more from in the future. If they could prove it invalid, Monsanto would be in a world of hurt. The conglomerate could not only lose a sizable stream of revenue but also could face hundreds of millions of dollars in suits. And in all likelihood, many of the cases it had won against farmers could be thrown out. It was the kind of bombshell that could wreak havoc on any company, even one the size of Monsanto.

Michael enjoyed envisioning the reaction of Monsanto's CEO should they succeed in proving that one of the conglomerate's highly profitable patents was invalid. The executive would have a nightmare on his hands. From the board of directors, to stockholders, to fellow executives, he would never hear the end of it. He would be under siege; he might even have to make do without his enormous bonus. Yet, for Michael, it was a trivial and cold comfort. The CEO still couldn't begin to imagine what it was like to be stalked and spied on for years, to have unmarked helicopters buzzing his home and businesses, to have his livelihood threatened and his family's peace of mind shattered. Like a lot of people, Michael felt bigwigs are thoroughly insulated from the consequences their actions have on others, yet few of them—if any—could survive even one day in the hell they routinely dump onto hardworking people.

The issue of the patent's validity led Michael back to a question that had kept him up more nights than he wanted to recall. 'Just how did it come to pass that plants were patentable?' It just didn't make any sense whatsoever to him that a company could patent something that had been on earth for thousands of years. Using that logic—or lack of it, Michael feared that Monsanto or some other company could soon get patents on trees and tell every little kid with a tree house to either pay a hefty royalty fee or have their lawyers demand that the child 'remove his tree house forthwith.'

The matter of whether or not GM plants were entitled to patents was more or less decided when the case of *J.E.M. AG Supply Inc. v. Pioneer Hi-Bred International Inc.* snaked its way through a maze of courts until it finally wound up at the U.S. Supreme Court. On December 10, 2001, the High Court found that "newly developed plant breeds are patentable under the general utility laws of the United States."

Critics pointed to a number of flaws regarding the Court's decision, not least of which was that it spat in the face of the Plant Variety Protection Act of 1970. The PVPA stated that plants can't be patented because they're "products of nature." It was based on common sense as well as the fact that many botanists and horticulturists would gladly explain that the "newly developed" plants in question were simply off-shoots of an original plant. They had been altered in someone's laboratory, nothing more, nothing less. Nevertheless, several of the justices on the High Court— none of whom were horticulturalists or botanists—had somehow made a decision to blur the lines between what is manmade and what is natural.

Michael had heard it takes a pharmaceutical company almost a decade to get approval for a new prescription medicine, and that process includes exhaustive tests and clinical trials to insure the safety and effectiveness of the drug. And once they're finally approved, you still can't take them without first obtaining a prescription from a duly licensed physician who must determine if the drug is right for you, and vice versa. Did it not stand to reason then that Monsanto's 'so-called' newly developed plant breeds should have to pass at least a few tests by independent labs to insure their safety? Apparently not. He felt that an unsuspecting public would serve as the ultimate guinea pigs for GMOs.

Given the problematic ruling by the Court, Michael and others felt it stood to reason that it was now possible for every fast-buck artist in the world with a petri dish and a cheap microscope to cook up "newly developed" GM plants and, once they got a toehold in the market, then the patent holders would own a crucial link in the food chain. Such a far-reaching ruling potentially gave all the wrong people a government endorsed license to steal from nature and make a profit doing so. What would happen, Michael wondered, if the Taliban secretly instructed some of its minions to jump on the bandwagon? Could the day be far off when consumers, unwittingly, were supporting terrorists simply by making a purchase at their local grocery store?

* * *

One evening while Michael and Troy were discussing the matter, Troy had commented that Justice Clarence Thomas had written the majority opinion on the ruling. "It was really strange," Troy had said, "'cause Thomas rarely ever writes an opinion. He pretty much says 'yea' or 'nay.'" He had followed up by making a cutting and sarcastic remark about the justice's lack of qualifications and honesty.

Back when Thomas was nominated for the High Court, a number of people were vehemently opposed to the Georgia native, yet Michael had always been an ardent supporter. Even so, Michael had let Troy's terse comment pass without rebuttal because Troy had done so much for him. It wasn't worth it to battle him over a simple difference of opinion.

* * *

Bedding down for the night at a safe house, Michael tossed and turned for the longest time before conceding that, once again, sleep would be elusive. For a time he simply laid in bed, but to Michael that always seemed like such a waste. So he got up and tiptoed into the kitchen, going to great pains not to wake anyone in the house.

After getting a glass of water, Michael sat down at the kitchen table and realized that for some reason the less-than-flattering remark Troy had been made about Clarence Thomas was really eating at him. Perhaps Troy had mistakenly lumped Thomas in with politicians in general? Even so, it seemed that there was more to it than that, even coming from a man who had no use for politicians and other publicly funded parasites.

Michael's mind wandered back to the hearings that were held for Thomas in 1991. Normally, Michael didn't have time for such things. What farmer did? But he had kept up with the hearings as best as he could because he, like so many others with traditional values, had been impressed by Thomas's life story, a classic Horatio Alger style tale. Plus, he felt Thomas shared many of his beliefs and values.

Naturally, it had troubled Michael that Anita Hill, a one-time friend and colleague of Thomas's, had seemingly turned on him. Siding with like-minded people, he believed that Hill was out to sabotage her old pal because of his conservative values. Almost a decade and a half later, he could still remember what Hill had said about Thomas, testifying under oath that her former boss had made 'highly inappropriate comments to her that were of a sexual nature.' Michael had been skeptical of her allegations back then. Based on what Michael had heard, it seemed totally out of character for Thomas to have said those terribly crude, vulgar and unseemly remarks.

Like most people who followed the hearings, Michael could vividly remember that Thomas had not only denied Hill's accusations, but complained bitterly that he was being subjected to a "*high-tech lynching*." That last phrase was so powerful few could forget it. It had seemed obvious to Michael that Thomas was indeed the victim.

Wanting a quick refresher on the hearings, Michael figured it wouldn't hurt to Google Thomas and do a little checking. If he couldn't sleep, why not keep occupied?

As expected, Michael found there was a lot of information online about Thomas. But what threw him a curve was the amount of negative information. It seemed Troy had a lot of company.

For better or worse, a quote that cropped up often about Thomas was one made by then Pres. George H. W. Bush when he proclaimed Thomas to be "the most qualified [nominee] at this time." Even Michael, with no legal background, knew that hadn't been the case. It turned out that what Michael hadn't realized in 1991 was that up until he was nominated for the highest court in the land, Thomas had never written a legal book, article, or brief of serious consequence. But what was truly unsettling was that at the time of his nomination he'd only had about one year of experience as a judge. Michael couldn't believe it: "One year of experience and he was the most qualified person in the entire country?" It was the equivalent of proclaiming a first-year medical resident was qualified to perform a heart transplant. However, in this instance, each and every American citizen had apparently wound up flat on their backs on a gurney while Thomas went about learning which end of the scalpel was up.

Michael couldn't believe that back in 1991 he never heard a word about the fact that Thomas had so little experience. Then again, perhaps he hadn't wanted to hear it back then and had simply tuned it out. It was now impossible to know for sure.

Digging a bit deeper, Michael discovered that Hill did not ask to testify against Thomas. In fact, she had been called as a reluctant witness, and only after a secret interview she had with the FBI was leaked to the media. In reality, Hill neither sought the spotlight nor wanted it. Yet in the end she was the one whom many people had vilified.

Staring at the screen, Michael stretched a bit, exhaled, and then asked no one in particular, "So Clarence Thomas is the one who wrote the opinion that gave Monsanto the right to take over our food supply?" Then, as an afterthought, he threw out a second question, "Wonder if he had any idea what a mess he was getting all of us into?"

Scrolling down the screen, Michael found himself perusing Thomas's biography. It could've been the bio of practically any hyper-ambitious person who aspired to a higher position in life and wasn't afraid to step on a few toes or kiss the right asses if that's what it took to get there.

Michael was about to stop reading when something in Thomas's biography caught his attention. At first he thought his eyes were playing a cruel and sadistic trick on him; they had to be. After all, it was the wee hours of the night, and he was very tired. Besides, what he thought he saw was beyond unthinkable. Actually, it was far worse than that. It was an absolute abomination of all things Michael held dear. Nevertheless, after reading the paragraph a second, and even a third time, his worst nightmare was indeed confirmed. The biography stated without equivocation that Clarence Thomas, a U.S Supreme Court Justice, had previously worked as an in-house attorney for the very company that now benefited the most from his ruling that "newly developed plant breeds are patentable" . . . *Monsanto*.

In Michael's opinion, the very notion that Thomas did not recuse himself from hearing a case that had the potential to directly and greatly benefit his former employer's revenues to the tune of billons and billons of dollars amounted to a *high-tech fleecing* of every man, woman and child in America, if not the planet.

CHAPTER 52

A trial can be an exorbitantly expensive proposition, and not only for a defendant like Michael. Given the sheer number of cases filed each year, the state shoulders an enormous financial load in the process. The government encourages plaintiffs and defendants to sit down together at the bargaining table and negotiate in good faith to find out if they can come to a meeting of the minds without burdening the system with the time and expense of a full-blown trial. Given all that he and his family had been through, and all he knew about Monsanto, Michael was skeptical that the conglomerate could do anything in 'good faith.' Only after his own lawyers convinced him that it was normal for both sides to go to the bargaining table before opting for a trial did Michael consent.

There was, of course, a major downside to mediation. Without the bright lights and attention a trial can provide, the evidence, the incessant spying, and complicated legal theory Michael's attorney's had prepared in hopes of invalidating one of Monsanto's patents probably wouldn't be given much more than a perfunctory glance.

Initially, the mediation was held at the federal courthouse in Birmingham, Alabama, but it quickly devolved into a complete waste of Michael's time. One reason things fell apart was that Monsanto had sent Ken Lesman, a corporate executive, to monitor the process. Michael was convinced that Lesman was a major cog in the blitzkrieg the conglomerate had unleashed on him and his family, one that had lasted for years and had stolen an incalculable part of their lives, including their peace of mind.

In Michael's estimation, Lesman epitomized big business run amok, and he wanted no part of him or his kind. It wasn't only because of what he thought Lesman had done to him and his family, it was also because of what he felt Lesman and company had done to all the "Tommys and Blanchards" of the world, many of whom had had their livelihoods yanked right out from under them and their lives destroyed in the process. And as far as Michael could tell, Lesman showed no remorse whatsoever; he was the poster boy for unbridled arrogance and greed.

But the real fuel on the fire for Michael was the manner in which Lesman operated. He reminded him of an obnoxious neighbor, the kind who is constantly sticking his nose in everyone else's business and spewing unwanted, inappropriate and unneeded advice when his own house is the one in dire need of repairs. In short order it became evident to Michael that there could be no resolution in Birmingham, not with Lesman parading around and making a spectacle of himself. Luckily, the proceedings were soon moved to Huntsville and, Michael learned, Lesman would be a no-show. Michael wasn't sure why Lesman wouldn't be there, but his absence served as something positive.

* * *

After the aborted attempt at mediation in Birmingham, the day of reckoning in Huntsville finally arrived. For Michael, the abomination that had started almost four years ago with the malicious spying, escalated with the break-in of his elderly father's home, and culminated with the loss of his family was finally coming to a head on a hot summer day in 2006.

The federal courthouse in Huntsville was a stately old building that had served the community well for many years. But it was also a bit long in the tooth. From its antiquated plumbing to its outdated electrical system to a host of other issues, it simply could no longer handle the demand that a growing region required of it. Long before Michael's hearing was set, a plan was put in motion to tear the old building down. A new and modern structure would take its place. Nevertheless, Michael's mediation would be heard at the old building, and that was exactly the way he wanted it.

Michael made his first visit to the old courthouse in Huntsville the previous year for his case, and it was during that trip when he first spied "the mural," which immediately caught his attention. Painted in 1937 by Xavier Gonzalez, an artist from Spain, the mural was a 12' by 13'6" masterpiece depicting a scene with an agricultural theme. Given the era when it was painted, it wasn't uncommon that it focused on farming. More Americans earned their living as farmers back then than at any other single occupation. But it wasn't a standard painting of a barn, a cow, a few chickens, and a farmer; instead it featured five distinct adult characters and one small child as its central focus. Each of the adults appeared to be pursing a life and calling all his or her own, yet they were all intertwined. Michael didn't have to be an art connoisseur to recognize that the majestic piece had been created by a gifted and visionary painter and that it was filled with dramatic and powerful symbolism.

Every time Michael came by the courthouse he found that he was drawn to the mural. He couldn't see it enough. And each time Michael saw it he found something new, something he hadn't seen before, something that provoked his interest even more than before.

There was a special feeling of comfort Michael found when he was close to the mural. Yet it was something that took him by surprise. Art had never been a big part of his life. And yet, gazing at Gonzalez's mural, for the first time Michael understood how people can stand in an art gallery, viewing only one painting, and do so for hours on end. Although it wasn't something he could readily explain, he hoped that simply being in the same courthouse with the mural would serve to his advantage during mediation, if for no other reason than the comfort and calming effect it provided him.

* * *

The mediation would be conducted behind closed doors. Neither the public nor press would be allowed inside. And the results would be sealed by the judge. However, before the judge could sign off on the proceedings both parties would have to come to a mutual agreement. That meant if either side was not satisfied they could demand a trial by jury. Michael felt that Monsanto would do practically everything in its power to keep the videos he had made of its goons away from the public. On the other hand, he wanted a trial by jury. His lawyers had stated as much on his behalf. He wanted the world to know what Monsanto had done to him and his family and what he was certain it was doing to the food supply. After all the laws Monsanto's henchmen had broken in their efforts to get Michael and their relentless assault on his rights, and the bogus suit filed against his father, he had mixed emotions about sitting in the same room with their lawyers.

No one in attendance at the mediation, save for Michael, would have any firsthand knowledge about the case. That meant it was up to him, and him alone, to explain to a gathering of people—all virtual strangers to him except his own lawyers—what it had been like to be hunted down like a wanted man for years, even though he had never been convicted of a felony - - - never even been charged with one.

In the course of a few minutes Michael was expected to explain to these people what it was like to be stalked and harassed for years, to have his livelihood yanked out from under him, to lose his sense of safety in his own home, and all perpetrated by cruel, merciless goons who hid their identities behind bogus tags, false identities, and through the use of unmarked aircrafts. It was a daunting task for anyone, especially for a man who was now face-to-face with some people he perceived to be the agents of the very hooligans who had orchestrated this abominable campaign of harassment and intimidation that had not only deeply affected him for years, but also his former wife, elderly parents, and young children.

* * *

After quite a few hours, the door of the room where the mediation was taking place opened. Michael had excused himself and left the room for a break. But it was more than that. Unbeknownst to anyone, not even his own lawyers, Michael was at a crossroads. Back inside the room there was an agreement on the table. He could either sign it and be done with the nightmare once and for all, or pass and go to trial. After everything that had happened, it all came down to him choosing one option or the other. It seemed so simple, yet it was anything but that. So before he made that monumental decision he wanted to see the mural. He was certain that the calming effect it had on him would not only make the decision easier, but it might even help him choose the right option. He could no more explain this compulsion to others than he could rationalize it in his own head. But he truly felt there was a message in the painting, and maybe this time he would finally figure it out.

Unfortunately, because the mediation had lasted so long, the courtroom containing the mural had been locked for the evening, and the judge who had the key had gone home. Upon hearing this news, Michael feared he might get physically ill. For awhile he simply leaned against a wall, not even sure if he could summon the strength to return to the mediation room.

Monsanto had filed the suit against Michael, and then tried to bully and intimidate him into settling. Nevertheless, it was Michael's prerogative to do what he felt was in his best interest. Succinctly, the conglomerate couldn't take away his right to a trial by jury. He still had the option to make them answer to twelve citizens. And the way Michael saw it, "I don't think anybody around here'll take kindly to a big old conglomerate that stalks and spies on a farmer and his family. And I'd love for 'em to hear about the threat Raymer made."

On the flipside—his Constitutional rights and a jury's reaction aside, Michael knew the cold, hard truth. Even his own lawyers had advised him that a jury trial was the wrong route to take. Would he win? They couldn't guarantee it, but the odds were good that he might. Still, winning a civil case at this level, even in federal court, served as little more than a fleeting moral victory when facing an opponent with cavernous pockets. Monsanto could appeal the case and appeal the case and appeal it some more . . . drag it out for years, decades even. Michael, the father of relatively young children, could be a grandfather or even a great-grandfather by the time the case was finally settled.

Michael's most immediate problem, however, was his financial situation. With his seed business ruined by Monsanto's manipulation of his customers, and his farm just barely keeping everything else afloat, insolvency, if not outright financial ruin, wasn't far down the pike.

Although Michael felt certain he was in the right, he literally could not afford to win - - - at least not through a lengthy appeals process. His plight highlighted one of the most appalling and tragic pitfalls of the American judicial system. In a civil case with a litigant of average means facing off against a rich one the deck is clearly stacked in favor of the litigant with the most money. A litigant with no scruples, yet enormous resources, can ferret out his opponents financial situation and then—exploiting that information—purposely drag the proceedings out until his opponent is flat broke. Even though some reputable attorneys are loathe to acknowledge it, there is an abundance of lawyers who use this ploy (denying someone their day in court) and even refer to it as "good legal strategy"—justice, truth and the Constitution be damned.

Given what Monsanto had put Michael and his family through, he had to wonder if it even cared about the truth. After all, the conglomerate had gone to extremes in the past to hide it. It was proven beyond a reasonable doubt that Monsanto hid the truth about PCBs in Anniston, did so for decades, and went to great lengths to accomplish that sordid scheme. And what about Agent Orange?

Admiral Elmo R. Zumwalt, Jr., a highly respected, decorated and innovative leader credited with improving life for enlistees and modernizing race relations in the military, was tasked by the U.S. Government with determining the facts about Agent Orange. In a 'classified' report submitted in 1990 to The Secretary of The Department of Veterans Affairs, Zumwalt provided substantial and credible evidence that Agent Orange was not only extremely harmful, but also that Monsanto knowingly used "fraudulent" means to cover-up the fact that people exposed to a contaminant present in a significant portion of the Agent Orange used in Vietnam, namely, 2,3,7, 8-tetrachlorodibenzo-p-dioxin (TCDD), faced a very real possibility of incurring serious and even fatal health problems.

Ironically, while serving in Vietnam, Zumwalt himself ordered the use of Agent Orange because he believed it was safe. Tragically, his own son, also serving in the war, was exposed to the toxic chemical and later died of cancer at forty-two. And to compound the tragedy, the Admiral's grandson—born after his son's exposure to Agent Orange—suffers from a rare and severe congenital dysfunction, a condition thought to be linked to the toxic herbicide.

Zumwalt's report stated unequivocally that employees of Monsanto committed fraud by altering data relating to an explosion at one of its plants in 1949 to make the TCDD present in Agent Orange appear safe when, in fact, it was anything but safe. Although it's beyond unconscionable for decent people to comprehend, Monsanto's employees manipulated the data to make TCDD appear harmless. When that same data was reanalyzed by a neutral party, the conclusion was that the cancer rate for Monsanto's workers who had been exposed to TCDD was 65 percent higher than their co-workers who had not been exposed to it, a rate so staggeringly high that no reasonable person would have any doubts about the toxicity and potential danger Agent Orange posed to humans.

The notion that Monsanto buried vital evidence about the toxicity of Agent Orange was eerily reminiscent of the scheme it orchestrated to hide the toxic nightmare it created in Anniston. Michael couldn't help but wonder, "If Monsanto discovered that GMOs were harmful to people, or bees, or any other form of life: Would it tell the public? Or bury the information for decades?"

The Admiral's findings were so alarming, appalling and compelling that Congress, operating posthaste—a true rarity during its 200 plus year history, enacted the Agent Orange Act a few months later. It not only provided Vietnam veterans with much needed and woefully long overdue benefits, but also made provisions for The National Academy of Sciences to determine the toxicity and harm Agent Orange had caused them, a far cry from the dubious tests and data that had been tainted by special interests.

Under the auspices of The National Academy of Sciences, the Institute of Medicine conducted extensive evaluations and provided their unbiased results. The IOM determined that when a human being is exposed to the TCDD in Agent Orange there is "sufficient evidence of an association" with: Hodgkin's lymphoma (cancer), non-Hodgkin's lymphoma (cancer), soft-tissue sarcoma (cancer), chronic lymphocytic leukemia (cancer), hairy cell leukemia (cancer), as well as other chronic B-cell leukemias (cancers). Additionally, the IOM stated that there is "limited or suggestive evidence of an association" with: lung cancer, trachea cancer, bronchus cancer, larynx cancer, prostate cancer, and multiple myeloma (cancer). There are also formidable links to: chloracne, porphyria cutanea tarda, type 2 diabetes, as well as spina bifida in children of soldiers who'd been exposed to the toxic herbicide.

Finally, the decades long campaign of misinformation, half-truths and outright concealment regarding the toxicity of Agent Orange to humans had been replaced with independent scientific information that was not polluted, manipulated or falsified by PR specialists, lobbyists or "corporate scientists."

After the IOM weighed in with its results, reasonable people who had been inundated over the years with an avalanche of misinformation, half-truths and lies to portray Agent Orange as nothing more than a benign herbicide realized it had been a snow job. They also understood why Arthur Galston had passed on the opportunity to become an extremely wealthy man from the toxic herbicide and, instead, was one of its biggest opponents. The lesson was clear: an honorable man will not sell his soul, not at any price, and Galston had passed the test in heroic style.

It took tremendous courage, honesty and integrity for Zumwalt to present the information he uncovered about Agent Orange, especially given that he had not only authorized its use in Vietnam, but also because he came to believe that his son's death was brought on by exposure to the toxic herbicide . . . the result of an order he gave.

Like so many leaders before him, and after, Zumwalt could have easily swept the facts under the dark and ominous rug of history to protect his own legacy. Instead, once he discovered the truth, he not only acknowledged it, but also took responsibility for the fateful decisions that he made in the Agent Orange travesty.

Although Zumwalt's report answered a number of questions about Agent Orange, more than two decades later, one still lingers for Vietnam veterans and their loved ones: Would a soldier whose health and quality of life were permanently destroyed by the toxic herbicide have gotten a fair settlement—instead of the paltry and insulting $5,700 most got stuck with, or the utterly obscene and demeaning $1,800 for those who died prematurely—had Monsanto not falsified its own documents and buried the link it found between the TCDD in Agent Orange and cancer? [14] [15]

Another sore point with Michael was the fact that a number of people in government agencies in key positions tasked with policing Monsanto have either worked for the conglomerate or had close ties with it. Was it possible that all these people were simply altruistic, civic minded, patriots who wanted nothing more than to serve their country for the good of mankind? Michael knew that, theoretically, it was possible. Of course, he also knew it was possible for a fiery meteor to come blasting through the earth's atmosphere at 160,000 mph and then land smack dab in the middle of his soybean field. However, he knew it was far more likely for a blue and white helicopter with no tail number to trespass and land on his property without permission while he was planting natural soybeans—and then come back later and do it again under cloak of darkness.

Monsanto's reason for this was all too obvious for Michael; he believed it was unbridled greed at its absolute worst. Considering that a substantial number of processed foods utilize soy, and an unsettling majority of the soybeans grown in American are now genetically modified, it meant everyone who ate those foods got stuck paying what Michael derisively called the

---

[14] On May 7, 1984, just hours before a class action suit for veterans harmed by Agent Orange was set to commence, the companies that made the toxin hastily settled out of court, with Monsanto responsible for the lion's share of the settlement. Veterans decried it as grossly inadequate and unfair, and were outraged that the companies did not have to admit any fault.

[15] On May 7, 2014, three decades after Monsanto dodged Vietnam veterans in court, this quote was retrieved from the company's website summarizing its 'opinion' about Agent Orange: "While a casual connection linking Agent Orange to chronic disease in humans has not been established, some governments have made the decision to provide certain medical benefits to veterans and their families even though there has not been a determination that an individual's health problem was caused by Agent Orange."

'Monsanto Tax.'[16] No one had voted on it, at least not the citizens, nor had they even been told about it. Even so, they were certainly paying it.

It certainly was not lost on Michael that—based on his firsthand experience, plus what he'd read and heard—Monsanto was not beyond throwing its weight around in an attempt to bully people like him into submission via the court system. And it was also his experience that Monsanto had no qualms about hiring thugs who would trample on the Constitution—if need be, exactly the opposite of highly principled men like Adm. Zumwalt who would have died for it.

With all this blasting through his head, and his mind in overdrive, suddenly, a thought came to Michael. What if *not* being able to see the mural was a sign? Perhaps it was an omen, the kind that he had to follow, even if no one else understood. It didn't take much to convince Michael that if he couldn't see the mural he was meant to choose a jury trial.

When he got back near the room where the mediation was being held, his lawyers, Stephen and J. R., were waiting outside to meet him. As soon as Michael told Stephen his decision, Stephen tried to reason with him, but to no avail. Michael was adamant. If he couldn't see the mural, they had better be prepared for trial. Michael knew it wasn't as if Stephen hadn't prepared, or that he didn't want to go to trial. Both he and J. R. had done nothing short of a miraculous job working on Michael's case; everyone at the firm who had worked on it had done a bang-up job. Even so, as they had explained to him, there was always a certain element of danger in a trial, especially when going up against an opponent with deep pockets. Unlike a trial, with mediation there would be closure once and for all. Once a deal was made and agreed upon by both parties, they would have to live with it. Monsanto couldn't turn its nose up at the decision a

---

[16] According to the Grocery Manufacturers Association, approximately 75 - 80 of the processed foods sold in grocery stores contain GMOs.

few months or years down the line and go shopping for one it liked better at another courthouse. Case in point: When it was battling claims brought by former U.S. soldiers who were suffering unmercifully and dying from exposure to Agent Orange, many of the soldiers were convinced the conglomerate purposely strung out the legal proceedings for years and years. They felt as if Monsanto had lifted a page from disgraced former Pres. Richard Nixon's infamous play book: *stonewall and deny*. More than a few soldiers lamented that delays stacked on top of delays had served only one purpose, i.e., Monsanto had hoped they would all simply die off, and that their claims would die right along with them.

No one wanted a resolution to the nightmare he had suffered through more than Michael. Yet like others before him, he wanted justice. He wanted his day in court. But justice for a man with shallow pockets who must battle a giant can be as elusive as a unicorn; an army of brave American warriors could attest to that.

Finding a quiet space where he could be by himself, Michael prayed. Although he knew it was impractical to pray for instant miracles, he did so anyway. And his prayer was simple. He wanted to see the mural.

A few moments later, Fess Caulder walked over and joined Michael. Fess was at the courthouse in hopes of settling his own case with Monsanto without a trial. He was tapped out long ago, and just wanted an end to his legal nightmare. The irony was, more than three years earlier, Monsanto's spies had used Fess as a pawn in their attempt to lasso Michael in their scheme of entrapment, one that ultimately backfired on them when Judge Smith chastised the conglomerate in open court for using the sordid ploy. The federal judge went so far as to call it a "scheme of entrapment."

Since Fess didn't have any money for his own legal council he was piggybacking on the advice of Michael's lawyers; he was more or less bound by whatever course Michael took. With one look at Michael, Fess had a good idea what his friend was going to do. "You're going to trial, ain't ya?"

Michael nodded. "Yep."

Fess was distraught by Michael's decision and begged him to reconsider. A lengthy trial would only prolong Fess's misery, and that of his family. He had nothing left to fight for; he wanted this abomination over and done with. As he pleaded with Michael something quite unusual happened. Judge John Ott, the mediator, joined the two men and spoke in a soft, low voice, "Michael, let's go up to the other courtroom and see the painting."

Michael was shocked. As far as he knew, no one had asked Judge Ott for this privilege. Yet somehow he had ascertained Michael's wishes and also located a key to the courtroom. Michael was elated. There was, however, a hitch. They were on break from meditation, and Judge Ott couldn't invite Michael without extending the same invitation to everyone else, even Monsanto's lawyers. Nearly everyone took the opportunity to stretch their legs and see the mural, everyone, that is, except Ernie Arden. For some reason he passed on the chance. And that suited Michael just fine.

With only a small group of people present in the large courtroom, there was no shortage of space. Each person was able to amble around the large room unencumbered. Michael took a vantage point that gave him a bird's eye view of the mural.

Michael was staring at a man in the painting holding a stalk of corn that had borne a perfect ear of corn. Judge Ott sidled up beside Michael and asked him why he thought Monsanto had never sued anyone for saving corn seed. Michael replied that if someone tried to save genetically modified corn seed the yield would be all but zero. There wouldn't be enough kernels from an entire field to make a side dish for even one person. Turning his gaze back to the stalk of corn in the painting, Michael was reminded of an incident back in 2004 when a stalk of genetically modified corn had "volunteered" in one of his soybean fields. It had been blatantly obvious that it wasn't supposed to be there because no one ever plants a single stalk of corn in the middle of a large field of soybeans. Michael had even made a photo of it because, instead of having six to eight hundred kernels like a normal ear, it had only few . . . and they were all rotten. It was proof to him that not only was the genetically modified corn inferior to natural varieties, but that no one can control nature. Odds were that a bird dropped it there, and Michael couldn't possibly police the bird population for "seed violations." Anyone—lay person, farmer, gardener, horticulturist or conglomerate—who thought he could was only kidding themselves, or trying to pull the wool over a lot of people's eyes.

About this time one of the lawyers took it upon himself to read the plaque below the mural out loud. The first part was a biography of the artist. The second was an explanation of the mural, something Michael had chosen not to read in the past. He felt it might taint or skew his personal interpretation of the work. But now, unless he covered his ears, he had no choice but to hear it read aloud. He chose to listen.

Reading from the plaque, the lawyer informed those present that the adult figures in the mural each represented a different facet of life. A woman shouldering a basket of fruit symbolized youth and fertility. A man pounding iron with a hammer stood for work. And the young man holding the cornstalk with the husk pulled back to reveal the perfect ear of natural corn—exactly the opposite of the genetically modified volunteer ear of corn in Michael's field—was symbolic of an open book, and represented scientific agriculture and the transition of learning from the environment to learning through the written source.

One of the lawyers commented, "How did that man know to use 'scientific agriculture'? I don't think the term existed back then."

No one answered or commented on the lawyer's assessment. Michael had barely heard it. The wheels in his head were too busy turning in a way they never had before. He realized more than ever that his needs were secondary to those of the world. People deserved to know what was going on. They had to know. At that moment, everything came together for him. It was a point of clarity that served as the defining moment of his ordeal.

More than anything, Michael wanted his story to be an open book that everyone could read and hear about. And just as the plaque described, it was certainly about scientific agriculture and the environment. More aptly, he felt it was about the pitfalls of what could happen to the environment if scientific agriculture fell into the wrong hands.

The world needed to know that Monsanto had not merely targeted a farmer in rural Alabama; this wasn't simply a case of alleged "patent misuse." Cases involving patent disputes were common. But this one had been different. The spying, the strong-arm tactics, the scheme of entrapment, the unmarked aircrafts—Michael didn't think for a moment these hardcore messages were solely intended for him, he felt they had been warnings for farmers everywhere. He was just being used as an example, one that seemed to say, "Here's what happens if a farmer doesn't jump on Monsanto's genetically modified bandwagon wearing a great big toothy grin and singing their praises." In his mind he saw this as only a few steps removed from the repugnant minstrel shows of the past, with hapless farmers frightened into playing the derisive role of shill for Monsanto.

Michael knew that if he went to trial and won Monsanto would simply appeal the decision. The appeals process would take at least two or three years, if not more. And if he won the next round, that would only lead to yet another appeal by Monsanto. It was certain to be a long, lonely and bumpy ride for Michael. It was the truly dark side of the legal process; Monsanto could tie him up in court for years, decades even. And as long as Michael was battling Monsanto in court it would be impossible for him to get his side of the story out to the public.

Staring at the mural, Michael actually looked through it. It was his way of looking past the personal transgressions Monsanto's goons had committed against him and his family. He had to do this in order to fully see the big picture. The way Michael saw it, a company that had once made Agent Orange and PCBs was in the process of creating a seed cartel that could give it unprecedented power over the world's food supply. The mere notion of remaining silent was beyond unthinkable.

For the past few years Michael had been secretly writing a biblically based book about seed and its place in the world. His efforts were genuinely altruistic. It would be self-published—paid for out of his own pocket, so profit certainly wasn't his motivation. He felt so strongly about it that—once it was published—if someone truly wanted a copy, yet couldn't afford it, he hoped he'd be in a position to give them one. But if the lawsuit continued, it could be many, many years before it ever saw the light of day.

With a newfound sense of peace and a genuine mission to accomplish, Michael got the attention of his lawyers and said in a quiet and solemn voice, "I'll sign the papers now."

The End

AFTERWORD

Fall of 2006

From the cool, crisp breeze to the fiery explosion of leaves covering the mountain, the hot, humid, insufferable days of summer were long gone and replaced by the splendor of autumn. Yet even though months had passed since his case was settled, Michael had not taken time off to savor the conclusion of his long and maddening legal nightmare. Like most farmers, taking a full-fledged vacation was impractical, if not unthinkable, especially during the harvest season. So on this day he was hard at work on a piece of farmland high up on the mountain.

Work kept him occupied, but it was no panacea for what ailed him. There were things on his mind that he could not shake, the kind of things that still kept him up into the wee hours of the morning.

Looking out at the beautiful fall foliage covering the mountainside below, he was reminded that he had once thought of this place as awe-inspiring, from the mountain itself to the Tennessee River below. It was one of the most beautiful places on earth, especially in the fall. But now it was tainted.

Officially, his case had been settled, though nothing much had changed. In his estimation Monsanto was still resorting to obstreperous measures to impose its will on farmers, and that was the same as imposing it on every man, woman and child on the planet who depends on them for food.

The details of Michael's case were sealed by a federal judge, and Michael had sworn an oath to God that he wouldn't discuss it. And no one took an oath before God more seriously than Michael White. Nevertheless, even a casual observer could see that he still had his farm, tractors and farm equipment, the land and buildings that once housed his seed business, his house, vehicles, even his beloved horses and mules. Essentially, more or less what he had before the suit . . . except the tranquility which came with living on the mountain and the peace of mind that he and his family were safe from interlopers, both of which had been stolen forever.

There was, however, one thing Michael could discuss without any legal or ethical ramifications, and he wasn't shy about it: the nature of the suit itself. Monsanto claimed it was nothing more than a civil case. Michael felt the conglomerate wanted people to believe it was just a benevolent multibillion dollar global enterprise trying to protect itself from a greedy, self-centered, money-hungry farmer in rural Alabama out to rip it off. A hard look took hold of Michael's face whenever he discussed it. "There wasn't nothing *civil* about the illegal and shameful things their sloppy privates done to me and my family and my elderly parents."

He often thought about one of the spies, Lowden Brown. One instance in particular stood out in his mind. It was the day the Deckers boxed Lowden in with their trucks. Michael had caught Lowden red-handed with a fake tag on his truck and he just laughed about it; Lowden even demonstrated how they switched the tags out. Michael could still hear Lowden's chilling proclamation, 'We're above the law! We can do anything we want!'

Operating with hindsight, Michael wasn't so sure that Lowden wasn't far off the mark. That was a bold assessment, but Michael was dead serious about it, and it wasn't like him to say things of that nature unless he thought they were true. Moreover, he felt he could substantiate his theory with facts from his own ordeal. Michael felt that anyone who truly reviewed the information objectively would come to the same conclusion.

* * *

Michael's conclusion was backed up by more than the words of Lowden Brown. He had Monsanto's unmarked blue and white helicopter on video, plus a number of eye witnesses had seen it. The copter alone was damning evidence, but there was more.

Geographically, Sand Mountain has a unique position in relation to some highly sensitive locations. The Marshall Space Flight Center, located on the Redstone Arsenal (Army base), is about forty miles due west as the crow flies. Marshall, NASA's largest center, provides crucial support for the space program, while the Redstone Arsenal develops and tests missiles for the Army. The Anniston Chemical Agent Disposal Facility is approximately sixty-five miles southeast of the mountain. ACADF held one of America's largest caches of chemical weapons, which included nerve agents such as Sarin and VX. Some of the most volatile chemicals on the planet were stored there; several of them were officially classified as *weapons of mass destruction*, the kind that could decimate the population of a large city in short order.[17] [18] Lastly, only a few miles from the base of the mountain is the Bellefonte Nuclear Generating Station, a nuclear plant. [19]

Individually, these locations were highly sensitive areas, the kinds that should have been protected by the most sophisticated early warning systems available. Collectively, the safekeeping of these three sites should

---

[17] Atlanta's metropolitan area has a population of approximately 5.5 million people (9th largest metro area in the U.S.) and is located less than 65 miles from these chemical weapons as the crow flies.

[18] Throughout the time unmarked aircrafts flew around Michael White's home and farm the ACADF was one of the most highly sensitive and volatile sites in the entire U.S. Since that time, all the weapons at the site have been destroyed by the U.S. Government, the last of which were incinerated on September 22, 2011, more than five years after Monsanto's case against Michael White was settled.

[19] Bellefonte Nuclear Generating Station is located in Hollywood, Alabama. It is not yet operational.

have been of the utmost priority for purposes of national security.

In theory, if a duly licensed and registered aircraft with an easy-to-read tail number enters or gets too close to a highly restricted area (air space) fighter jets should be scrambled, they should intercept the interloper, escort it to a secure airfield, and then the pilot should be interrogated to the nth degree by the proper authorities until they can determine exactly why he attempted to breach a highly sensitive location.

It's understandable that Michael, and others, wondered why the swift moving and highly agile blue and white JetRanger with no tail number was allowed to fly at will within minutes of all three of those highly sensitive locations and for such a long period of time. A reasonable person could come up with a number of scenarios why it was possible, yet the four most likely explanations seem to be: (1) All three sites were woefully unprepared for an attack—including attacks orchestrated by terrorists—and did not have early warning systems which would have alerted them that an unmarked aircraft had breached their air space, or was within minutes of doing so. (2) The sites had early warning systems, yet the systems at all three locations failed simultaneously, and did so on numerous occasions. (3) Each site had an early warning system, they all worked, yet none of the people monitoring the systems thought an unmarked aircraft posed a significant threat. (4) Someone with connections at the highest level in government made sure that the helicopter with no tail number was allowed to fly freely around Sand Mountain with no restrictions or consequences.

* * *

For almost four years Michael battled Monsanto, no matter what it threw at him. Even at his lowest moments—defying all odds and overcoming enormous obstacles, he would miraculously find a way to bounce back. He credited his strong faith for bringing him through this tumultuous ordeal, the kind that would have humbled any number of people who are far smarter, better educated and with more resources. Even now, when it seemed the battle was over, and he could go on with his life, he would not do it. This was because although the battle was done, the war was not.

It was the selfless nature of Michael White, coupled with the old time values his parents had instilled in him, his unshakable faith, and his conviction that good people do not sit idly by while bad things happen, that spurred him on—even now, when so many others would have been content to take a safe and comfortable seat in the bleachers.

Staring off into the distance as the sun slowly disappeared into the valley below, leaving only an orange and gray haze in the sky, a familiar thought crept into Michael's mind, one that haunted him day and night. It was the abominable admission made by Monsanto's very own director of corporate communications, Phil Angell. "Monsanto should not have to vouchsafe the safety of biotech food," he said. "Our interest is in selling as much of it as possible. Assuring its safety is the F.D.A.'s job."

Chills shot down Michael's spine each time he thought about that cavalier attitude toward the safety and well-being of more than 300 million people in the United States alone, to say nothing of other countries. Toss in Monsanto's sordid history of covering up horrific information to protect its bottom-line, plus the way its spies treated Michael and his family, and it was understandable why he felt the way he did.

There were reasons why Michael White could not rest, could not sleep, could not let his ordeal with Monsanto go. And anyone who knew him, truly knew what was in his heart, understood why.

EPILOGUE

In 2007, little more than a year after Michael White's lawsuit with Monsanto was settled, he broke ground on Camp Cross, a Christian camp for children situated on a picturesque piece of ground high atop Sand Mountain. Michael donated a substantial sum of his own money to make this project a reality.

In 2007, while on the campaign trail for president, Sen. Barack Obama pledged he would make the labeling of foods containing GMOs a priority because people deserved to know what they are buying.

In 2008 Michael White published a biblically based book about seed, *The 666's are in the Seed.*

In 2009 the United States Justice Department announced its intentions to investigate whether or not Monsanto has a monopoly in the area of genetically modified technology as it relates to our food supply.

In 2010 Pres. Obama appointed Michael R. Taylor, an attorney and former Vice-President for Monsanto, to a newly created post at the FDA, Deputy Commissioner for Foods. Taylor opposes the public's right to know if food contains GMOs, exactly the opposite of Obama's pledge to the American people to label food containing GMOs during his initial run for the presidency. [20]

In 2011 Wayne White passed away at age 87. He never received an apology from Monsanto or its attorneys for the baseless suit filed against him, or for the harassment that he and his terminally ill wife, Virginia, were subjected to during their 'golden years.'

In 2012 a grassroots effort in California placed Proposition 37 on the ballot. It would have given consumers the right to know if the food they are eating contains GMOs. Backed by concerned citizens, $9 million

---

[20] The FDA's policy on GMOs, which dates back to 1992, was crafted by Michael R. Taylor. It alleges that GM plants are "substantially equivalent" to natural ones and, therefore, should not be labeled as such or checked for safety. The first public mention of this policy was made during a speech by Vice-President Dan Quayle in May of 1992.

dollars was raised in support of the proposition. However, it failed because a number of large companies opposed the public's right to know. These businesses spent more than $46 million to combat the measure, flexing their financial muscles by outspending the citizens group by a margin of greater than five to one. Monsanto, the largest single contributor to the campaign, poured more than $8 million dollars into the opposition's war chest to silence the public's right to know.

In 2012, approximately 90 percent of the U.S. soybean, canola and sugar beet crops were grown from GM seeds, and about 80 percent of the corn. In 1992, a scant twenty years earlier, virtually all of those same crops were grown from non-GM seeds. In order to put these percentages into perspective, the U.S.'s dependency on foreign oil is only about 45 percent.

In 2012 Monsanto announced that the United States Justice Department's antitrust investigation of its company had ended. After spending three years and an untold amount of the tax payer's money, the Justice Department would only say that "marketplace developments" affected its decision to terminate the probe.

In 2013 Pres. Obama signed a bill, H.R. 933, into law with a provision that effectively strips the federal courts of their ability to halt the sale or planting of GM seeds, even if serious health issues arise concerning the edible crops raised from those seeds. Given that Monsanto paid lobbyists, lawyers and others to have this highly contentious provision included in the bill, and it stands to benefit from it, the law is often referred to as the "Monsanto Protection Act."

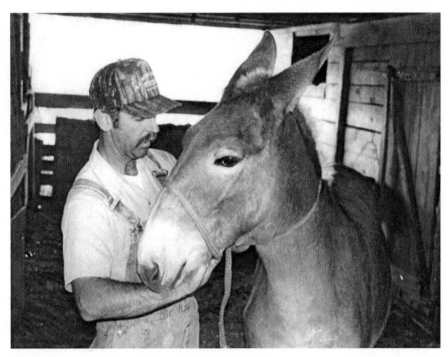

Years before Monsanto's spies turned his life upside down, Michael White is seen caring for one of his mules. – Courtesy of *The Daily Sentinel*

In his soybean field during Monsanto's suit against him, Michael White is standing beside a "volunteer" stalk of corn that's almost 6 feet high. "Volunteer" refers to a plant that takes root by accident, such as when a seed is dropped by a bird. – Courtesy of Michael White

This undated photo of Wayne and Virginia White and their first child, Stanley, is believed to have been taken in late 1945, soon after Wayne returned home from overseas duty in WWII. Both Wayne and Virginia were 22 years old at the time.

– Courtesy of Michael White

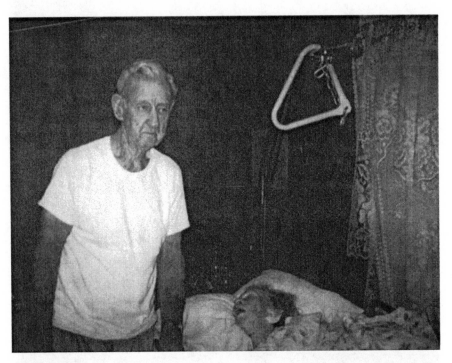

This was taken in 2003, soon after Monsanto filed suit against Wayne White. Both Wayne and Virginia White were 80 years old. He was in failing health and she was bedridden and dying of cancer. – Courtesy of Michael White

END NOTES

"Monsanto Hid Decades of Pollution, PCBs Drenched Ala. Town, But No One Was Ever Told," Michael Grunwald, Washington Post, Jan. 1, 2002

"Alabama Jury Says Monsanto Polluted Town," David Firestone, New York Times, Feb. 23, 2002

"Monsanto's Harvest of Fear," Donald L. Barlett and James B. Steele, Vanity Fair, May 2008

"Oakhurst Lawsuit: David vs. Goliath; Chemical Giant Monsanto Moves Against a Family-Owned Maine Dairy in a High-Stakes Battle over Growth Hormones in Dairy Cows," Edward D. Murphy, Portland Press Herald, July 13, 2003

"Monsanto Protection Act: 5 Terrifying Things to Know About the HR 933," Connor Adams Sheets, International Business Times, March 27, 2013

"$700 Million Settlement in Alabama PCB Lawsuit," New York Times, Thursday, August 21, 2003

"World Braced for Terminator 2, GM Food: Special Report," John Vidal, The Guardian, UK, October 6, 1999

"Playing God in the Garden," Michael Pollan, New York Times Magazine, October 25, 1998

"PCB Contamination in Anniston, Alabama: Hearing before a Subcommittee on the Committee on Appropriations," United States Senate, One Hundred Seventh Congress, Second Session, Special Hearing, April 19, 2002

"Solutia Files For Bankruptcy, Cites Monsanto Liabilities," Steven Mackay, Birmingham Business Journal, December 17, 2003

"GM Presence in Seeds Inevitable, EU Group Says," David Brough, Reuters News Service, April 6, 2001

"Clarence Thomas: A Silent Justice Speaks Out," Jan Crawford Greenburg, ABC News, September 30, 2007

"Understanding Court Nominee Evaluation and Approval: Mass Opinion in the Bork and Thomas Cases," James G. Gimpel and Lewis S. Ringel, Political Behavior, Volume 17, Number 2, June, 1995

"FDA Promotes Unsafe Milk Due to Industry Pressure," Jeffrey Smith, Huff Post Politics, April 8, 2009

"Agent Orange on Trial: Mass Toxic Disasters in the Courts," Peter H. Schuck, Harvard University Press/Belknap Press, 1987

"Study Links Prostate Cancer, Agent Orange," Kelly Kennedy, Army Times, August 7, 2008

"FDA Needs to Dismiss Former Monsanto Counsel," Samuel S. Epstein, Huffington Post, August 11, 2009

"VA Extends Agent Orange Benefits to More Veterans," News Release issue from the Office of Eric K. Shinseki, Secretary of Veterans Affairs, Department of Veterans Affairs, United States of America, October 13, 2009

"The Monopolization of Biodiversity: Terminator Bioscience and the Criminalization of the Harvest," Prof. Brian Wolf, Ph.D., University of Idaho, (Theory & Science) 2007

"Crops 'Widely Contaminated' by Genetically Modified DNA," Fred Pearce, New Scientist, February 23, 2004

"The Outcry over 'Terminator' Genes in Food: Critics Fear Such Safeguards Present Fresh Genetic Perils," Arlene Weintraub, with Pallavi Gogoi, Business Week, July 14, 2003

"The Mysterious Deaths of the Honeybees: Honeybee Colony Collapse Drives Price of Honey Higher and Threatens Fruit and Vegetable Production," Amy Sahba, CNN Money, March 29, 2007

"Monsanto vs. U.S. Farmers," Andrew Kimbrell and Joseph Mendelson, Center for Food Safety, January 2005

"The American Heritage Dictionary of The English Language," Editors: William Morris & Peter Davies, Dell Publishing Company, 1969

Circuit Court, Thirteenth Judicial Circuit, Hillsborough County, Florida, Case No. 98-2439, Exhibit C - February 21, 1997

"Agent Orange, A Deadly Member of the Rainbow," Brandon Schneider, Yale Scientific, Winter 2003

The Bible, King James Version, Genesis, Chapters 1 & 47, Thomas Nelson Publishers, 1972

"Arthur Galston, Agent Orange Researcher, Is Dead at 88," Jeremy Pearce, New York Times, June 23, 2008

"Monsanto Under Antitrust Review by the DOJ," Christopher Hinton, MarketWatch, October 9, 2009

"Obama's Broken Promise on GMO Food Labeling," Tom Philpott, Mother Jones, October 6, 2011

U.S. Census, Population Data, 2012

"America's Worst Vice Presidents," Kate Pickert, Time, August 21, 2008

"The Value and Vitality of V.P.s," Lionel Van Deerlin, The San Diego Union-Tribune, July 21, 2004

"Michael R. Taylor, Food Safety Czar," Laura Rambeau Lee, Examiner.com, December 10, 2010

"Monsanto GMO Ignites Big Seed War," Frank Morris, NPR and KCUR, January 12, 2010.

"Antitrust Probe of Monsanto Intensifies," Christopher Leonard, AP, Denver Post, January 15, 2010

"Essay, Administration of the 2003 Tolbert PCB Settlement in Anniston, Alabama: An Attempted Collaborative and Holistic Remedy," Edgar C. Gentle, III, Alabama Law Review, Vol. 60, No. 5, 2009

"Monsanto Sells off Controversial Milk-Hormone Unit to Focus on Seed Product Lines," Jennifer Yousfi, Money Morning, August 21, 2008

"Agent Orange Study Called Botched or Rigged," Paula Yost, Washington Post, July 12, 1989

"Court OKs Hormone-Free Label on Dairy Products in Ohio," April Fulton, NPR, October 1, 2010

"Modified Crops Tap a Wellspring of Protest," Julia Moskin, New York Times, February 7, 2012

"Rudolph gets Life for Birmingham Clinic Attack," David Mattingly, Henry Schuster, Matt Smith, CNN, July 18, 2005

"Prop. 37 backers vow to continue food regulation efforts," Marc Lifsher, Los Angeles Times, November 7, 2012

"The GM Genocide: Thousands of Indian Farmers are Committing Suicide after Using Genetically Modified Crops," Andrew Malone, Daily Mail, UK, November 2, 2008

"How NPR Got it Wrong on Monsanto's Superweeds," Tom Philpott, Mother Jones, March 14, 2012

"Genetic Changes to Food May get Uniform Labeling," Stephanie Strom, New York Times, January 31, 2013

"MTSU Becomes First in State to Offer Forensic Science Degree Beginning in Spring," Lisa L. Rollins, Examiner.com, December 4, 2009

"A Time for Peace: The Legacy of the Vietnam War," Robert D. Schulzinger, Oxford University Press, 2006

"Spina Bifida and Agent Orange," U.S. Department of Veterans Affairs, publichealth.va.gov., as per U.S. Public Law 104-204, enacted September 26, 1996

"Agent Orange Continues to Poison Vietnam," Marjorie Cohn, Huff Post World, June 15, 2009

"20 Years of GMO Policy That Keeps Americans in the Dark About Their Food," Dave Murphy, Huff Post Green, May 30, 2012

"Justice Department ends Monsanto Antitrust Probe," Georgina Gustin, St. Louis Dispatch, November 19, 2012

"Why Do G.M.O.'s Need Protection?," Mark Bittman, Editorial, The New York Times, April 2, 2013

"Gone: Workers Incinerate Last of Anniston Depot's Chemical Weapons Stockpile," Cameron Steele, The Anniston Star, September 22, 2011

Monsanto vs. Michael White, Wayne White, et. al., 5:03-cv-02804-CLS, U.S. District Court, Northern District of Alabama, Northeastern Division, October 15, 2003

"Delta and Pine Land Now a Division of Monsanto," Pam Golden, Prairie Farmer, Farm Progress, June 20, 2007

"The History, Use, Disposition and Environmental Fate of Agent Orange," Alvin Young, Springer, 2009

"How the world's oceans could be running out of fish," Gaia Vince, BBC, September 21, 2012

"The Chemical Scythe Lessons of 2,4,5-T and Dioxin (Disaster Research in Practice)," Alastair Hay, Springer, 1982

Kemner. et. al. v. Monsanto Company, No. 5--88--0420 (5th Dist., Illinois Appellate Court), October 3, 1989

Margaret Miller, U.S. FDA/NCTR, Resume, as posted on The Toxicology Forum

"Agent Orange Victims Sue Monsanto," Tom Fawthrop, CorpWatch, November 4, 2004

"Environmental Law: Cases and Materials," Philip Weinberg, University Press of America, 2006

Google Maps; maps.google.com

Report to Secretary of the Department of Veterans Affairs on the Association Between Adverse Health Effects and Exposure to Agent Orange, Classified, Confidential Status (1), As reported by Special Assistant Admiral E. R. Zumwalt, Jr., May 5, 1990, Warning: Not for Publication and Release to the General Public

Cancer.org/cancer/cancercauses/othercarcinogens/intheworkplace/agent-orange-and-cancer

"GMO Field Trials: Contamination Concerns," Conan Milner, Epoch Times, September 4, 2013

Monsanto.com/newsviews/pages/agent-orange-background-monsanto-involvement.aspx

"Hypocrisy and Intransigence - Mainstays of the Agent Orange Controversy," Dr. Wayne Dwernychuk, Salem News, February 2, 2012

"Agent Orange: Diseases Associated with Agent Orange Exposure," Department of Veterans Affairs Office of Public Health and Environmental Hazards, May 25, 2010

"Calif. to vote on labeling GMO foods, but you may already eat them," Elisa Zied, R.D., NBC News, November 2, 2012

"Health Effects of PCBs," U.S. Environmental Protection Agency, January 31, 2013

"Food safety group demands U.S. probe in tainting of alfalfa crop," Carey Gillam, Reuters, September 27, 2013

"FSA 'endangering public health' by ignoring concerns over GM food," John Vidal, The Guardian, September 5, 2013

"Monsanto Law Undermines Democracy, Public Health," Rekha Basu, Minneapolis Star Tribune, April 9, 2013

CPSIA information can be obtained at www.ICGtesting.com
Printed in the USA
LVOW12s2308130115

422741LV00005B/404/P